Houghton Mifflin Mathematics 7

Les Dukowski
Richard Holmes
Irvin K. Burbank
Walter Szetela
George Scroggie
Doug Super

Houghton Mifflin Canada Limited

150 Steelcase Road West • Markham, Ontario • L3R 1B2

Houghton Mifflin Mathematics

Program Authors
Irvin K. Burbank
Florine Koko Carlson
Les Dukowski
Richard Holmes
Heather J. Kelleher
Carol Poce
George Scroggie
Doug Super
Walter Szetela

Art Director and Designer
Tom Sankey

Assembly and Technical Art
Dave Hunter

Cover Art
Glenn Priestley

Illustrations
Tom Sankey
Bob Seguin

Editorial Adviser
Doug Super

Editor
Fran Seidenberg

Canadian Cataloguing in Publication Data

Main entry under title:
Houghton Mifflin mathematics 7

For use in grade 7.
Includes index.

ISBN 0-395-34662-2

1. Mathematics—1961–   I. Dukowski, Les.
II. Title

QA107.H68 1984 510   C83-099201-4

Printed in Canada

Metric Commission, Canada, has granted use of the national symbol for metric conversion.

CONTENTS

UNIT 1
Addition and Subtraction

Problem Solving:
Choosing the Right Facts

Wayne Gretzky has broken many records in hockey.
Look at the incredible facts!

1980–81 Season: He scored 164 points to break Phil Esposito's record by 12.
His 109 assists broke Bobby Orr's record by 7.

1981–82 Season: He scored 92 goals to break Esposito's record of 76.
He broke his own record for assists with 120.

1982–83 Season: He scored 125 assists, breaking his record again.

1983–84 Season: He scored in his first 51 games breaking his own record of
30 consecutive games set in 1982–83.

By how many goals did Gretzky break Esposito's record?

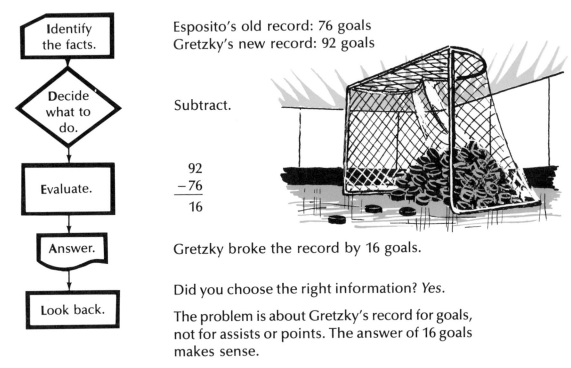

Identify the facts.

Esposito's old record: 76 goals
Gretzky's new record: 92 goals

Decide what to do.

Subtract.

Evaluate.

$$\begin{array}{r} 92 \\ -76 \\ \hline 16 \end{array}$$

Answer.

Gretzky broke the record by 16 goals.

Look back.

Did you choose the right information? *Yes.*

The problem is about Gretzky's record for goals, not for assists or points. The answer of 16 goals makes sense.

The facts listed on the previous page contain much more information than is needed to solve the problem.

EXERCISES

Choose the right facts about Wayne Gretzky's records to solve each problem. If there are not enough facts, tell what is needed.

1. How many points did Gretzky score in the 1980–81 season?

2. How many points did Gretzky score in the 1981–82 season?

3. Who held the record for assists before Gretzky?

4. How many points did Gretzky score in the 1982–83 season?

5. In how many consecutive games did Gretzky score in 1983–84?

6. By how much did Gretzky break his own record for assists in 1982–83?

7. How many goals did Gretzky score in the 1983–84 season?

8. How many goals did Gretzky score in the 1980–81 season?

A gold-record award is given when the sales of a recording reach one million. About 3000 gold records have been awarded.

The Beatles hold the record for the most gold records with 42.

Paul McCartney of the Beatles went on to earn 21 more gold-record awards with the group, Wings.

The most gold-record awards for an individual is held by Elvis Presley with 38.

A best-selling record of all time is the double-album soundtrack of the film, *Saturday Night Fever*, with over 25 million albums sold.

Choose the right facts above to solve each problem.

1. How many gold records were awarded on which Paul McCartney performed?

2. If each record costs five dollars, what would be the total cost of one copy of each of all the Beatles' gold records?

3. If Elvis Presley received at least 50¢ for each of his gold-record sales, what is the least amount he could have received from the total sales?

4. If each side of the *Saturday Night Fever* album takes 24 min to play, how long would it take to play the whole album?

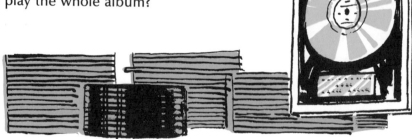

Five Largest Lakes in North America

Lake	Area (km²)	Length (km)	Depth (m)
Superior	82 103	563	405
Huron	59 570	332	229
Michigan	57 757	494	281
Great Bear	31 328	306	413
Great Slave	28 570	483	614

Choose the right facts from the table to solve each problem.

5. Lake Superior is the largest lake, but it is not the deepest lake. Which lake is the deepest? How much deeper is it than Lake Superior?

6. Three lakes in the table are longer than Lake Huron. Yet Lake Huron is larger than two of those lakes. Explain how this can be possible.

7. Which is larger, the area of Lake Huron or the combined areas of Great Bear Lake and Great Slave Lake?

8. The CN Tower in Toronto is one of the world's highest free standing structures. It is 553 m tall.
In which lakes would part of the CN Tower still be visible if it were placed in the deepest part?
What length of the tower would be visible if it were placed in the deepest part of Lake Michigan?

Great Bear
Lake

Great Slave
Lake

Lake
Superior

Lake
Huron

Lake
Michigan

How Resourceful Are You?

Make a table like the one above for the large lakes of other continents: South America, Europe, Africa, Asia, and Australia.

Place Value: Whole Numbers

The oldest solid ground in North America is the Canadian Shield which is about 3 600 000 000 years old.

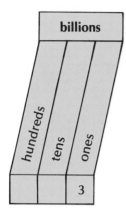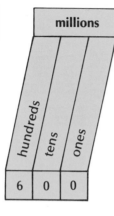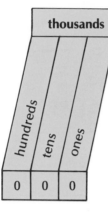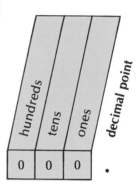

Expanded form: (3 × 1 000 000 000) + (6 × 100 000 000)
Standard form: 3 600 000 000
Words: *three billion, six hundred million*

EXERCISES

What is the place value of the 6 in each numeral?

1. 26 349
2. 6 201 785
3. 18 602
4. 617 843 920
5. 463 021
6. 9865
7. 6 000 000 000
8. 4 132 986

Write in standard form.

9. (3 × 10 000) + (9 × 1000) + (4 × 100) + (7 × 1)

10. (2 × 100 000) + (5 × 100)

11. (6 × 1000) + (8 × 100) + (1 × 10) + (5 × 1)

12. (4 × 1 000 000) + (8 × 100 000) + (5 × 10 000)

13. (4 × 1000) + (9 × 10) + (8 × 1)

14. (9 × 10 000) + (7 × 1000) + (6 × 100)

15. (7 × 100 000) + (5 × 1000) + (3 × 100) + (6 × 10)

16. (8 × 1000) + (2 × 10) + (6 × 1)

Write in expanded form.

17. 9421
18. 306 857
19. 8 327 961
20. 27 005

Write in expanded form.

1. 10 313   2. 5000   3. 439 187   4. 34 900 008

Write the next four whole numbers.

5. 352 098   6. 6 714 999 998   7. 1 409 997   8. 400 309

Copy and complete. Use < or >.

9. 2 493 156 ● 2 493 165

10. 800 900 ● 800 899

11. 403 751 678 ● 403 752 678

12. 9 602 759 400 ● 9 602 759 040

13. 7 126 400 ● 899 400

14. 30 950 ● 9817

Write in order from smallest to largest.

15. 189 040, 18 904, 189 004, 1890, 18 940

16. 5 682 031, 5 682 301, 5 682 310, 5 862 031, 5 862 301

Dizzy Digits

The following sequences show how you could change 123 into 321
by switching pairs of digits.

A. 123 ⟶ 321

Switch.

B. 123 ⟶ 213 ⟶ 231 ⟶ 321

Switch.   Switch.   Switch.

In each sequence, the number is made larger at every step.
Sequence **A** has the least possible number of steps.
Sequence **B** has the greatest.

1. Write another sequence of digit switches to change 123 into
   321, making the number larger at each step.

2. Write such a sequence to change 1234 to 4321.

3. How many steps are in the shortest possible sequence to
   change 1234 into 4321? The longest possible sequence?

4. Investigate 12 345 and larger numbers.

Place Value: Decimals

Find the quotient on a calculator.

$$2 \quad 5 \quad \div \quad 1 \quad 6 \quad =$$

How do you say the answer in words?

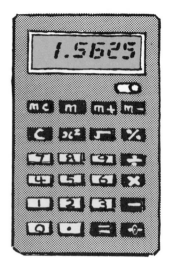

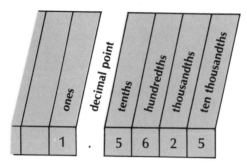

ones	decimal point	tenths	hundredths	thousandths	ten thousandths
1	.	5	6	2	5

Expanded form: $1 + \left(5 \times \frac{1}{10}\right) + \left(6 \times \frac{1}{100}\right) + \left(2 \times \frac{1}{1000}\right) + \left(5 \times \frac{1}{10\,000}\right)$

$1 + (5 \times 0.1) + (6 \times 0.01) + (2 \times 0.001) + (5 \times 0.001)$

Standard form: 1.5625

Words: *one* **and** *five thousand six hundred twenty-five ten thousandths*

EXERCISES

Write the place value of the 9 in each numeral.

1. 7.9   **2.** 29.6713   **3.** 148.2975   **4.** 0.4296

5. 3.7529   **6.** 90.24   **7.** 47.6392   **8.** 36.9507

Write in standard form.

9. $(5 \times 1000) + (9 \times 100) + (2 \times 10) + (4 \times 1) + \left(3 \times \frac{1}{10}\right) + \left(8 \times \frac{1}{100}\right)$

10. $(6 \times 10\,000) + (1 \times 100) + (3 \times 1) + \left(5 \times \frac{1}{10}\right) + \left(6 \times \frac{1}{1000}\right) + \left(4 \times \frac{1}{10\,000}\right)$

11. $(4 \times 1) + (6 \times 0.1) + (3 \times 0.01) + (2 \times 0.0001)$

Write in expanded form using fractions.

12. 97.65   **13.** 4.301   **14.** 26.0084   **15.** 0.4607

Write in expanded form using decimals.

16. 7.108   **17.** 3.1275   **18.** 33.4175   **19.** 904.6023

Write in standard form.

1. $(4 \times 1) + \left(1 \times \frac{1}{10}\right) + \left(5 \times \frac{1}{1000}\right) + \left(8 \times \frac{1}{10\,000}\right)$

2. $(3 \times 1000) + (9 \times 100) + (2 \times 1) + \left(6 \times \frac{1}{100}\right)$

3. $(2 \times 10) + (4 \times 1) + \left(3 \times \frac{1}{10}\right) + \left(7 \times \frac{1}{100}\right) + \left(5 \times \frac{1}{1000}\right) + \left(2 \times \frac{1}{10\,000}\right)$

4. $(8 \times 1000) + (6 \times 100) + (7 \times 10) + (5 \times 1) + \left(2 \times \frac{1}{10}\right) + \left(6 \times \frac{1}{1000}\right)$

5. $(6 \times 10) + (2 \times 1) + (3 \times 0.01) + (7 \times 0.001)$

6. $(9 \times 100) + (7 \times 1) + (2 \times 0.1) + (4 \times 0.01) + (2 \times 0.001) + (6 \times 0.0001)$

7. $(5 \times 100) + (4 \times 10) + (3 \times 1) + (2 \times 0.1) + (8 \times 0.01) + (7 \times 0.001)$

8. $(2 \times 1000) + (4 \times 100) + (7 \times 10) + (5 \times 1) + (9 \times 0.01) + (4 \times 0.001)$

Write in expanded form using both fractions and decimals.

9. 3.25   10. 72.55   11. 0.089   12. 1.3025

13. 189.013   14. 24 597.08   15. 5200.0091   16. 9.0603

Write in words.

17. 233.1   18. 80.22   19. 0.5602   20. 43.156

Find the quotient on your calculator.
Write it in standard and expanded form.

21. $\boxed{7} \div \boxed{1}\,\boxed{6} =$ 22. $\boxed{3}\,\boxed{5} \div \boxed{1}\,\boxed{6} =$

23. $\boxed{1}\,\boxed{7} \div \boxed{4}\,\boxed{0} =$ 24. $\boxed{1}\,\boxed{2}\,\boxed{5} \div \boxed{4}\,\boxed{0} =$

Canadian Facts

Insert a decimal point in each number to make a
true statement.
a. The highest temperature ever recorded in Canada is 43 °C at Regina in 1937.
b. Canada's overall population density is 245/km².
c. In 1867, Canada was a rural agricultural society of 35 million people.
d. The length of the Connaught Railway Tunnel at Rogers Pass, Canada's longest tunnel, is 808 km.

Comparing

Which is greater, 9.2, 9.20, or 9.200?

9.2
9.20
9.200

Each number has 9 ones, 2 tenths, 0 hundredths, and 0 thousandths.

So: 9.2 = 9.20 = 9.200   They are **equivalent** decimals.

Which is greater, 0.481 or 0.474?

same number of decimal places

Look at the farthest place to the left that has different digits. Compare.

0.481
0.474

We know: 8 > 7
So: 0.481 > 0.474

Which is greater, 6.49 or 6.5?

different number of decimal places

Annex a zero so both numbers have the same number of decimal places. Compare.

6.5 = 6.50

We know: 6.49 < 6.50
So: 6.49 < 6.5

EXERCISES

Write an equivalent decimal in tenths.

1. 7.20 = 7.■   2. 4.000 = 4.■   3. 6 = 6.■

4. 9.000   5. 32   6. 195

Write an equivalent decimal in hundredths.

7. 7.9 = 7.■   8. 3.200 = 3.■   9. 16.9 = 16.■

10. 71.5   11. 8.100   12. 43

Copy and complete. Use <, = , or >.

13. 7.4 ● 7.3   14. 3.147 ● 3.201   15. 65.22 ● 64.22

16. 9.60 > 9.57   17. 12.061 < 12.070   18. 3.00 > 2.99
    9.6 ● 9.57   12.061 ● 12.07   3   ● 2.99

19. 6.4 ● 6.39   20. 8.558 ● 8.6   21. 32.09 ● 32.074

22. 2.675 ● 2.78   23. 1 ● 0.625   24. 175.6 ● 174.79

Write an equivalent decimal in tenths.

1. 6.10   2. 4   3. 79   4. 342   5. 9.800

Write an equivalent decimal in hundredths.

6. 3.2   7. 28   8. 7.600   9. 7   10. 575

Copy and complete. Use <, =, or >.

11. 6.175 ● 6.174   12. 12 ● 11.86   13. 1.40 ● 1.4

14. 15.087 ● 16   15. 3.04 ● 3.040   16. 29.634 ● 29.643

17. 483.6 ● 483.15   18. 186.72 ● 185.72   19. 98.75 ● 98.750

20. 44.8 ● 48.4   21. 36 ● 35.999   22. 72 351 ● 72 351.02

23. 0.473 ● 0.4371   24. 652.31 ● 652.301   25. 4925.816 ● 4952.016

Write the smallest decimal.

26. 17, 1.7, 170, 0.17   27. 2.06, 2.6, 2.006, 26   28. 4.112, 4.212, 4.102, 4.1

29. 7.5, 7.05, 75, 5.07   30. 18.1, 8.11, 1.18, 1.81   31. 68.1, 8.61, 8, 6.18

Write the next four decimals.

32. 0.005, 0.006, 0.007, ■, ■, ■, ■

33. 3.4956, 3.4957, 3.4958, ■, ■, ■, ■

34. 6.94, 6.95, 6.96, ■, ■, ■, ■

35. 36.35, 36.36, 36.37, ■, ■, ■, ■

36. 1.095, 1.096, 1.097, ■, ■, ■, ■

Betwixt and Between

Use some or all of the digits at the right.
Make a number between:

a. 2.11 and 2.140

b. 95.02 and 95.2

c. 0.1 and 0.4

d. 31.5 and 32

e. 410 and 512.7

Rounding

A Commonwealth Games record for the 100 m backstroke was set in 1982 by Michael West of Waterloo, Ont. with a time of 57.12 s. What is his record time to the nearest second?

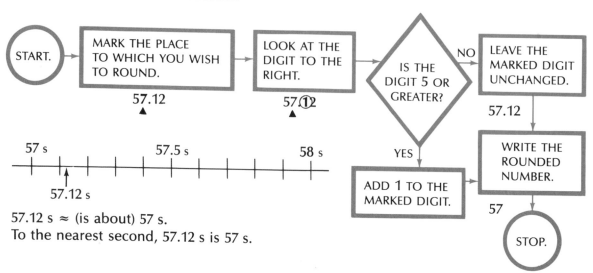

57.12 s ≈ (is about) 57 s.
To the nearest second, 57.12 s is 57 s.

EXERCISES

Round to the nearest hundred.

1. 778   2. 9180   3. 356   4. 4317

Round to the nearest ten.

5. 972   6. 6759   7. 3875   8. 9414

Round to the nearest one.

9. 17.45   10. 24.7   11. 3.625   12. 409.2

Round to the nearest tenth.

13. 3.892   14. 434.128   15. 4.16   16. 27.559

Round to the nearest hundredth.

17. 0.125   18. 4.1666   19. 68.293   20. 0.9708

Round to the nearest thousandth.

21. 1.4496   22. 7.6735   23. 2.2361   24. 31.4648

Round to the nearest million.

1. 4861 649
2. 2358 075
3. 9630 224
4. 862 156
5. 36 006 245
6. 80 874 047
7. 99 521 633
8. 409 328

Round to the nearest ten thousand.

9. 47 443
10. 83 313
11. 99 437
12. 65 121
13. 697 745
14. 358 278
15. 103 947
16. 7835 130

Round to the nearest tenth.

17. 24.72
18. 73.55
19. 15.99
20. 31.03
21. 25.875
22. 896.305
23. 627.556
24. 45.008

Round to the nearest dollar.

25. $89.61
26. $11.34
27. $48.50
28. $99.98
29. $583.46
30. $251.03
31. $229.69
32. $426.55

Round to the nearest tenth of a second.

33. 100 m free-style swim: 55.41 s
34. 400 m run: 43.86 s
35. 100 m run: 9.95 s
36. Calf roping: 7.50 s

Round to the nearest cent.

37. $6.732
38. $8.9695
39. $42.0458
40. $1.9999

Round to the nearest thousandth.

41. 22.0432
42. 8.5408
43. 1.2401
44. 46.4995

Computer Rounding

When I type: PRINT 94 783.216 95 on my computer keyboard, it displays 94 783.217. My computer rounds numbers to 8 digits. What would my computer display for these commands?

a. PRINT 347 185.2839
b. PRINT 761.794 16
c. PRINT 8657.993 477
d. PRINT 95 106.36

Adding and Subtracting Whole Numbers

Joan has read 845 pages in her book. She has 275 pages left to read. How many pages are in the book?

total pages in book = 845 + 275

	Add the ones.	Add the tens.	Add the hundreds.
845 +275	1 8 4 5 + 2 7 5 ――― 0	1 1 8 4 5 + 2 7 5 ――― 2 0	1 1 8 4 5 + 2 7 5 ――― 1 1 2 0
	10 ones are renamed as 1 ten.	12 tens are renamed as 1 hundred and 2 tens.	11 hundreds are renamed as 1 thousand and 1 hundred.

The book has 1120 pages.

There are 1050 students attending Melvale Junior High School. Five hundred sixty-three students are male. How many students at Melvale are female?

female students = 1050 − 563

	Subtract the ones.	Subtract the tens.	Subtract the hundreds.
1050 −563	4 10 1 0 5 0 − 5 6 3 ――― 7	9 14 10 1 0 5 0 − 5 6 3 ――― 8 7	9 14 10 1 0 5 0 − 5 6 3 ――― 4 8 7
	5 tens are renamed as 4 tens 10 ones.	10 hundreds and 4 tens are renamed 9 hundreds and 14 tens.	

There are 487 female students at Melvale school.

EXERCISES

Find the sum.

1.	34 +68	**2.**	90 +51	**3.**	72 +49	**4.**	395 + 86
5.	546 +934	**6.**	6794 + 307	**7.**	2664 +9385	**8.**	758 +6934
9.	534 628 + 7 825	**10.**	693 284 + 29 010	**11.**	845 360 + 90 431	**12.**	392 675 +5 128 304

13. 579 + 864

14. 9675 + 279

15. 5308 + 12 726

16. 96 713 + 587 105

17. 413 807 + 7962

18. 375 + 795 108

Find the difference.

19.	56 −32	**20.**	95 −41	**21.**	80 −36	**22.**	74 −57
23.	609 − 20	**24.**	3154 − 836	**25.**	5006 −1428	**26.**	7000 − 832
27.	169 352 −109 478	**28.**	605 000 − 97 132	**29.**	693 084 −297 175	**30.**	5 421 283 −2 794 395

31. 54 − 38

32. 132 − 84

33. 500 − 125

34. 7038 − 165

35. 94 006 − 6273

36. 400 000 − 76 243

Add or subtract.

37. 74 + 65 927

38. 50 500 − 38 792

39. 6 175 248 − 4153

40. 93 846 + 9987

41. 142 937 + 51 362

42. 40 005 − 562

43. 1600 students
757 females
How many males?

44. 732 km from A to B
429 km from B to C
How far is it from A
to C?

45. 10 000 books
5179 fiction
How many are
non-fiction books?

Add or subtract.

1.   78
    − 29

2.   923
    + 35

3.   500
    − 211

4.   1867
    + 979

5.   9805
    + 3726

6.   4003
    − 3528

7.   324 036
    −   8 179

8.   36 512
    + 826 543

9. 9406 − 977

10. 390 870 + 9986

11. 421 563 + 3 384 767

12. 100 300 − 52 648

Round to the nearest thousand. Estimate the answer.

13.   38 503
    + 12 698

14.   45 709
    − 6 493

15.   30 564
    − 19 447

16.   9 006
    + 51 994

17. 3815 + 16 060

18. 4380 − 795

Copy and complete using = or ≠.

19. 917 − 136 ● 556 + 225

20. 468 + 950 ● 2100 − 652

21. 5600 − 945 ● 3537 + 1078

22. 763 + 4975 ● 5986 − 248

23. 5972 + 418 ● 6956 − 566

24. 7602 − 462 ● 6519 + 623

Solve.

25. The highest place on earth is Mount Everest, 8848 m above sea level. The lowest point on earth is in the Pacific Ocean, a depth of 11 022 m to the ocean floor. What is the total distance from the highest point to the lowest point?

26. Ellesmere Island in the Canadian Arctic has an area of 196 236 km^2. It is 312 215 km^2 smaller than Canada's largest island, Baffin Island. What is the area of Baffin Island?

27. The sum of 2569 and 1143 is 805 more than a certain number. What is the number?

28. On a series of math quizzes, Glenda got 12 out of 15; 8 out of 10; 17 out of 20; 6 out of 7; and 5 out of 8. What was the total possible number of marks on the five quizzes? How many marks did Glenda get?

Palindromes

A **palindrome** is a number which reads the same forwards and backwards.

44, 686, and 497 794 are palindromes.

Most numbers can be made into palindromes after a few steps like these:

$$\begin{array}{r} 59 \\ +95 \\ \hline 154 \\ +451 \\ \hline 605 \\ +506 \\ \hline 1111 \end{array}$$

1. Add its reversal to the number.

2. If the sum is not a palindrome, add the sum and its reversal.

3. Continue until the sum is a palindrome.

Make each number into a palindrome.

a. 49   **b.** 598   **c.** 78   **d.** 876   **e.** 198

Make It Magic

a. Use the numbers 1, 2, 3, 4, 5, 6, 7, 8, and 9 to make a magic square. Each row, diagonal, and column will have a sum of 15.

b. Copy and complete this magic square.

	39	24
	27	
	15	

c. Change one number to make a magic square.

35	20	17	34	19
32	28	23	24	18
14	21	25	29	36
13	26	27	38	37
31	30	33	16	15

Adding and Subtracting Decimals

Mr. Taylor bought 1.675 kg of T-bone steaks and 2.55 kg of strip steaks. How much meat did Mr. Taylor buy in all?

total meat bought = 1.675 + 2.55

Line up the decimals.	Add the thousandths.	Add the hundredths.	Add the tenths.	Add the ones.

1.675
+2.55
	1 . 6 7 5
	+ 2 . 5 5
	――――
	        5
		¹
		1 . 6 7 5
		+ 2 . 5 5
		――――
		     2 5
			¹ ¹
			1 . 6 7 5
			+ 2 . 5 5
			――――
			. 2 2 5
				¹ ¹
				1 . 6 7 5
				+ 2 . 5 5
				――――
				4 . 2 2 5

		12 hundredths are renamed as 1 tenth and 2 hundredths.	12 tenths are renamed as 1 one and 2 tenths.	

Mr. Taylor bought 4.225 kg of meat.

Ms. Givani had 6.25 kg ham to sell in her meat store. After closing time, there was 4.175 kg of the ham left. How much ham was sold that day.

ham sold = 6.25 − 4.175

Annex a zero.	Subtract the thousandths.	Subtract the hundredths.	Subtract the tenths.	Subtract the ones.

6.250
−4.175
	⁴ ¹⁰
	6 . 2 5 0
	− 4 . 1 7 5
	――――
	        5
		¹ ¹⁴ ¹⁰
		6 . 2 5 0
		− 4 . 1 7 5
		――――
		     7 5
			¹ ¹⁴ ¹⁰
			6 . 2 5 0
			− 4 . 1 7 5
			――――
			. 0 7 5
				¹ ¹⁴ ¹⁰
				6 . 2 5 0
				− 4 . 1 7 5
				――――
				2 . 0 7 5

	50 thousandths are renamed as 4 hundredths and 10 hundredths.	24 hundredths are renamed as 1 tenth and 14 hundredths.		

2.075 kg of ham was sold.

16

EXERCISES

Find the sum.

1. 0.8
      +0.5

2. 4.7
      +1.2

3. 11.9
      + 3.2

4. 15.0
      + 7.4

5. $0.34
      + 0.89

6. $6.05
      + 3.28

7. $75.94
      + 30.85

8. $168.51
      +   9.27

9. 48.7
      + 6.675

10. 90.09
       + 8.453

11. 36.436
       +869.7

12. 148.092
       + 61.35

13. 7 + 6.5

14. 11.4 + 9

15. $16.55 + $2.95

16. $488 + $36.95

17. 2.1012 + 75.323

18. 300.546 + 120.4

Find the difference.

19. 1.0
       −0.6

20. 9.2
       −6.6

21. 14.1
       − 8.5

22. 43.2
       −17.3

23. $0.51
       − 0.28

24. $3.00
       − 2.47

25. $98.90
       − 5.91

26. $237.10
       − 64.58

27. 4.7
       −0.249

28. 8.006
       −3.64

29. 68.4
       −23.795

30. 431.34
       − 1.759

31. 4 − 2.2

32. 16.5 − 8

33. $20 − $6.59

34. $42.60 − $4.75

35. 65.1053 − 4.75

36. 1190.001 − 693.027

Add or subtract.

37. 7.4 + 18.36

38. 10 − 6.25

39. $75 − $16.95

40. $3.29 + $18.35

41. 386 + 21.542

42. 50.6 − 2.7962

Round to the nearest whole number. **Estimate** the answer.

43. 7.394 − 2.76

44. 19.885 + 3.9

45. 28.42 − 6.757

46. 12.8 + 40.2478

47. 89.684 − 39.5218

48. 9.3 + 0.7758

PRACTICE

Add or subtract.

1.   0.8
   $+4.0$

2.   7.5
   -0.62

3.   19.0
   $-\ 6.45$

4.   9.2
   $+0.487$

5. $48.00
   $-\ 13.26$

6. $25.48
   $-\ 6.39$

7. $30.00
   $-\ 28.75$

8. $500.00
   $-\ 129.50$

9.   13.687 9
   $+\ 6.3$

10.   52.105
   -39.4

11.   653.477
   $+\ 7.5332$

12.   1528.8
   $-\ 53.736$

13. 16 + 12.2

14. 8 − 1.375

15. $40 − $1.95

16. $62.50 + $7.95

17. 22.37 + 41.796

18. 4.7 − 2.825

Copy and Complete using >, = , or <.

19. 16.35 + 9.267 ● 39.12 − 13.5

20. 3.4 − 1.095 ● 1.86 + 0.5

21. 146.3 + 59.75 ● 381.55 − 176

22. 24.68 − 14.9 ● 4.5 + 5.28

Round to the nearest whole number. **Estimate** the answer.

23.   2.78
   $+7.64$

24.   8.7324
   -5.39

25.   6.8521
   -0.343

26.   12.99
   $+\ 2.186$

Solve.

27. A swimmer swam 100 m in 49.44 s. A runner ran the same distance in 9.95 s. How much faster was the runner than the swimmer?

28. What number can be added to 12.9 so that the sum is 2.8 less than 270?

29. In a figure skating competition, each competitor's score was found by eliminating the highest and lowest score and adding the remaining scores. Brian was given scores of 5.5, 5.8, 5.7, 5.7, 5.9, 5.6, and 5.7. What was Brian's total score?

30. Mr. Rupert bought an electric chainsaw for $42.97. The cashier gave him $17.05 in change when he paid for the saw. How much money did Mr. Rupert give the cashier?

Calculator Code

Match each numbered question with the lettered question that has the same answer. Find the message.

1	2	3	4	5	6	7

1. 213.54 − 58.96

2. 27.107 + 43.919

3. 86.45 + 91.67

4. 51.026 − 37.896

5. 13.5 + 109.2

6. 81.9042 − 26.3542

7. 200 − 94.62

G. 23.91 + 154.21

H. 680.04 − 666.91

I. 134.506 − 63.48

N. 34.088 + 71.292

O. 204.18 − 148.63

R. 89.01 + 65.57

T. 35.66 + 87.04

REVIEW

Write in expanded form.

1. 125   2. 706 521   3. 98 400 000   4. 6 245 900 000

5. 3.17   6. 0.562   7. 0.9708   8. 36.0461

Copy and complete. Use <, =, or >.

9. 36.475 ● 36.474   10. 4.2 ● 4.200   11. 9.081 ● 9.09

Round to the nearest tenth.

12. 0.78   13. 396.125   14. 42.75   15. 8.6291

Add or subtract.

16. 7923 + 46 157   17. 90 408 − 6764   18. 809 + 9524

19. $50 − $32.45   20. 7.5 + 38.162   21. 16 − 5.475

Column Addition

A fast method for calculating the sum of the bill at the right is to look for tens.

```
    2  2
 $ 0 . 2 5
   3 . 3 9
   0 . 8 4
   5 . 9 5
   0 . 1 6
 ─────────
 $10 . 5 9
```

Stanley's Hardw

23210 88 Street
Lethbridge, Alta.

nails	$0.25
wrench	3.39
sandpaper	0.84
paint	5.95
washers	0.16
Total	$10.59

To see if this answer is *reasonable*, the sum is **estimated**.

Round each
number
to the
nearest
dollar.

```
 $ 0
   3
   1
   6
 + 0
 ────
 $10
```

The estimated sum is $10.
Then, the calculated sum of $10.59 is reasonable.

EXERCISES

Look for tens. Find the sum.

1.	2.	3.	4.	5.
3	4	9	6.4	27
9	8	9	3.0	80
7	3	5	2.5	16
5	6	11	8.0	3
+1	2	+ 5	7.6	44
	+4		+4.2	+65

Round to the nearest dollar. *Estimate* the sum.

6.	7.	8.	9.	10.
$3.76	$ 4.82	33¢	$6.45	$ 3.12
4.39	10.50	29¢	8.62	42.95
+ 7.94	0.42	59¢	9.48	1.65
	+ 0.95	78¢	3.89	0.26
		+99¢	+ 6.95	+ 5.88

PRACTICE

Find the sum.

1.	2.	3.	4.	5.
3	29	38	2.9	4.54
9	36	5	5.6	3.8
4	81	52	3.8	653.
2	20	17	8.7	5.7
7	17	9	6.2	0.161
8	43	3	1.0	3.21
+5	+50	+64	+5.4	+ 0.489

Round to the nearest whole number. Estimate the sum.

6. 7.8 + 3.946 + 12.32 + 0.2

7. 5.1372 + 20.775 + 34.675

8. 9.823 + 0.875 + 6.4773 + 6.9

9. 30.2 + 10.459 + 2.88 + 5 + 4.9172

Par for the Course

Below is a copy of the score card Laura and Rex used when they played 18 holes of golf at the Spruce Edge Golf Course.

First Nine

Hole	Metres	Par	Laura	Rex
1	320	4	3	4
2	485	5	4	5
3	353	4	4	3
4	164	3	4	3
5	415	4	4	4
6	542	5	4	4
7	385	4	4	4
8	132	3	3	3
9	421	4	4	4

Second Nine

Hole	Metres	Par	Laura	Rex
10	325	4	3	3
11	470	5	4	4
12	359	4	5	4
13	162	3	4	3
14	406	4	3	4
15	541	5	4	4
16	384	4	4	4
17	133	3	3	3
18	427	4	4	4

a. Find each player's score for the first nine; the second nine; and the course.
b. Find par for the first nine; the second nine; and the course.
c. Find the total length of the first nine holes; the second nine holes; and the whole course.

21

Evaluating Expressions

A letter that is used to represent an unknown number is called a **variable**. Below are some English *phrases* translated into mathematical **expressions** containing a *variable*.

Phrases	Expressions
1. the sum of a number and 50:	$n + 50$
2. 14 increased by a number:	$14 + x$
3. a number reduced by 12:	$a - 12$
4. Mary's mass increased 5 kg. Mary's mass is:	$(m + 5)$ kg
5. Tom earns $6 more per hour than Ian. Tom's hourly earnings are:	$\$(i + 6)$
6. Sue finished 16 problems less than Joan. Sue's finished problems are:	$j - 16$

An expression can be *evaluated* if a value is substituted for the variable. For example 6, suppose that Joan finished 50 problems.
Since $j = 50$, then $j - 16 = 50 - 16 = 34$.
Sue then finished 34 problems.

EXERCISES

Choose an expression for each phrase.

1. 38 increased by a number $\qquad$ $38 + x$ or $38 - n$

2. the difference between a number and 15 $\qquad$ $n + 15$ or $n - 15$

3. 24 more than a number $\qquad$ $b + 24$ or $b \times 24$

4. 95 reduced by a number $\qquad$ $95 + d$ or $95 - d$

Choose a letter to represent the unknown number.
Then write an expression.

5. the sum of 17 and a number
6. a number increased by 9
7. a number less 6
8. 14 more than a number
9. a number increased by 31
10. 6 less than a number

Evaluate each expression. Suppose $a = 7$, $b = 12$, and $c = 9$.

11. $a + 4$ 12. $17 - b$ 13. $c - 9$ 14. $b + c$ 15. $b - a$

Choose a letter to represent the unknown number.
Then write an expression for each.

1. a number plus 16

2. 67 reduced by a number

3. the difference between a number and 4

4. 8 more than a number

5. 12 increased by a number

6. 32 less than a number

7. 41 more than a number

8. a number decreased by 28

9. the difference between a number and 56

10. the sum of a number and 48

11. The temperature this morning was 22°C. By afternoon it dropped an unknown number of degrees. What is the temperature now?

12. George ate 3 cookies less than Mario. How many cookies did Mario eat?

13. Janet scored 15 points more than Sheila. How many points did Sheila score?

14. A record costs $6.95 plus tax. What is the total cost of the record?

15. Mrs. Fox's mass is decreased by 4 kg. What is Mrs. Fox's mass?

Evaluate each expression. Suppose $c = 42$, $d = 84$, and $e = 50$.

16. $48 - c$

17. $d + 16$

18. $e - 29$

19. $19 + a$

20. $e - c$

21. $c + d$

22. $d - c$

23. $a + b + c$

Evaluate each expression. Suppose $x = 1.5$, $y = 8$, and $z = 3.04$.

24. $14 + x$

25. $y - 5.2$

26. $y + z$

27. $z - 1.2$

28. $x + y + z$

29. $z - x$

30. $3.7 + x$

31. $y - x$

When Wrongs are Right

Each different letter stands for a different digit.
Find their value and check by adding.

```
  WRONG
+ WRONG
-------
  RIGHT
```

23

Guessing and Testing

In the Grey Cup games from 1978 through 1982, a total of 203 points were scored. The Edmonton Eskimos played each year and scored a total of 75 more points than their opponents. How many points did the Eskimos score in all five games? How many points did their opponents score?

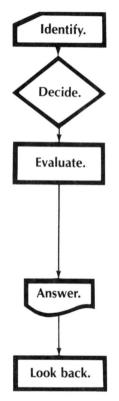

Identify.

Decide.

Evaluate.

Answer.

Look back.

203 points scored by both teams
75 more points scored by the Eskimos

Guess the total for the Eskimos. Subtract this from 203 to find the opponents' total. Then test if the difference is 75. If not, try another guess.

1st guess:
The Eskimos scored 140 points.
203 − 140 = 63 opponents' points
140 − 63 = 77

77 is too much!

2nd guess:
The Eskimos scored 139 points.
203 − 139 = 64 opponents' points
139 − 64 = 75

Just right!

The Eskimos scored 139 points, and the opponents scored 64 points.

The answer makes sense. The numbers 139 and 64 add up to 203, the total number of points for both teams. The difference in point totals is exactly 75.

EXERCISES

1. Eleven runs were scored in a high school baseball game. The winning team scored 5 more runs than the losing team. What was the score of the game?

2. The sum of Bill and Bob's ages is 22. Bill is 2 years older than Bob. How old is each boy?

3. Janet has 7 coins in her purse, all nickels and dimes. In all, she has $0.55. How many of each coin does Janet have?

PRACTICE

Guess and test the solution to each problem.

1. It took Jake 14 h to read a book and write a book report. Jake spent 4 more hours reading the book than writing the report. How long did he spend writing the report?

2. The entire Doucette family is watching television, even the cats and dogs. Altogether there are 11 people and pets. Janelle counts 32 legs altogether. How many pets do the Doucettes have?

3. In a new car lot there are 15 cars for sale. A small car sells for $7000 and a large car sells for $11 000. The total value of all the cars is $121 000. How many of the cars are large?

4. Forty-eight points were scored in a Grey Cup game by the Edmonton Eskimos and the Toronto Argonauts. The difference between the points scored by the Eskimos and the Argonauts is 16. What was the game score?

5. Sugar cookies cost 25¢ each, donuts cost 35¢ each. Mr. Geiss bought twice as many sugar cookies as donuts. Altogether he spent $3.40. How many sugar cookies did he buy?

6. Marcy, Tracy, and Lacy are sisters. Marcy is the youngest, Tracy is a year older, and Lacy is two years older. When their ages are multiplied, the result is 1716. How old is each girl?

For Imaginative Thinkers

Imagine that you are on a distant planet. You notice that the strange inhabitants have 4 legs. Their pets have 10 legs. Make up a problem about the planet that you can solve, and try it out on your teacher and classmates.

25

Guessing and Testing to Solve Equations

An **equation** is a mathematical sentence that uses the symbol = .

A question about an unknown number can be stated as an equation.

What number plus 9 is 15?	23 decreased by what number is 19?
$n + 9 = 15$	$23 - a = 19$

1st guess and test:
Let $n = 6$
$6 + 9 = 15$

The solution to the equation
is **$n = 6$.**

1st guess: Let $a = 5$
1st test: $23 - 5 = 18$ Too large!

2nd guess: Let $a = 4$
2nd test: $23 - 4 = 19$ Just right!

The solution to the equation
is **$a = 4$.**

When the unknown number, represented by a letter, has been
determined, the equation has been solved.

EXERCISES

Choose an equation for each question.

1. What number increased by 4 is 21? $x + 4 = 21$ or $x - 4 = 21$

2. Fifty is what number less 35? $50 - 35 = n$ or $50 = n - 35$

3. Six more than what number is 47? $a + 6 = 47$ or $6 + 47 = a$

Write an equation with an unknown for each question.

4. The sum of what number and 300 is 503.3?

5. What number decreased by 7 is 48?

6. Fifty-two more than what number is 118?

Guess and test the solution for each equation.

7. $6 + x = 13$
$x = \blacksquare$

8. $18 - r = 4$
$r = \blacksquare$

9. $m + 6 = 15$
$m = \blacksquare$

10. $16 - b = 7.5$

11. $g + 3 = 12$

12. $f - 8 = 11$

13. $n - 12 = 45$

14. $y + 23 = 48.2$

15. $50 + r = 81$

PRACTICE

Guess and test the solution for each equation.

1. $14 + x = 26$
2. $c - 8 = 30$
3. $s + 400 = 525$
4. $n + 23 = 48$
5. $9 = b - 38.2$
6. $98 - 36 = j$
7. $36 = a + 22$
8. $30 - p = 22$
9. $45 = x - 60.5$
10. $34 + x = 56.7$
11. $y - 84 = 35$
12. $16 + 23 = a - 40$
13. $231 - r = 16$
14. $400 + s = 25$
15. $89 = n - 38$
16. $x = 351 - 182$
17. $44.2 + b = 129 - 84$
18. $290.3 + 36.2 = m$

Choose a letter to represent what is unknown.
Then write an equation and guess and test the solution.

19. The sum of what number and 30 is 48?

20. What number subtracted from 63 is 50?

21. Four more than what number is 27?

22. Twelve less than what number is 6.5?

23. The sum of what number and 35.2 is 47?

24. Twenty-four more than what number is 33.8?

Rainbow's End

Solve each equation. Write the variable above its value below to decode the answer.

What do you find at the end of "The Rainbow"?

$h - 16 = 27$ $46 + l = 82$

$14.3 + w = 52.3$ $e - 71 = 104$

$e + 19 = 63$ $117.2 = t + 22.2$

$78 + 52 = t$ $r - 47 = 18 + 44$

$36.9 - t = 17.9$ $149 - e = 35$

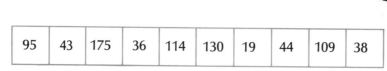

95	43	175	36	114	130	19	44	109	38

Using Equations to Solve Problems

Alex had 48 math problems to do for homework. He did 20 problems at school and 15 problems before supper. How many problems did Alex have left to do after supper?

To solve the problem:

1. Let x represent the unknown number of problems Alex had left to do.

2. Write an equation. $20 + 15 + x = 48$

3. Guess and test the solution of the equation.

1st guess and test:
Alex had 10 problems left.

$$\text{Let } x = 10$$

$$20 + 15 + x = 48$$
$$20 + 15 + 10 = 45$$
$$45 < 48$$

Too small! $x \neq 10$

2nd guess and test:
Alex had 13 problems left.

$$\text{Let } x = 13$$

$$20 + 15 + x = 48$$
$$20 + 15 + 10 = 48$$
$$48 = 48$$

Just right! $x = 13$

Alex had 13 problems left to do after supper.

EXERCISES

Complete the equation for the problem.
Then guess and test the solution.

1. Bernice will be 34 years old in 15 years. How old is she *now*?

   $a + \blacksquare = \blacksquare$

2. Gordon had $10 in small coins and bills in his pocket. He discovered that he lost some of this when he counted only $2.50 left. How much did he lose?

   $\blacksquare - m = \blacksquare$

3. The sum of Gina and Rita's ages is 27. If Rita is 8 years old, how old is Gina?

   $\blacksquare + g = \blacksquare$

4. When a number is subtracted from sixty-three, the result is fifty. What is the number?

   $\blacksquare - n = \blacksquare$

PRACTICE

Complete the equation for this problem.
Then guess and test the solution.

1. After coming home from work, Mr. Daniels said, "I must have had a thousand phone calls today!" Actually, he had only 58 calls. How many more calls would he have to have to bring his total to a thousand? ■ + c = ■

2. Thomas Douglas, the Earl of Selkirk, established a settlement at present-day Winnipeg in 1812. Sixty-two years earlier, a fur trading post called Fort Toronto was built. In what year was Fort Toronto built? $t + $ ■ = ■

3. Lake Superior's total area is 82 103 km². If 53 354 km² of this area is on the American side of the boundary, how much of Lake Superior lies on the Canadian side? ■ + c = ■

4. Janice took $59.49 out of the bank to buy a bicycle. She then had $26.26 left in her account. How much did Janice have in her account before buying the bicycle? $m - $ ■ = ■

REVIEW

Look for tens. Find the sum.

1. 8 + 6 + 2 + 7 + 3 + 2
2. 0.2 + 0.7 + 0.5 + 0.4 + 0.6 + 0.3
3. 9 + 3 + 7 + 8 + 4 + 3 + 1 + 2
4. 0.5 + 0.6 + 0.8 + 0.4 + 0.5 + 0.1

Evaluate each expression. Suppose $x = 4$, $y = 5.5$, and $z = 0.2$.

5. $16 + x$
6. $38 - y$
7. $z + 1.5$
8. $x - z$
9. $y - x$
10. $x + y + z$

Guess and test the solution for each equation.

11. $14 + r = 25$
12. $v - 6 = 12$
13. $a + 9 = 33$
14. $48 - n = 25.3$
15. $t + 20.5 = 180$
16. $s - 12.4 = 17$

Applications

Study each computer program. Then write the computer *output* if
the program were RUN.

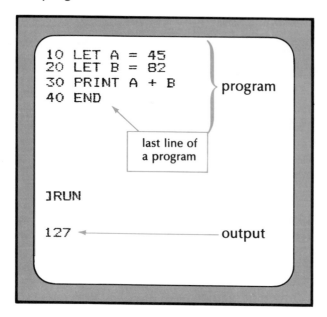

```
10 LET A = 45
20 LET B = 82
30 PRINT A + B
40 END
```
program

last line of
a program

]RUN

127 ←——————————— output

1.
```
10 LET M = 176
20 LET N = 58
30 PRINT M + N
40 END
```

2.
```
10 LET F = 647.3
20 LET G = 8.65
30 PRINT F - G
40 END
```

3.
```
10 LET L = 9.4
20 LET M = 0.173
30 LET N = 67.88
40 PRINT L + M + N
50 END
```

```
10 LET X = 905
20 LET Y = 132
30 PRINT "PROBLEM 1"
40 PRINT X + Y
50 PRINT "PROBLEM 2"
60 PRINT X - Y
70 END
```

]RUN

The computer prints
whatever is typed between
the quotation marks.

```
PROBLEM 1
1037
PROBLEM 2
773
```
output

4.
```
10 LET K = 6.84
20 LET T = 0.657
30 PRINT "PROBLEM 1"
40 PRINT K + T
50 PRINT "PROBLEM 2"
60 PRINT K - T
70 END
```

5.
```
10 LET Q = 94605
20 LET R = 3879
30 LET S = 2423
40 PRINT "PROBLEM 1"
50 PRINT Q + R
60 PRINT "PROBLEM 2"
70 PRINT Q - S
80 PRINT "PROBLEM 3"
90 PRINT Q + R + S
100 END
```

Calculators and Populations

Use the information in the table and a calculator to answer each question.

1. How many more people live in Ontario than live in Quebec?

2. Alberta, Saskatchewan, and Manitoba are called the Prairie provinces. What is their combined population?

3. Nova Scotia, New Brunswick, and Prince Edward Island are called the Maritimes. What is their combined population?

4. How many more people live in the Prairie provinces than the Maritimes?

5. What was Canada's total population in 1981?

Population 1981	
B.C.	2 744 467
Alta.	2 237 724
Sask.	968 313
Man.	1 026 241
Ont.	8 625 107
Que.	6 438 403
N.S.	847 442
N.B.	696 403
P.E.I.	122 506
Nfld.	567 681
Y.T.	23 153
N.W.T.	45 741

Calculator Safe Cracking

In the grid below are sums of two numbers printed on the sides of the safe. The only way to open the safe is to:

1. add all possible combinations of two numbers on the safe.

2. find the vertical, horizontal, or diagonal row that contains five of these sums.

43 956
78 104
34 376
87 524

439.56
875.24
343.76
781.04

78 332	34 719.76	87 963.56	88 399.24	1656.28
44 737.04	1124.8	44 299.76	112 480	35 251.24
1220.6	44 831.24	1219	88 305.04	78 543.56
44 395.56	87 867.76	35 157.04	78 979.24	122 060
78 885.04	121 900	78 447.76	1314.8	34 815.56

Problems

Use the table below to answer questions 1–3.

AREA OF THE PROVINCES AND TERRITORIES			
Province or Territory	Land (km²)	Freshwater (km²)	Total (km²)
Newfoundland	370 485	34 032	404 517
Prince Edward Island	5657	—	5657
Nova Scotia	52 841	2650	55 491
New Brunswick	72 092	1344	73 436
Quebec	1 356 792	183 889	1 540 681
Ontario	891 195	177 388	1 068 583
Manitoba	548 495	101 592	650 087
Saskatchewan	570 269	81 531	651 900
Alberta	844 389	16 796	661 185
British Columbia	930 529	18 068	948 597
Yukon Territory	478 034	4481	482 515
Northwest Territories	3 046 392	133 294	3 379 588
CANADA	9 157 170	755 165	9 922 335

1. Which province or territory has the greatest amount of freshwater? the least?

2. Which province has a total area which is nearly 10 times greater than the total area of Prince Edward Island?

3. Lake Superior has an area of 82 103 km². Which provinces have a total area less than that of Lake Superior?

Solve.

4. The world's largest drum was built for Disneyland in 1961. It has a diameter of 320 cm and a mass of 204 kg. You want to know how many grade 7 students it would take to be as heavy as the drum.
   a. What information do you need that is not given?
   b. What information is given which is unnecessary?

5. On the 21st of September, Marlene baby-sat for 5 h and earned $7.50. On the 28th of September, she earned $6 by baby-sitting 4 h. How much money did she earn in all?

Write in expanded form.

1. 7 095 300   2. 68 276   3. 4 902 700 000

Write the place value of the 8 in each numeral.

4. 3 082 165   5. 42.6781   6. 8 176 000 000

Copy and complete. Use <, = , or >.

7. 80.3512 ● 80.3521   8. 6.09 ● 6.9   9. 4.5 ● 4.4999

Round to the nearest dollar.

10. $14.75   11. $116.25   12. $0.92   13. $3.56

Add or subtract.

14.
```
  730
+ 865
```
15.
```
  243 018
 −  65 237
```
16.
```
  1 067 416
 +   382 933
```
17.
```
   425 803 182
 − 385 973 285
```

18. 7000 − 395   19. 47 262 + 9678   20. 18 − 3.625

21.
```
  19.6
 − 9.08
```
22.
```
  $164.51
 +   85.67
```
23.
```
  3.0025
 − 1.23
```
24.
```
  $4 782.64
 + 3 985.65
```

Round to the nearest whole number. **Estimate** the sum.

25. 6.42 + 0.8 + 9 + 8.763 + 4.2 + 0.5

26. 12.4 + 0.3 + 6.7968 + 4.8 + 9.2 + 6

Evaluate each expression. Suppose $a = 4$, $b = 6.2$, and $c = 15$.

27. $a + 39$ 28. $60 - b$ 29. $c - b$ 30. $b - a$ 31. $a + b$

Guess and test the solution for each equation.

32. $n + 6 = 18$ 33. $40 - b = 12$ 34. $r - 11 = 13$

35. $12 - c = 3.5$ 36. $9 + n = 9.8$ 37. $25 - g = 14.5$

Write an equation. Then guess and test the solution.

38. When you subtract 15 from a number, the result is 24. What is the number?

39. The sum of 6.2 and a number is 11. What is the number?

UNIT 2
Multiplication and Division

Multiplying by Powers of Ten

A **power of 10** is a *product* in which each *factor* is 10.

10^1	ten to the first power	$= 10$	$= 10$
10^2	ten to the second power	$= 10 \times 10$	$= 100$
10^3	ten to the third power	$= 10 \times 10 \times 10$	$= 1000$
10^4	ten to the fourth power	$= 10 \times 10 \times 10 \times 10$	$= 10\,000$

It is easy to multiply by powers of ten.

$62 \times 10 = 620$

$62 \times 100 = 6200$

$62 \times 1000 = 62\,000$

$62 \times 10\,000 = 620\,000$

62 0.

62 00.

62 000.

62 0000.

Rule:

The decimal point moves *right*

the same number of places

as there are zeros in the power of 10.

1. $10^2 = 10 \times 10 = \blacksquare$　　　　**2.** $10^4 = 10 \times 10 \times 10 \times 10 = \blacksquare$

3. $10^3 = \blacksquare$　　**4.** $10^6 = \blacksquare$　　**5.** $10^1 = \blacksquare$　　**6.** $10^5 = \blacksquare$

Multiply each by 10.

7. 32　　　　**8.** 175　　　**9.** 7.8　　　**10.** 0.09　　　**11.** 1.274

Multiply each by 100.

12. 77　　　　**13.** 648　　　**14.** 9.2　　　**15.** 3.15　　　**16.** 0.007

Multiply each by 1000.

17. 26　　　　**18.** 275　　　**19.** 4.9　　　**20.** 7.05　　　**21.** 0.102

Multiply each by 10 000.

22. 6.08　　　**23.** 194　　　**24.** 3.071　　　**25.** 82　　　**26.** 0.5

PRACTICE

Copy and complete.

1.

n	$n \times 10$
6	
342	
0.8	
1.75	
0.253	

2.

n	$n \times 1000$
18	
2.95	
0.006	
0	
4.5	

3.

n	$n \times 100$
0.017	
6.2	
1	
2741	
0.04	

4.

n	$n \times 10\ 000$
0.0001	
0	
0.001	
0.01	
0.1	

5.

n	$n \times 100$
424	
89	
20.6	
0	
2.98	

6.

n	$n \times 10\ 000$
16.7	
924	
1	
0	
86	

Estimating Products

Mrs. Zenon earns $475/week.
About how much does she earn
per year?

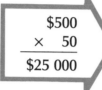

yearly earnings = $475 × 52 weeks

Round each number to
its first digit.

$475 $500
× 52   × 50

Multiply.

$500
×   50
─────────
$25 000

$475 × 52 ≈ $500 × 50
So: $475 × 52 ≈ $25 000

Mrs. Zenon earns about $25 000 per year.

EXERCISES

Estimate the product.

1.   53 ⟶ 50
     × 9 ⟶ ×10
            ■

2.   905 ⟶ 900
     × 18 ⟶ × ■
            ■

3.   733 ⟶ ■
     × 46 ⟶ ×■
            ■

4.   28 ⟶ 30
     ×3.2 ⟶ × 3

5.   62 ⟶ 60
     ×1.8 ⟶ ×■
            ■

6.   29.5 ⟶ ■
     ×12 ⟶ ×■
            ■

7. $4.95 ⟶ $5.00
     ×   6   ×   6

8. $32.15 ⟶ ■
     ×   3 ⟶ ×3
               ■

9. $58.75 ⟶ ■
     ×   18 ⟶ ×■
                ■

10. 74 × 8 ≈ ■

11. 62 × 11 ≈ ■

12. 23 × 96 ≈ ■

13. 372 × 9 ≈ ■

14. 841 × 97 ≈ ■

15. 214 × 588 ≈ ■

16.   32
      × 8

17.   69
      × 7

18.   54
      ×25

19.   482
      × 12

20.   317
      × 28

21.   2.4
      ×0.5

22.   9.5
      ×3.1

23.   72.3
      × 1.6

24. $12.25
      ×   4

25. $17.92
      ×   83

36

PRACTICE

Estimate the product.

1.	18 × 7	**2.**	29 ×51	**3.**	66 × 3	**4.**	67 ×82	**5.**	17 ×63
6.	41 ×48	**7.**	571 × 12	**8.**	27 ×54	**9.**	396 × 92	**10.**	816 × 41
11.	27 ×1.5	**12.**	48.2 × 9	**13.**	34.1 × 11	**14.**	4.96 × 3	**15.**	7.85 × 72
16.	$9.25 × 7	**17.**	$19.42 × 38	**18.**	$29.95 × 66	**19.**	$41.08 × 92	**20.**	$62.14 × 304

Estimate the solution. Use ≈ to express the estimate.

21. Robert's average score for each of 12 gold tournaments was 282. About what was his total score for the 12 tournaments?

22. A large airplane has 9 seats in each row. There are 41 rows in the plane. About how many seats are there altogether?

23. Calculators are on sale for $12.99. Mr. Spencer is thinking of ordering one for each of his 28 math students. About how much would a classroom set of calculators cost?

24. Chicken dinners cost $4.75. Estimate the cost of 18 chicken dinners. Is $70 enough money to pay for them?

In Conclusion

The two statements are true.
Label each conclusion as true or false.

A rectangle has four right angles.
A certain figure has no right angles.

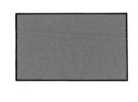

1. The figure has to be a circle.

2. The figure is not a rectangle.

3. The figure could be a parallelogram.

4. No certain conclusion can be made.

Multiplying Whole Numbers

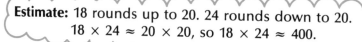

Jennifer sold 18 cases of pop at the school fair. Each case held 24 cans. How many cans of pop did Jennifer sell in all?

total cans sold = 18 × 24

Estimate: 18 rounds up to 20. 24 rounds down to 20.
18 × 24 ≈ 20 × 20, so 18 × 24 ≈ 400.

Multiply
4 ones × 18.

```
  3
  18
× 24
────
  72
```

Multiply
2 tens × 18.

```
  7
  18
× 24
────
  72
 360
```

Add.

```
  18
× 24
────
  72
 360
────
 432
```

```
  18
× 24
────
  72
 360
────
 432
```

Jennifer sold 432 cans of pop in all.

For the school fair, Sam filled 153 bags of popcorn, each bag having a mass of 248 g. What was the total mass of the popcorn Sam bagged?

total mass = 248 × 153

Estimate: 248 rounds down to 200. 153 rounds up to 200.
248 × 153 ≈ 200 × 200, so 248 × 153 ≈ 40 000

Multiply
3 ones × 248.

```
 1 2
 248
×153
─────
 744
```

Multiply
5 tens × 248.

```
 2 4
 248
×153
─────
  744
12400
```

Multiply
1 hundred × 248. Add.

```
  248
 ×153
─────
  744
12400
24800
```

```
  248
 ×153
─────
  744
12400
24800
37944
```

```
  248
 ×153
─────
  744
12400
24800
37944
```

The total mass of the popcorn was 37 944 g.

EXERCISES

Find the product.

1. 94 × 6	**2.** 94 ×40	**3.** 94 ×46	**4.** 68 × 3
5. 68 ×70	**6.** 68 ×73	**7.** 492 × 8	**8.** 492 × 50
9. 492 × 58	**10.** 357 × 4	**11.** 357 × 50	**12.** 357 × 54
13. 603 × 5	**14.** 603 × 50	**15.** 603 ×700	**16.** 603 ×755
17. 25 ×53	**18.** 276 × 38	**19.** 187 ×490	**20.** 704 ×325

How many dots in all?

21.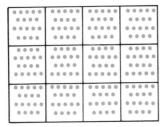

22.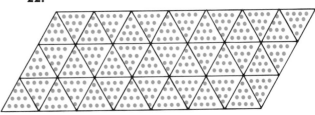

23.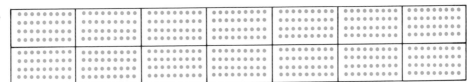

Estimate. Then solve.

24. 21 buses
 55 students per bus
 How many students in all?

25. 48 chairs in each row
 72 rows
 How many chairs in all?

26. 60 min = 1 h
 24 h = 1 d
 How many minutes in one day?

27. 24 h = 1 d
 365 d = 1 a
 How many hours in a year?

Find the product.

1.	32 ×25	**2.**	89 ×64	**3.**	90 ×65	**4.**	26 ×72	**5.**	56 ×54
6.	410 × 84	**7.**	888 × 13	**8.**	306 × 62	**9.**	185 × 95	**10.**	202 × 47
11.	410 ×728	**12.**	974 ×831	**13.**	158 ×302	**14.**	7014 × 363	**15.**	3897 × 145

Estimate the product.

16. $27 \times 38 \approx$ ■

17. $92 \times 25 \approx$ ■

18. $44 \times 77 \approx$ ■

19. $322 \times 86 \approx$ ■

20. $672 \times 47 \approx$ ■

21. $845 \times 119 \approx$ ■

22. $619 \times 781 \approx$ ■

23. $7325 \times 469 \approx$ ■

24. $8017 \times 592 \approx$ ■

Solve.

25. How many days are there in a decade?

26. A case of eggs has 24 one-dozen cartons in it.
How many eggs are in each case?

27. Today is Tom's 13th birthday.
a. About how many days has Tom lived?
b. About how many hours has Tom lived?

28. Joyce makes $62 every two weeks.
How much money does she make in one year?

29. A pocket book averages 8 words per line and 27 lines per page.
About how many words are in the book if it has 159 pages?

Summing Out

Study how the multiplication is checked.

```
   386          3 + 8 + 6 = 17    1 + 7 = 8
  ×273          2 + 7 + 3 = 12    1 + 2 = 3     8 × 3 = 24    2 + 4 = 6
 105 378    1 + 5 + 3 + 7 + 8 = 24    2 + 4 = 6
```

Check problems 11 to 15 above by *Summing Out*.

Calculator Code

Why does a hen lay eggs?

The answer to the riddle can be found by finding each product.
Match the letters of the calculator exercises with the product below.

A. 810 ×786	D. 954 ×129	I. 428 ×831	U. 655 ×406	E. 240 ×119
B. 271 ×344	E. 716 ×518	P. 102 ×399	M. 821 ×456	H. 159 ×207
K. 573 ×134	H. 466 ×271	E. 316 ×398	W. 449 ×230	S. 861 ×511
P. 625 ×431	L. 697 ×205	F. 358 ×116	R. 473 ×154	O. 726 ×300
Y. 870 ×325	E. 900 ×667	D. 487 ×192	H. 148 ×465	T. 379 ×160
T. 3054 × 624	O. 1808 × 207	R. 4856 × 139	E. 5600 × 300	D. 9146 × 288

| 355 668 | 41 528 | | 439 971 | 68 820 | 1 680 000 |

| 123 066 | 674 984 | 217 800 | 40 698 | 269 375 | 370 888 | 93 504 |

| 60 640 | 32 913 | 28 560 | 374 376 | | 1 905 696 | 126 286 | 125 768 | 282 750 |

| 103 270 | 374 256 | 265 930 | 142 885 | 2 634 048 |

| 93 224 | 72 842 | 600 300 | 636 660 | 76 782 |

41

Multiplying Decimals

How many litres of paint are in the 6 cans?

4.54 × 6 = total litres

Estimate: 4.54 × 6 ≈ 5 × 6, so 4.54 × 6 ≈ 30.

$$\begin{array}{r} 4.54 \\ \times\ \ \ \ 6 \\ \hline 27.24 \end{array}$$

The factors have a total of
2 decimal places.

The product has
2 decimal places

There are 27.24 L of paint in 6 cans.

How many litres of paint are there in 1.5 cans?

4.54 × 1.5 = total litres

Estimate: 4.54 × 1.5 ≈ 5 × 2, so 4.54 × 1.5 ≈ 10.

$$\begin{array}{r} 4.54 \\ \times\ \ 1.5 \\ \hline 2270 \\ 4540 \\ \hline 6.810 \end{array}$$

The factors have a total of
3 decimal places.

The product has
3 decimal places.

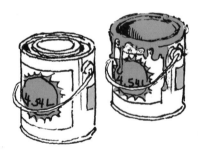

There are 6.81 L of paint in 1.5 cans.

It is easy to calculate the total litres of paint when you must
multiply by a power of 10.

100 cans	= 100 × 4.54 =	454.	The decimal moves *right*.
10 cans	= 10 × 4.54 =	45.4	The product is larger than 4.54.
1 can	= 1 × 4.54 =	4.54	
0.1 of a can	= 0.1 × 4.54 =	0.454	The decimal moves *left*.
0.01 of a can	= 0.01 × 4.54 =	0.0454	The product is smaller than 4.54.

42

EXERCISES

Find the product.

1.	243 × 8	**2.**	24.3 × 8	**3.**	2.43 × 8	**4.**	0.243 × 8
5.	243 × 0.8	**6.**	24.3 × 0.8	**7.**	2.43 × 0.8	**8.**	0.243 × 0.8
9.	243 ×0.08	**10.**	24.3 ×0.08	**11.**	2.43 ×0.08	**12.**	0.243 × 0.08

13.
75×100
75×10
75×1
75×0.1
75×0.01

14.
7.5×100
7.5×10
7.5×1
7.5×0.1
7.5×0.01

15.
7.05×100
7.05×10
7.05×1
7.05×0.1
7.05×0.01

16.
7.005×100
7.005×10
7.005×1
7.005×0.1
7.005×0.01

17.	51.5 × 33	**18.**	5.15 × 33	**19.**	5.15 × 3.3	**20.**	5.15 ×0.33

Estimate. Then find the product.

21.	37.2 × 2.4	**22.**	9.56 × 7.5	**23.**	53.6 ×0.43	**24.**	12.5 ×0.079

Copy and complete.

25. One box of cereal is 675 g.

2.5 boxes = ■ g
0.5 box = ■ g
0.1 box = ■ g

26. One can of juice concentrate is 355 mL.

4 cans = ■ mL
3.5 cans = ■ mL
0.5 can = ■ mL

27. One bag of flour is 2.5 kg.

7 bags = ■ kg
2.5 bags = ■ kg
0.1 bag = ■ kg

28. One can of paint is 4.54 L.

3.5 cans = ■ L
0.5 can = ■ L
0.25 can = ■ L

PRACTICE

Find the product.

1. $0.26 × 3	**2.** $0.05 × 9	**3.** $0.84 × 6	**4.** $2.57 × 4	**5.** $6.50 × 8
6. 841 × 0.6	**7.** 428 × 0.5	**8.** 28.4 × 0.2	**9.** 2.02 × 0.7	**10.** 5.98 × 0.8
11. $53.19 × 0.25	**12.** $91.26 × 0.42	**13.** $34 × 0.50	**14.** $75 × 0.25	**15.** $34.61 × 0.08
16. 25.70 × 0.08	**17.** 276.1 × 0.073	**18.** 1452 × 0.368	**19.** 6183 × 0.245	**20.** 430.6 × 0.661

Estimate the product.

21. $97.6 × 0.8 ≈$ ■ **22.** $2.195 × 1.9 ≈$ ■ **23.** $\$675 × 0.75 ≈$ ■

24. $\$94.31 × 1.5 ≈$ ■ **25.** $6.08 × 0.8 ≈$ ■ **26.** $123.4 × 10.8 ≈$ ■

27. $99.2 × 2.3 ≈$ ■ **28.** $78.3 × 0.02 ≈$ ■ **29.** $334 × 1.09 ≈$ ■

Calculate the cost of the gasoline sold at each pump.
Round to the nearest cent.

30.
55.3¢
Cost Per Litre
62.5
Litres Sold

31.
62.4¢
Cost Per Litre
58.7
Litres Sold

32.
48.9¢
Cost Per Litre
61.4
Litres Sold

Solve.

33. Mrs. Baxter bought 3.455 kg of beef.

She packed all but about $\frac{1}{5}$ (or 0.2) of it for the freezer.

  a. About how many kilograms of beef did Mrs. Baxter leave unfrozen?

  b. About how many kilograms of beef did Mrs. Baxter freeze?

34. Mr. Werley made a frame that is 3 times as long as one he already has. The frame he has is 0.5 m long. How long will the new frame be?

Decimal Search

Some members of the 7th-grade class participated in a *Decimal Search*. The rules were that they each had $\frac{1}{2}$ h to find 3 decimals mentioned in newspapers or magazines in the school library. Then, each student used a calculator to multiply his or her decimals together to get one product. The winner of the *Decimal Search* was the student whose product was the smallest.

Find each student's product. Who was the winner?

Student's Name	Three Decimals Found		
Janice	0.6	0.001	0.41
Brian	0.02	0.4	0.5
Sara	0.7	0.3	0.01
Charles	0.01	0.02	0.06
Jim	0.16	0.105	0.9
Caroline	0.81	0.045	0.11
Matt	0.5	0.1	0.02
Martha	0.2	0.4	0.01
Ted	0.9	0.11	0.2
Elaine	0.15	0.05	0.003
Juan	0.1	0.001	0.3
Lynne	0.04	0.09	0.1
Ingrid	0.01	0.001	0.1
Ian	0.34	0.009	0.012

Letter Math

Each different letter stands for a different digit. Find the digits that make the problem work.

One-Digit Divisors

Six history books have a mass of 2.52 kg.
What is the mass of one history book?

2.52 ÷ 6 = mass of one book

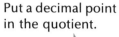

Put a decimal point in the quotient.	There are no ones.	**Long Division**	**Short Division**	Check

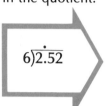

$$6)\overline{2.52}$$
with decimal point above

$$6)\overline{2.52}$$
$$\ \ 0.$$

Long Division
$$\begin{array}{r} 0.42 \\ 6)\overline{2.52} \\ -2\,4 \\ \hline 12 \\ -12 \\ \hline 0 \end{array}$$

Short Division
$$\begin{array}{r} 0.42 \\ 6)\overline{2.52} \end{array}$$

Check
$$\begin{array}{r} 0.42 \quad \text{quotient} \\ \times \quad 6 \quad \text{divisor} \\ \hline 2.52 \quad \text{dividend} \end{array}$$

One history book has a mass of 0.42 kg.

EXERCISES

Find the quotient. Check your answer.

1. $9)\overline{81}$
2. $2)\overline{8.1}$
3. $6)\overline{84}$
4. $6)\overline{8.4}$

5. $4)\overline{96}$
6. $4)\overline{9.6}$
7. $7)\overline{98}$
8. $7)\overline{9.8}$

9. $8)\overline{456}$
10. $8)\overline{4.56}$
11. $9)\overline{144}$
12. $9)\overline{\$1.44}$

13. $3)\overline{552}$
14. $3)\overline{5.52}$
15. $6)\overline{738}$
16. $6)\overline{\$7.38}$

17. $8)\overline{3656}$
18. $8)\overline{3.656}$
19. $5)\overline{2230}$
20. $5)\overline{\$22.30}$

21. $8.7 \div 3$
22. $316 \div 4$
23. $\$19.25 \div 7$
24. $2624 \div 8$

25. $\$4.50 \div 9$
26. $33.6 \div 7$
27. $1698 \div 3$
28. $648.9 \div 9$

Solve.

29. 3 pairs of socks for $7.47

What does one pair cost?

30. 354 km driven in 4 h

How many kilometres per hour?

PRACTICE

Find the quotient.
1. 3)$\overline{57}$
2. 2)$\overline{98}$
3. 9)$\overline{117}$
4. 5)$\overline{345}$

5. 4)$\overline{3404}$
6. 8)$\overline{5216}$
7. 9)$\overline{3366}$
8. 7)$\overline{4361}$

9. 4)$\overline{7.2}$
10. 8)$\overline{5.6}$
11. 7)$\overline{25.2}$
12. 3)$\overline{\$4.68}$

13. 6)$\overline{\$53.70}$
14. 7)$\overline{\$17.15}$
15. 4)$\overline{\$38.24}$
16. 9)$\overline{\$51.66}$

17. 222 ÷ 3
18. 612 ÷ 9
19. 3372 ÷ 6
20. 3205 ÷ 5

21. 1144 ÷ 8
22. 1508 ÷ 4
23. 47.6 ÷ 7
24. 76.5 ÷ 9

25. 168.6 ÷ 6
26. 432.8 ÷ 8
27. $4.80 ÷ 5
28. $29.44 ÷ 4

Solve.

29. An airplane travelled 2655.9 km in 3 h. How far did it go in 1 h?

30. Seven theatre tickets cost $115.50. What is the cost per ticket?

31. When a mystery number is added to 53.4, the sum is 334.4 ÷ 5. What is the mystery number?

32. When a mystery number is subtracted from 294.6, the difference is 915.2 ÷ 4. What is the mystery number?

REVIEW

Find the product.
1. 100 × 3.5
2. 0.52 × 10
3. 0.766 × 100

Estimate the product.
4. 9.9 × 3.2
5. 507 × 89
6. $78.59 × 187

Multiply.
7. 107 × 54
8. 216 × 513
9. 7009 × 588
10. 0.7 × 0.3
11. $11.96 × 0.5
12. 5089 × 0.273

Divide.
13. 3)$\overline{7962}$
14. 9)$\overline{21.6}$
15. 4)$\overline{\$19.76}$

Powers of Ten as Divisors

Dividing by powers of 10 is easily calculated.

$84 \div 10^1$	=	$84 \div 10$	=	8.4
$84 \div 10^2$	=	$84 \div 100$	=	0.84
$84 \div 10^3$	=	$84 \div 1000$	=	0.084
$84 \div 10^4$	=	$84 \div 10\ 000$	=	0.0084

Rule:
The decimal point moves *left* the same number of places as there are zeros in the power of 10.

Divide $84 among 10 people.

Each person gets $84 ÷ **10** or $8.40.	means the same as	Each person gets $84 × **0.1** or $8.40.

Divide $84 among 100 people.

Each person gets $84 ÷ **100** or $0.84.	means the same as	Each person gets $84 × **0.01** or $0.84.

EXERCISES

Divide each by 10.

1. 36 **2.** 129 **3.** 8957 **4.** 24.3 **5.** $8.20

Divide each by 100.

6. 425 **7.** 7660 **8.** 12 **9.** 2.5 **10.** $43.75

Divide each by 1000.

11. 29 475 **12.** 325 **13.** 6 **14.** 24.7 **15.** $80

Compare the answers. Are they the same?

16. $10\overline{)465}$ $465 \times 0.1 =$ **17.** $100\overline{)24.5}$ $24.5 \times 0.01 =$

18. $1000\overline{)3695}$ $3695 \times 0.001 =$ **19.** $10\ 000\overline{)57.30}$ $57.30 \times 0.0001 =$

Divide to complete each statement.

20. | 1000 g = 1 kg |

625 g = ■ kg
48 g = ■ kg
100 g = ■ kg

21. | 1000 m = 1 km |

750 m = ■ km
9 m = ■ km
85 m = ■ km

22. | 1000 mm = 1 m |

2254 mm = ■ m
48 mm = ■ m
912 mm = ■ m

Find each quotient.

1.
$$
\begin{array}{l}
346 \div 1 \\
346 \div 10 \\
346 \div 100 \\
346 \div 1000
\end{array}
$$

2.
$$
\begin{array}{l}
6500 \div 10 \\
6500 \div 100 \\
6500 \div 1000 \\
6500 \div 10\,000
\end{array}
$$

3.
$$
\begin{array}{l}
7 \div 1 \\
7 \div 10 \\
7 \div 100 \\
7 \div 1000
\end{array}
$$

4.
$$
\begin{array}{l}
35.2 \div 1 \\
35.2 \div 10 \\
35.2 \div 100 \\
35.2 \div 1000
\end{array}
$$

5. $10\overline{)887}$

6. $100\overline{)2}$

7. $1000\overline{)\$60}$

8. $10\,000\overline{)\$400}$

9. $100\overline{)2.4}$

10. $10\overline{)0.15}$

11. $1\overline{)0.02}$

12. $1000\overline{)72.5}$

Copy and complete. Use <, =, or >.

13. $3.2 \times 10 \bullet 3200 \div 100$

14. $237 \times 100 \bullet 237\,000 \div 100$

15. $0.41 \times 100 \bullet 4100 \div 100$

16. $400 \times 0.1 \bullet 400 \div 10$

17. $20 \times 0.001 \bullet 20\,000 \div 100$

18. $78 \times 0.01 \bullet 78 \div 1000$

Rewrite each fact in kilometres.

19. Brenda swims 500 m every day.

20. Brenda's swimming pool is 25 m long.

Solve.

21. One thousand sheets of paper are 85 mm thick. How thick is each sheet?

22. The longest ice skating race held regularly is 200 km long. How many metres long is the race?

Calculator Constants

Some calculators have a *constant* feature. This enables a number to be multiplied or divided many times.

$12\,345 \div 100$ (or $12\,345 \div 10^2$):

| 1 | 2 | 3 | 4 | 5 | ÷ | 1 | 0 | = | = |

18×1000 (or 18×10^3):

| 1 | 8 | × | 1 | 0 | = | = | = |

For each set of key presses, write the calculator display.
Write an equation for each using exponents.

a. | 1 | 7 | 4 | 9 | ÷ | 1 | 0 | = | = |

b. | 1 | 0 | × | 1 | . | 7 | = | = | = | = | = |

49

Estimating Quotients

Mr. Kraus earned $3045 for 21 days of work during the month of October. About how much did he earn per day in October?

daily earnings = $3045 ÷ 21 days

Round each number to its first digit.

Divide.

$$21\overline{)3045} \longrightarrow 20\overline{)3000}$$

$$20\overline{)3000} = 150$$

Estimated earnings per day ≈ $150.

Mr. Kraus earned *about* $150 per day in October.

EXERCISES

Round each number to its first digit.
Then **estimate** the first digit of the quotient.

1. $84\overline{)345}$ ⟶ $80\overline{)300}$ ■

2. $17\overline{)857}$ ⟶ $20\overline{)900}$ ■

3. $62\overline{)3247}$ ⟶ ■$\overline{)}$■ ■

4. $76\overline{)2449}$ ⟶ ■$\overline{)}$■ ■

5. $13\overline{)4182}$ ⟶ ■$\overline{)}$■ ■

6. $88\overline{)7528}$ ⟶ ■$\overline{)}$■ ■

Estimate the quotient.

7. $19\overline{)117}$ ⟶ $20\overline{)100}$

8. $47\overline{)388}$ ⟶ ■$\overline{)}$■

9. $22\overline{)815}$ ⟶ ■$\overline{)800}$

10. $32\overline{)8027}$ ⟶ ■$\overline{)}$■

11. $71\overline{)1215}$ ⟶ ■$\overline{)1000}$

12. $28\overline{)8910}$ ⟶ ■$\overline{)}$■

13. $18\overline{)67.5}$ ⟶ ■$\overline{)70}$

14. $48\overline{)435.2}$ ⟶ ■$\overline{)}$■

15. $95\overline{)788.4}$ ⟶ ■$\overline{)800}$

16. $33\overline{)612.9}$ ⟶ ■$\overline{)}$■

17. $996 ÷ 22 ≈$ ■

18. $3711 ÷ 39 ≈$ ■

19. $8146 ÷ 8 ≈$ ■

20. $98.2 ÷ 49 ≈$ ■

21. $417.8 ÷ 9.5 ≈$ ■

22. $64 ÷ 0.9 ≈$ ■

Estimate the quotient.

1. $58\overline{)506}$ 2. $83\overline{)673}$ 3. $19\overline{)864}$ 4. $28\overline{)747}$

5. $23\overline{)8510}$ 6. $61\overline{)2076}$ 7. $47\overline{)9480}$ 8. $11\overline{)5230}$

9. $32\overline{)86.3}$ 10. $78\overline{)587.9}$ 11. $1.8\overline{)\$82}$ 12. $2.3\overline{)\$398}$

13. $657 \div 21 \approx$ ■   14. $7550 \div 58 \approx$ ■   15. $8176 \div 38 \approx$ ■

16. $\$92.25 \div 32 \approx$ ■   17. $\$48.75 \div 25 \approx$ ■   18. $\$372 \div 98 \approx$ ■

19. $28 \div 1.2 \approx$ ■   20. $39 \div 7.9 \approx$ ■   21. $82 \div 2.2 \approx$ ■

Estimate the solution. Use ≈ to express the estimate.

22. 895 students in all
33 classes
About how many
students per class?

23. $812 earned
37 h worked
About how much money
is earned per hour?

24. 28 poetry books bought
$278.60 paid for the books
About how much was
paid per book?

25. 625 eggs
About how many dozen?

26. $984 shared
32 people
About how much
money per person?

27. 415 apartments
18 floors
About how many
apartments per floor?

28. 9360 auditorium seats
65 rows
About how many
seats per row?

29. $7800 paid in all
24 payments
About how much
money for each payment?

Who's Who?

Sarah, Freda, and Gail are the girlfriends of Jack, Ken, and Bryan although not necessarily in that order.

Sarah's boyfriend and Jack's girlfriend play as a mixed doubles badminton team against Jack and Freda. No girl plays with her boyfriend. Bryan does not play badminton.

Who is each girl's boyfriend?

	Jack	Ken	Bryan
Sarah	?	?	?
Freda	?	?	?
Gail	?	?	?

Dividing by Whole Numbers

A broadway show ran for 4118 performances. If the show was put on 294 times each year, how many years did the show run?

years the show ran = 4118 ÷ 294

Estimate.

$$\begin{array}{r} 1 \\ 300\overline{)4000} \end{array}$$

Multiply. Subtract.

$$\begin{array}{r} 1 \\ 294\overline{)4118} \\ -294 \\ \hline 117 \end{array}$$

Estimate.

$$\begin{array}{r} 3 \\ 300\overline{)1000} \end{array}$$

Multiply. Subtract.

$$\begin{array}{r} 13 \\ 294\overline{)4118} \\ -294 \\ \hline 1178 \\ -882 \\ \hline 296 \end{array}$$

Estimate again.

STOP!
3 is too small.
Try 4.

Multiply. Subtract.

$$\begin{array}{r} 14R2 \\ 294\overline{)4118} \\ -294 \\ \hline 1178 \\ -1176 \\ \hline 2 \end{array}$$

Check.

$$\begin{array}{r} 31 \\ 294 \\ \times\ 14 \\ \hline 1176 \\ 2940 \\ \hline 4116 \\ +\ \ 2 \\ \hline 4118 \end{array}$$

294 divisor
× 14 quotient

+ 2 remainder

4118 dividend

The broadway show ran about 14 years.

EXERCISES

Is the first estimate too small or too large?
Complete the second division.

1. $38\overline{)748}$ $38\overline{)748}$
   -76

2. $46\overline{)3264}$ $46\overline{)3264}$
   -176

Divide.

3. $20\overline{)502}$ 4. $23\overline{)502}$ 5. $50\overline{)3983}$ 6. $47\overline{)3983}$

7. $219\overline{)786}$ 8. $579\overline{)1962}$ 9. $32\overline{)902.4}$ 10. $17\overline{)\$21.52}$

PRACTICE

Divide. Check your answers.

1. 12)84 2. 15)75 3. 48)492 4. 18)3600

5. 24)7008 6. 13)5226 7. 26)13 078 8. 94)29 477

9. 104)650 10. 173)8026 11. 18)529.2 12. 81)4106.7

Find the divisor.

13. $5152 \div \blacksquare = 92$ 14. $\$75.60 \div \blacksquare = \$3.50$ 15. $607.6 \div \blacksquare = 0.7$

Find the dividend.

16. $\blacksquare \div 64 = 355$ 17. $\blacksquare \div 32 = \$2.98$ 18. $\blacksquare \div 192 = 53.4$

Solve.

19. A building has a fire escape with 375 steps. If there are 15 steps for each floor, how many floors are in the building?

20. The Schaefers average 88 km/h when driving on a highway. About how long will it take them to drive 530 km?

21. When a mystery number is divided by 64, the quotient is $85 + 17$. What is the mystery number?

22. When 2088 is divided by a mystery number, the quotient is $71 - 13$. What is the mystery number?

How is an Icicle Like a Goose?

The answer to the riddle can be found by matching the letters of the problems with the quotients below.

G. $7.13 \div 2$ O. $56.8 \div 4$ D. $370.215 \div 5$ H. $0.675 \div 3$

E. $72.42 \div 6$ R. $1938.48 \div 8$ O. $10.913 \div 7$ T. $0.081 \div 9$

W. $583.098 \div 6$ Y. $20\ 795.2 \div 4$ O. $81.515 \div 5$ N. $193.47 \div 3$

H. $9.416 \div 8$ B. $5371.02 \div 9$ T. $605.14 \div 2$ W. $109.186 \div 7$

302.57	0.225	12.07	5198.8

596.78	14.2	0.009	1.177

3.565	242.31	16.303	15.598

74.043	1.559	97.183	64.49

Rounding Quotients

What is the cost
of one cupcake?

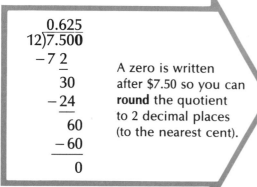

CHOCOLATE
CUPCAKES $7.50/
Dozen

$7.50 ÷ 12 = cost of one cupcake

Divide to 3 decimal places.

Round the quotient
to 2 decimal places.

$$
\begin{array}{r}
0.625 \\
12\overline{)7.500} \\
-7\,2 \\
\hline
30 \\
-24 \\
\hline
60 \\
-60 \\
\hline
0
\end{array}
$$

A zero is written
after $7.50 so you can
round the quotient
to 2 decimal places
(to the nearest cent).

$0.625 rounds up
to $0.63.

One cupcake costs $0.63.

EXERCISES

Round the quotient to one decimal place.

7.24	5.63	1.28	2.33
1. 12)86.88	**2.** 32)180.16	**3.** 48)61.44	**4.** 69)162.15

Round the quotient to two decimal places.

1.783	4.255	6.319	0.266
5. 25)44.575	**6.** 47)199.985	**7.** 18)113.742	**8.** 95)21.470

Divide. Round the quotient to one decimal place.

9. 6)53.9   6)53.90

10. 7)684   7)684.00

11. 12)189.6   **12.** 31)955   **13.** 52)64.7   **14.** 98)768

Divide. Round the quotient to the nearest cent.

15. 16)$45.65   16)$45.650

16. 25)$968   25)$968.000

17. 33)$4.75   **18.** 75)$46.25   **19.** 14)$114   **20.** 62)$900

Divide. Round the quotient to one decimal place.

1. $12\overline{)46.3}$ 2. $35\overline{)206}$ 3. $52\overline{)517}$ 4. $11\overline{)738.6}$

Divide. Round the quotient to two decimal places.

5. $3\overline{)1.9}$ 6. $48\overline{)21.2}$ 7. $14\overline{)73}$ 8. $22\overline{)686}$

Divide. Round the quotient to the nearest cent.

9. $16\overline{)\$4.12}$ 10. $25\overline{)\$42.10}$ 11. $32\overline{)\$187.60}$ 12. $98\overline{)\$24.38}$

Find the cost of one. Then tell which is the better buy.

13.
| Oranges 12 for $1.99 | 4 oranges for 79¢ |

14.
| 4 grapefruit for 89¢ | Grapefruit $2.99 a dozen |

15.
| Limes $1.29 a dozen | 3 Limes for 25¢ |

16.
| Lemons 12 for 99¢ | Lemons 3/$0.19 |

17.
| Yogurt 500 g $2.59 | Yogurt 850 g $3.59 |

18.
| Peas 2 cans for $1.15 | Peas 5 cans/$1.79 |

19.
| Green Peppers 6/99¢ | Green Peppers 5 for $0.79 |

20.
| 3 Sesame Seed Rolls for 39¢ | Sesame Seed Rolls $1.29/dozen |

Logical Figures

Each different figure stands for a different digit. Can you find the numerical value of each figure?

$$\frac{\text{✳}\,32.\text{✳}\,\text{✳}}{\text{✳}} = \blacksquare\,0.6\,\text{✳}\,\blacksquare$$

$$\frac{5\,\blacksquare\,\blacksquare.\blacksquare\,⬡}{⬡} = \blacktriangle\,⬟.0\blacktriangle$$

Hint:
Division can be written 3 ways.

$8 \div 4 = 2$
$4\overline{)8}\,^{2}$
$\dfrac{8}{4} = 2$

55

Dividing by Tenths and Hundredths

How many 0.4 m pieces of cord can be cut from a 11.2 m ball of cord?

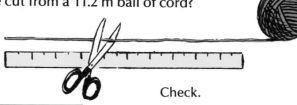

$$\frac{11.2}{0.4} = \text{number of pieces}$$

Divide.

```
      28.
04.)112.
    - 8
     32
    -32
      0
```

The dividend and divisor are *multiplied by 10* so you can divide by a whole number.

$$\frac{11.2}{0.4} = \frac{11.2 \boxed{\times\ 10}}{0.4 \boxed{\times\ 10}} = \frac{112}{4}$$

Check.

```
       3
      28    quotient
    ×0.4    divisor
    11.2    dividend
```

How many 3.25 m pieces of cord can be cut from 13 m of cord?

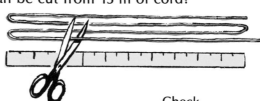

$$\frac{13}{3.25} = \text{number of pieces}$$

Divide.

```
        4.
325.)1300.
    - 1300
        0
```

The dividend and divisor are *multiplied by 100* so you can divide by a whole number.

$$\frac{13}{3.25} = \frac{13 \boxed{\times\ 100}}{3.25 \boxed{\times\ 100}} = \frac{1300}{325}$$

Check.

```
     3.25    divisor
    ×   4    quotient
    13.00    dividend
```

It is easy to calculate how many pieces of cord you can cut when you are dividing by powers of 10.

Size of Cord Pieces			Pieces	
10 m	=	32 ÷ 10	=	3.2
1 m	=	32 ÷ 1	=	32
0.1 m	=	32 ÷ 0.1	=	320.
0.01 m	=	32 ÷ 0.01	=	3200.
0.001 m	=	32 ÷ 0.001	=	32 000.

The decimal moves *left*.
The quotient is smaller than 32.

The decimal moves *right*.
The quotient is larger than 32.

32 m

EXERCISES

Multiply each number by 10.

1. 65   **2.** 1.7   **3.** 4.26   **4.** 5.627   **5.** 0.89

Multiply the dividend and divisor by 10. Divide by a whole number.

6. $0.4\overline{)16.8}$ ⟶ $04.\overline{)168.}$ **7.** $2.1\overline{)126}$ ⟶ $21.\overline{)1260.}$

8. $0.9\overline{)3.96}$ ⟶ $09.\overline{)39.6}$ **9.** $0.5\overline{)34}$ ⟶ $05.\overline{)340.}$

10. $0.6\overline{)81}$ **11.** $0.2\overline{)0.226}$ **12.** $2.2\overline{)209}$ **13.** $8.5\overline{)384.2}$

Multiply each number by 100.

14. 3.96   **15.** 0.143   **16.** 63.906   **17.** 411.9   **18.** 23

Multiply the dividend and divisor by 100. Divide by a whole number.

19. $0.06\overline{)21.6}$ ⟶ $006.\overline{)2160.}$ **20.** $0.25\overline{)75}$ ⟶ $025.\overline{)7500.}$

21. $0.04\overline{)108}$ ⟶ $004.\overline{)10800.}$ **22.** $0.06\overline{)67.308}$ ⟶ $006.\overline{)6730.8}$

23. $0.09\overline{)513.9}$ **24.** $0.03\overline{)5118}$ **25.** $0.64\overline{)2.240}$ **26.** $0.42\overline{)0.861}$

27. How many tenths are there in 2?   **28.** How many hundredths are there in 2?

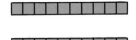 $0.1\overline{)2}$  $0.01\overline{)2}$

Copy and complete.

29.

125 ÷ 100	= ■
125 ÷ 10	= ■
125 ÷ 1	= ■
125 ÷ 0.1	= ■
125 ÷ 0.01	= ■

30.

40 ÷ 100	= ■
40 ÷ 10	= ■
40 ÷ 1	= ■
40 ÷ 0.1	= ■
40 ÷ 0.01	= ■

31.

8 ÷ 100	= ■
8 ÷ 10	= ■
8 ÷ 1	= ■
8 ÷ 0.1	= ■
8 ÷ 0.01	= ■

Divide. Round the quotient to one decimal place.

32. $0.3\overline{)7.564}$ ⟶ $03.\overline{)75.64}$ **33.** $0.03\overline{)7.564}$ ⟶ $003.\overline{)756.40}$

34. $0.7\overline{)65}$ **35.** $0.07\overline{)65}$ **36.** $0.9\overline{)33}$ **37.** $0.09\overline{)33}$

PRACTICE

Find the quotient.

1. $0.2\overline{)9.6}$ **2.** $0.05\overline{)125}$ **3.** $0.7\overline{)25.2}$ **4.** $0.03\overline{)141}$

5. $3.6\overline{)4.32}$ **6.** $0.52\overline{)936}$ **7.** $9.6\overline{)3.168}$ **8.** $0.44\overline{)926.2}$

Divide. Round the quotient to one decimal place.

9. $0.3\overline{)9.26}$ **10.** $0.7\overline{)167}$ **11.** $0.09\overline{)55.3}$ **12.** $0.25\overline{)389}$

Divide. Round the quotient to two decimal places.

13. $0.7\overline{)1.8}$ **14.** $2.3\overline{)3.4}$ **15.** $0.09\overline{)6.4}$ **16.** $0.35\overline{)12}$

Solve.

17. In the past month, an airline pilot has flown 36 h going from Calgary to Vancouver. Each of her Calgary-Vancouver flights has lasted 1.5 h. How many flights has the pilot made in the past month from Calgary to Vancouver?

18. John walks 0.75 km from his home to school each day. He attends school for 200 days in one year. How far does John walk back and forth to school in one year.

19. When 34 is divided by a mystery number, the quotient is 200 − 30. What is the mystery number?

20. When 4.5 is divided by a mystery number, the quotient is 50 × 30. What is the mystery number?

Calculating Mentally

To **divide by 5:**	To **divide by 0.5:**	To **divide by 0.05:**
1. Multiply by 2. 2. Move decimal point one place left.	1. Multiply by 2.	1. Multiply by 20.

$5\overline{)40} = 40 \times 2 = \mathbf{80}$ $00.5\overline{)40} = 40 \times 2 = 80$ $0.05\overline{)40} = 40 \times \mathbf{20} = 80$

Try these:

a. $60 \div 5$ **b.** $324 \div 0.5$ **c.** $743 \div 5$ **d.** $6.05 \div 0.5$

e. $60 \div 0.05$ **f.** $324 \div 0.05$ **g.** $743 \div 0.5$ **h.** $6.05 \div 0.05$

Food Labels

The food labels show the mass in kilograms, the price per kilogram, and the total cost. Find the missing information.

1.

Canada #1 White Honey		
Mass	Price per kilogram	Total $
0.500 kg	?	$1.53

2.

Medium Coconut (Bulk)		
Mass	Price per kilogram	Total $
?	$5.40	$2.16

3.

Long Grain Rice (Bulk)		
Mass	Price per kilogram	Total $
2.200 kg	$1.99	?

4.

Whole Wheat Flour (Bulk)		
Mass	Price per kilogram	Total $
2.500 kg	?	$1.25

5.

Unsalted Sunflower Seeds (Bulk)		
Mass	Price per kilogram	Total $
?	$4.62	$6.93

6.

Chocolate Chips (Bulk)		
Mass	Price per kilogram	Total $
0.300 kg	$6.79	?

7.

Lean Ground Beef		
Mass	Price per kilogram	Total $
0.615 kg	$4.17	?

8.

Pork Chops		
Mass	Price per kilogram	Total $
1.060 kg	?	$8.47

9.

Chicken Legs		
Mass	Price per kilogram	Total $
?	$2.88	$4.32

10.

Swiss Cheese		
Mass	Price per kilogram	Total $
0.125	$4.29	?

Evaluating Expressions

Some English phrases can be translated into mathematical **expressions.** Each expression has a letter called a *variable* which represents an unknown number.

Phrases	**Expressions**
1. 7 times a number	$7n$ (or $7 \times n$)
2. 28 divided by a number	$\dfrac{28}{b}$
3. the product of a number and 2	$2c$ (or $2 \times c$)
4. a number divided by 11	$\dfrac{n}{11}$
5. the product of 5 and two unknowns	$5xy$ (or $5 \times x \times y$)
6. Mary's grandmother is 5 times older than Mary. Mary's grandmother's age	$5m$ (or $5 \times m$)

An expression can be **evaluated** if a value is substituted for the variable. For example 6, suppose that Mary's age is 12.

Since $m = 12$, then $5m = 5 \times 12$
Mary's grandmother is 60 years old.

EXERCISES

Choose an expression for each phrase.

1. a number multiplied by 7 $7x$ or $7 + x$
2. a number divided by 6 $\dfrac{6}{n}$ or $\dfrac{n}{6}$
3. the product of 8 and two unknowns $8x$ or $8xy$

Choose a letter to represent what is unknown.
Then write an expression.

4. 24 divided by a number   5. 17 times a number

6. 12 times two unknowns   7. a number divided by 2

Evaluate each expression. Suppose $a = 12$, $b = 4$, and $c = 10$.

8. $16a$ 9. $\dfrac{60}{a}$ 10. $3ab$ 11. $\dfrac{c}{2}$ 12. abc

PRACTICE

Choose a letter to represent what is unknown.
Then write an expression.

1. 8 times a number
2. the quotient of a number and 4
3. 18 divided by a number
4. the product of 14 and two unknowns
5. a number is divided by 100
6. the product of 3 unknowns

7. Cedarbrook School has 500 students in an unknown number of classrooms. How many students are in each classroom?

8. Mr. Antonelli's house is 3 times older than Mr. Ali's house. How old is Mr. Antonelli's house?

9. A residential building has 120 apartments. It has an unknown number of apartments on each floor. How many floors does the building have?

10. A shoe box is completely filled with centimetre cubes. There are an unknown number of cubes along the box's length, width, and height. How many centimetre cubes are in the box?

Evaluate each expression. Suppose $d = 40$, $e = 5$, and $f = 90$.

11. $4d$
12. $\dfrac{d}{2}$
13. $12e$
14. $\dfrac{160}{e}$
15. $2f$

16. $\dfrac{f}{30}$
17. $2de$
18. $\dfrac{d}{e}$
19. $8ef$
20. def

Evaluate each expression. Suppose $m = 10$, $n = 0.1$, and $p = 100$.

21. $7m$
22. $3n$
23. $\dfrac{500}{p}$
24. $\dfrac{m}{5}$
25. mn

Letter Logic

Each letter stands for a different digit.
Can you find the numerical value of each letter?

$$\begin{array}{r} M \\ M\overline{)AT} \\ \underline{AT} \end{array}$$

$$M \div M = A$$

$$\begin{array}{r} H \\ H\overline{)TM} \\ \underline{TM} \end{array}$$

$$\begin{array}{r} H \\ T\overline{)MH} \\ \underline{MH} \end{array}$$

Guessing and Testing to Solve Equations

Equations can be used to guess and test possible solutions to a problem.

The product of 7 and what number is 84?
$7n = 84$

1st guess and test:

$$\text{Let } n = 12$$
$$7 \times 12 = 84$$

The solution to the equation is $n = 12$.

What number divided by 3 is 17?
$\dfrac{n}{3} = 17$

1st guess: Let $n = 48$

1st test: $\dfrac{48}{3} = 16$ Too small!

2nd guess: Let $n = 51$

2nd test: $\dfrac{51}{3} = 17$ Just right!

The solution to the equation is $n = 51$.

EXERCISES

Choose an equation for each question.

1. What number divided by 7 is 4? $\dfrac{n}{7} = 4$ or $\dfrac{7}{n} = 4$

2. What number times 6 is 72? $72n = 6$ or $6n = 72$

Choose a letter to represent what is unknown.
Then write an equation.

3. What number divided by 12 is 8?   4. Eleven times what number is 132?

5. Seventy-five divided by what number is 5?

Guess and test the solution for each equation.

6. $12n = 36$

   $n = \blacksquare$

7. $\dfrac{a}{5} = 4$

   $a = \blacksquare$

8. $\dfrac{28}{b} = 2$

   $b = \blacksquare$

9. $5a = 15$

10. $\dfrac{42}{x} = 7$

11. $3b = 33$

12. $\dfrac{36}{c} = 12$

13. $15x = 60$

14. $\dfrac{500}{m} = 50$

Choose a letter to represent what is unknown.
Then write an equation and guess and test the solution.

1. Fifteen times a certain number is 480. What is the number?

2. When a number is divided by 10, the quotient is 13. What is the number?

3. When an unknown number is multiplied by 8 the result is 376. What is the number?

4. Forty-eight divided by a certain number is 16. What is the number?

5. The product of 25 and an unknown number is 375. What is the number?

6. When an unknown number is divided by 18, the quotient is 6. What is the number?

Write the solution for each.

7. $4x = 24$

8. $10y = 90$

9. $2r = 42$

10. $3s = 48$

11. $21a = 84$

12. $15d = 615$

13. $8b = 56$

14. $25c = 125$

15. $6x = 96$

16. $\dfrac{x}{2} = 4$

17. $\dfrac{75}{n} = 15$

18. $\dfrac{w}{9} = 3$

19. $\dfrac{180}{n} = 18$

20. $\dfrac{u}{1} = 157$

21. $\dfrac{450}{k} = 5$

Two Variables

Dan has 27 coins in his pocket. He has only nickels and dimes.

1. Write an equation for this situation, using n for the number of nickels and d for the number of dimes.

2. If Dan has 7 nickels, how many dimes does he have?

3. If $d = 23$, what is n?

4. If Dan has 8 times as many dimes as nickels, how much money does he have?

Using Equations to Solve Problems

Donna earns $132 every 4 weeks from her paper route. How much does she earn each week?

To solve the problem:

1. Let x represent the unknown amount of money Donna earns each week.

2. Write an equation. $4x = 132$

3. Guess and test the solution of the equation.

1st guess and test:

Donna earns $32/week.

$$\text{Let } x = 32$$
$$4x = 132$$
$$4 \times 32 = 128$$

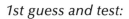

Too small!

2nd guess and test:

Donna earns $33/week.

$$\text{Let } x = 33$$
$$4x = 132$$
$$4 \times 33 = 132$$

Just right!

Donna earns $33 per week.

EXERCISES

Complete the equation for the problem.
Then guess and test the solution.

1. Ms. Terrell's annual salary was $18 000. How much did she *earn each month*?

   ■ e = ■

2. The school auditorium had 23 rows of chairs. There were 414 seats in the auditorium. *How many chairs* were in each row?

   $\dfrac{■}{x}$ = ■

3. Canada's highest waterfall has a drop of about 384 m. It is 8 times as high as Niagara Falls. About *how high* is Niagara Falls?

   ■ n = ■

4. Walter had a summer job packing small boxes of thumb tacks in large cartons for shipping. There were 144 small boxes in each carton. *How many cartons* had Walter filled when he packed 1872 boxes of tacks?

   $\dfrac{■}{c}$ = ■

Choose a letter to represent the unknown.
Then complete the equation and guess and test the solution.

1. Tickets to the school concert were $2.75 each.
   The first night of the concert, the school
   collected $654.50. How many *people* attended
   the concert on the first night?

   ■ p = ■

2. Ted bought a sheet containing 30 postage
   stamps. The cost of the sheet was $24. What was
   the *price* of each stamp?

   ■ c = ■

3. A store manager hired a grade seven class of 32
   students to deliver 8960 advertising flyers. How
   many *flyers* did each student have to deliver?

   ■ f = ■

Divide.

1. $27 \div 10$
   $27 \div 100$

2. $4651 \div 100$
   $4651 \div 1000$

3. $9.2 \div 10$
   $9.2 \div 100$

Estimate the quotient.

4. $341 \div 98$

5. $7921 \div 404$

6. $112 \div 0.8$

Divide. Write the remainder.

7. $56\overline{)6496}$

8. $948\overline{)5688}$

9. $64\overline{)89.6}$

Divide. Round to one decimal place.

10. $4\overline{)4.5}$

11. $92\overline{)86.3}$

12. $19\overline{)58}$

Divide.

13. $0.1\overline{)364}$

14. $3.9\overline{)5.46}$

15. $0.03\overline{)44.925}$

Evaluate each expression. Suppose $a = 20$, $b = 16$, $c = 0.2$.

16. $5a$

17. $\dfrac{a}{4}$

18. $8c$

19. $\dfrac{b}{c}$

20. $2ab$

Guess and test the solution for each equation.

21. $14a = 56$

22. $\dfrac{n}{8} = 15$

23. $25x = 105$

Applications

Computers do not use the symbols × and ÷ for multiplication and division. Instead they use these symbols:

* means *multiply*.
/ means *divide*.

Study how a RUN of this computer program would produce the *output*, 6.

1st statement → `10 PRINT 3*2*1`

2nd statement → `20 END`   } ← program

command → `]RUN`

`6` ← output

Show how a RUN of this computer program would produce the *output*, 48/4 = 12.

line numbers → `10 PRINT "48/4=";48/4`

`20 END`

`]RUN`

`48/4=12` ← output

The computer prints whatever is typed *between* quotation marks. Then it prints the quotient of 48/4.

Study how the FOR and NEXT statements in the computer program make a *loop*. Because of the loop, the computer multiplies by 0.5 over and over until the variable A is equal to 4.

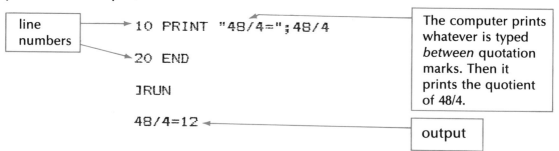
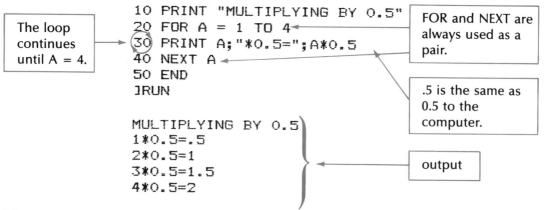

The loop continues until A = 4.

```
10 PRINT "MULTIPLYING BY 0.5"
20 FOR A = 1 TO 4
30 PRINT A;"*0.5=";A*0.5
40 NEXT A
50 END
]RUN

MULTIPLYING BY 0.5
1*0.5=.5
2*0.5=1
3*0.5=1.5
4*0.5=2
```

FOR and NEXT are always used as a pair.

.5 is the same as 0.5 to the computer.

← output

What is the computer *output* if the program were RUN?

1.  ```
    10 PRINT 275*24
    20 END
    ```

2.  ```
    10 PRINT 600/8
    20 END
    ```

3.  ```
    10 PRINT 6*5*4
    20 END
    ```

4.  ```
    10 PRINT 1000/.1
    20 END
    ```

5.  ```
    10 PRINT (7*6) + (4*9)
    20 END
    ```

6.  ```
    10 PRINT (12/2) + (65/5)
    20 END
    ```

7.  ```
    10 PRINT "13*7=";13*7
    20 END
    ```

8.  ```
    10 PRINT "192/32=";192/32
    20 END
    ```

10. ```
    10 PRINT "1.37*6*0*2.5=";1.37*6*0*2.5
    20 END
    ```

11. ```
    10 PRINT "(4*64) - (900/6)=";(4*64) - (900/6)
    20 END
    ```

12. ```
    10 PRINT "MULTIPLYING BY 0.05"
    20 FOR J = 1 TO 4
    30 PRINT J;"*0.05=";J*.05
    40 NEXT J
    50 END
    ```

13. ```
    10 PRINT "DIVIDING BY 0.2"
    20 FOR M = 1 TO 5
    30 PRINT M;"/0.2=";M/.2
    40 NEXT M
    50 END
    ```

Find the product.

1. 37 × 1000   **2.** 1.75 × 10   **3.** 0.3 × 10 000

Estimate the product.

4. 71	**5.** 392	**6.** 91.5	**7.** $28.95
× 9	× 34	×3.25	× 32

Multiply.

8. 86	**9.** 5189	**10.** 5.61	**11.** 5039
×94	× 136	× 4.3	×0.006

Divide.

12. 5)$\overline{425}$ **13.** 6)$\overline{5586}$ **14.** 4)$\overline{3.752}$ **15.** 7)$\overline{\$76.51}$

16. 46 ÷ 10   **17.** 382 ÷ 1000   **18.** 7.5 ÷ 10   **19.** 0.2 ÷ 1000

Estimate the quotient.

20. 18)$\overline{515}$ **21.** 37)$\overline{2856}$ **22.** 39)$\overline{238.2}$ **23.** 1.8)$\overline{99}$

Divide. Write the remainder.

24. 25)$\overline{189}$ **25.** 33)$\overline{\$60.39}$ **26.** 123)$\overline{6938}$ **27.** 542)$\overline{894.3}$

Divide. Round the quotient to one decimal place.

28. 9)$\overline{74.487}$ **29.** 64)$\overline{375}$ **30.** 22)$\overline{9.69}$

Divide.

31. 0.8)$\overline{606}$ **32.** 1.2)$\overline{256.8}$ **33.** 0.25)$\overline{6322}$ **34.** 0.03)$\overline{381}$

Evaluate each expression. Suppose $x = 12$, $y = 50$, and $z = 0.8$.

35. $3y$ **36.** $\dfrac{96}{x}$ **37.** $2xy$ **38.** $\dfrac{y}{z}$

Guess and test the solution for each question.

39. $7a = 63$ **40.** $\dfrac{n}{15} = 5$ **41.** $16f = 128$

Write an equation. Then guess and test the solution.

42. The product of a number and 6 is 84.
What is the number?

LOOKING BACK

Addition and Subtraction

Write in expanded form.

1. 475 020
2. 176 503 000
3. 37 245

Write the place value of the 4 in each numeral.

4. 9 724 317
5. 4 983 070
6. 34 000 000 000

7. 8.245
8. 0.416
9. 75.234

Copy and complete. Use < or >.

10. 46.74 ● 46.743
11. 7.2 ● 7.195

12. 79 126.3 ● 79 126.03
13. 0.38 ● 0.83

Round to the nearest dollar.

14. $23.75
15. $263.18
16. $0.78
17. $2.45

Add or subtract.

18. $\begin{array}{r} 4861 \\ -\ 875 \\ \hline \end{array}$
19. $\begin{array}{r} 657\ 231 \\ +\ 68\ 977 \\ \hline \end{array}$
20. $\begin{array}{r} 8\ 492\ 006 \\ -\ 546\ 547 \\ \hline \end{array}$
21. $\begin{array}{r} 925\ 443\ 354 \\ +436\ 858\ 462 \\ \hline \end{array}$

22. $\begin{array}{r} \$55.47 \\ +\ 48.69 \\ \hline \end{array}$
23. $\begin{array}{r} 963.1 \\ -\ 80.22 \\ \hline \end{array}$
24. $\begin{array}{r} 5.4 \\ -3.694 \\ \hline \end{array}$
25. $\begin{array}{r} \$3\ 610.24 \\ +\ 1\ 831.67 \\ \hline \end{array}$

26. 6000 − 782
27. 26 384 + 1775
28. 24 − 2.987
29. $16.05 + $4.99

Round to the nearest whole number. Estimate the sum.

30. 6.6 + 0.7 + 7 + 18.2 + 4.65 + 0.3

31. 42.8 + 1.9 + 0.2 + 12 + 6.78 + 2 + 0.4

Evaluate each expression. Suppose $x = 7$, $y = 16$, and $z = 9.5$.

32. $y + 22$
33. $104 - x$
34. $y - x$
35. $y - z$
36. $x + y + z$

Write the solution for each equation.

37. $g + 47 = 102$
38. $91 - r = 18$
39. $w - 26 = 45$

Write an equation. Then guess and test the solution.

40. When 24 is added to a number, the sum is 151. What is the number?

UNIT 3   Computation

Special Properties

Knowing about special properties makes computing easier.

Commutative Property: We can add or multiply in any **order.**

Computation: $17 + 83 = 83 + 17$ $4 \times 9 = 9 \times 4$

Rule: $a + b = b + a$ $ab = ba$

Associative Property: We can change **groups** when we add or multiply.

Computation: $(42 + 25) + 75$ $(7 \times 8) \times 5$

                $= 42 + (25 + 75)$ $= 7 \times (8 \times 5)$
                $= 42 + 100$ $= 7 \times 40$
                $= 142$ $= 280$

Regroup to
compute with
tens.

Rule: $(a + b) + c = a + (b + c)$ $(a \times b) \times c = a \times (b \times c)$
                                                            or $(ab)c = a(bc)$

Commutative and Associative Properties:
We can change **order** and **groups** when we add and multiply.

Computation: $(22 + 97) + 78$
$= (22 + 78) + 97$
$= 100 + 97$
$= 197$

Reorder and *regroup* to compute with tens.

$(6 \times 9) \times 5$
$= (6 \times 5) \times 9$
$= 30 \times 9$
$= 270$

Distributive Property: We can rewrite a number as a sum or difference.

Computation: 5×67
$= 5 \times (60 + 7)$
$= (5 \times 60) + (5 \times 7)$
$= 300 + 5$
$= 335$

Rewritten as a sum.

6×98
$6 \times (100 - 2)$
$= (6 \times 100) - (6 \times 2)$
$= 600 - 12$
$= 588$

Rewritten as a difference.

Rule: $a \times (b + c) = ab + ac$
or $a(b + c) = ab + ac$

$a \times (b - c) = ab - ac$
or $a(b - c) = ab - ac$

EXERCISES

Find the value of *n* using the *commutative property*.

1. $n + 9 = 9 + 14$ **2.** $6 \times 7 = n \times 6$ **3.** $98 + n = 49 + 98$

Find the value of *n* using the *associative property*.

4. $(8n) \times 5 = 8 \times (7 \times 5)$ **5.** $(9 + 3) + 7 = 9 + (n + 7)$

Find the value of *n* using the *distributive property*.

6. $7 \times (30 + 4) = (7n) + (7 \times 4)$ **7.** $(100 - 1) \times 4 = (100n) - (4 \times 1)$

Compute. Look for tens by *reordering* and *regrouping*.

8. $(37 + 65) + 35$
$= 37 + (65 + 35)$
$= \blacksquare$

9. $(5 \times 87) \times 2$
$= \blacksquare \times (\blacksquare \times \blacksquare)$
$= \blacksquare$

10. $(63 + 49) + 37$
$= \blacksquare + (\blacksquare + \blacksquare)$
$= \blacksquare$

Compute. Rewrite as a sum or difference.

11. 3×76
$= (3 \times 70) + (3 \times 6)$
$= \blacksquare$

12. 4×95
$= (\blacksquare \times \blacksquare) - (\blacksquare \times \blacksquare)$
$= \blacksquare$

PRACTICE

Write the name of the property used.

1. $r + s = s + r$

2. $(c + d) + e = c + (d + e)$

3. $a \times (b + c) = ab + ac$

4. $xy = yx$

5. $(xy) \times z = x \times (yz)$

6. $m \times (r - s) = mr - ms$

Find the value of n using the properties.

7. $(60 \times 24) \times 50 = (50 \times 60) \times n$

8. $5 \times (100 - 15) = (5 \times 100) - (5n)$

9. $(42 + 2) \times 6 = 42n + 2n$

10. $86 + 95 = n + 86$

11. $12 \times 14 = 14n$

12. $(28 + 64) + 32 = (32 + n) + 64$

13. $(4 \times 22) \times 5 = 4 \times (22n)$

14. $106 + (51 + 94) = (106 + n) + 51$

Compute. Use the commutative and associative properties.

15. $99 + (47 + 1)$

16. $(25 \times 41) \times 4$

17. $(50 \times 97) \times 2$

18. $5 \times (13 \times 2)$

19. $(96 + 79) + 4$

20. $25 \times (37 \times 4)$

21. $(200 + 653) + 800$

22. $(125 \times 93) \times 8$

23. $999 + (356 + 1)$

Complete each equation in the left column by matching it to an expression from the right column.

24. $(50 \times 25) + (20 \times 25)$

A. $80 \times (25 + 50)$

25. $50 \times (20 + 25)$

B. $(50 \times 80) + (50 \times 25)$

26. $50 \times (80 + 25)$

C. $(50 + 20) \times 25$

27. $(80 \times 25) + (80 \times 50)$

D. $(25 + 50) \times 20$

28. $(25 \times 20) + (50 \times 20)$

E. $(25 \times 80) + (25 \times 50)$

29. $25 \times (80 + 50)$

F. $(50 \times 20) + (50 \times 25)$

Tennis Trial

Copy the drawing.
Place the numerals 1, 2, 3, 4, 5, and 6 in the tennis balls so that the sum along each row of three balls is 9.

Can you place the numerals to get a sum of 10? a sum of 11? a sum of 12?

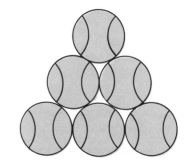

Multiplication Shortcuts

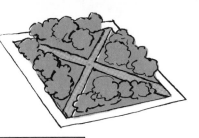

It is easy to compute a product using these shortcuts.

Multiplying by 25:

Shortcut: $\dfrac{n \times 100}{4}$

Example: 84×25

$= \dfrac{84 \times 100}{4}$

$= \dfrac{8400}{4}$

$= 2100$

Multiplying by 50:

Shortcut: $\dfrac{n \times 100}{2}$

Example: 64×50

$= \dfrac{64 \times 100}{2}$

$= \dfrac{6400}{2}$

$= 3200$

Multiplying by 9:

Shortcut: $(n \times 10) - n$
Example: 78×9
$\quad = (78 \times 10) - 78$
$\quad = 780 - 78$
$\quad = 702$

Multiplying by 19:

Shortcut: $(n \times 20) - n$
Example: 28×19
$\quad = (28 \times 20) - 28$
$\quad = 560 - 28$
$\quad = 532$

Multiplying by 11:

Example: 253×11

Shortcut:

$$
\begin{array}{r} 2\,5\,3 \\ \times\ 1\,1 \\ \hline 2\quad\ \ 3 \end{array}
\qquad
\begin{array}{r} 2\,5\,3 \\ \times\ 1\,1 \\ \hline 2\ 8\,3 \end{array}
\qquad
\begin{array}{r} 2\,5\,3 \\ \times\ 1\,1 \\ \hline 2\,7\,8\,3 \end{array}
$$

Compute using the shortcuts.

1. 88×25
   52×25
   124×25
   512×25

2. 72×50
   84×50
   106×50
   236×50

3. 16×9
   35×9
   48×9
   125×9

4. 8×19
   14×19
   25×19
   34×19

5. 427×11
   315×11
   824×11
   1526×11

6. Can you invent a shortcut for multiplying by 125? by 500? by 29?

Exponents

Exponents are a shortened way to write the repeated multiplication of the same number.

base   exponent

$16 = 2 \times 2 \times 2 \times 2 = 2^4$ *two to the fourth power*

$8 = 2 \times 2 \times 2 \quad\quad = 2^3$ *two to the third power, or two cubed*

$4 = 2 \times 2 \quad\quad\quad = 2^2$ *two to the second power, or two squared*

Exponents can be used to simplify the writing of numbers in *expanded form.*

$2946 = (2 \times 1000) + (9 \times 100) + (4 \times 10) + 6$
$\quad\quad = (2 \times 10^3) \quad + (9 \times 10^2) + (4 \times 10^1) + 6$

Large numbers are often written with exponents.

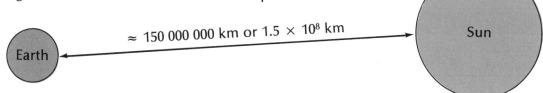

≈ 150 000 000 km or 1.5×10^8 km

Earth

Sun

EXERCISES

What is the *exponent*?   What is the *base*?

1. 10^3 **2.** 2^9 **3.** 4^{15} **4.** 6^4 **5.** 50^2

Write using exponents.

6. $2 \times 2 \times 2 \times 2 \times 2 = 2^{\blacksquare}$ **7.** $5 \times 5 \times 5$ **8.** 9×9

9. $4 \times 4 \times 4 \times 4 \times 4$ **10.** 21×21 **11.** $18 \times 18 \times 18 \times 18$

Write as a repeated multiplication.

12. $3^2 = \blacksquare \times \blacksquare$ **13.** 4^5 **14.** 2^7 **15.** 10^4 **16.** 1^8

Calculate the value.

17. $5^2 = \blacksquare$ **18.** 10^4 **19.** 1^5 **20.** 4^3 **21.** 2^6

Write in expanded form using powers of ten.

22. $327 = (3 \times 10^{\blacksquare}) + (2 \times 10^{\blacksquare}) + (7 \times 10^{\blacksquare})$ **23.** 9245 **24.** $10\ 286$

PRACTICE

Calculate the value.

1. 10^2 2. 4^3 3. 2^3 4. 6^2 5. 10^1

6. 8^2 7. 1^9 8. 10^5 9. 50^2 10. 3^2

11. 9^2 12. 6^3 13. 20^2 14. 1^{27} 15. 10^9

Guess and test the value of n in each equation.

16. $n \times n \times n = 1$ 17. $n^2 = 16$ 18. $n \times n \times n = 125$

19. $n^4 = 81$ 20. $n \times n = 49$ 21. $n^1 = 10$

22. $n \times n \times n \times n \times n = 32$ 23. $n^3 = 8$ 24. $n \times n = 10\,000$

25. $n^3 = 64$ 26. $n \times n = 90\,000$ 27. $n^{10} = 1$

Copy and complete. Use $<$, $=$, or $>$.

28. $2^2 \bullet 1^4$ 29. $5^2 \bullet 3^3$ 30. $10^4 \bullet 100^2$

31. $3^2 \bullet 2^3$ 32. $2^6 \bullet 8^2$ 33. $10^1 \bullet 1^{10}$

34. $6^3 \bullet 15^2$ 35. $2^4 \bullet 4^2$ 36. $5^2 \bullet 2^5$

Write in expanded form using powers of ten.

37. 729   38. 843   39. 7134   40. 70 625   41. 42 000 000

Write each amount without powers of ten.

42. The solar system is calculated to be at least 4.7×10^9 years old.

43. A normal human heart beats about 3.6×10^7 times in one year.

44. The volume of the earth is $1.083\,23 \times 10^{12}$ km³.

What's In a Name?

All of the expressions are names for 16.

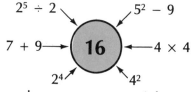

$2^5 \div 2$ $5^2 - 9$

$7 + 9 \rightarrow$ **16** $\leftarrow 4 \times 4$

2^4 4^2

Give these numbers an *exponential name*.

a. 4   b. 9   c. 8   d. 27   e. 36   f. 49

 g. 1   h. 64   i. 10   j. 100   k. 81   l. 32

Computing With Zero and One

<table>
<tr><td colspan="2">Zero   0</td><td colspan="2">One   1</td></tr>
</table>

Zero is the **identity element** for addition and subtraction.	One is the **identity element** for multiplication and division.
$a + 0 = a$ *a* can be $a - 0 = a$ any number.	$a \times 1 = a$ *a* can be $a \div 1 = a$ any number.
Ways to make zero: $a \ - a \ = 0$ $a \ \times 0 \ = 0$ $0 \ \div a \ = 0$ $8 \div 0$ It is impossible to divide by zero.	Ways to make one: $a \ \div a \ = 1$

$a^0 = 1$ *a* can be any
            number but zero.
	$a^1 = a$ *a* can be
	            any number.

EXERCISES

Which have a value of zero?   of one?

1. $a \times 0$	**2.** 5×0	**3.** $0 + 0$	**4.** 0×5
5. $16 \div 16$	**6.** $x - x$	**7.** $0 + 1$	**8.** 0×1

Evaluate.

9. $6 + 0$	**10.** $6 \div 6$	**11.** 6×1	**12.** $6 \div 1$
13. 52^0	**14.** 52^1	**15.** $52 \div 1$	**16.** $52 \div 0$
17. $r \times 1$	**18.** r^0	**19.** $0 \times r$	**20.** r^1
21. $0 + b$	**22.** $y \div 1$	**23.** $1 \times c$	**24.** $f - 0$
25. $n - 0$	**26.** $k - k$	**27.** $0 \div d$	**28.** $d \div 0$

PRACTICE

Evaluate.

1. $95 - 95$
2. 7^0
3. $24 \div 24$
4. $0 + 45$
5. 1×0
6. $0 \div 15$
7. $28 - 0$
8. $63^2 \times 0$
9. $14 - 14$
10. 4^1
11. 1^1
12. 2037×1
13. 10^0
14. $52 \div 1$
15. $236 - 236$
16. 12^1
17. $0 \div x$
18. $d \div 1^2$
19. 1^0
20. $f \times 1$
21. e^0
22. $0 + h$
23. 10^1
24. $s - s$

Find the value of n.

25. $6n \times 3 = 18$
26. $15 + n + 20 + 18 = 53$
27. $17 - 5 - n - 0 = 11$
28. $(27 + 12) - 0 + n = 44$
29. $3 \times 7n \times 8 = 0$
30. $(50 - n) + 2 + 7 = 9$
31. $46 + n + 4 + 50 = 100$
32. $8 \times 3n \times 2 = 48$
33. $(n - 23) + 5 + 6 = 11$
34. $(75 + n) + 16 - 16 = 100$

Choose a letter to represent the unknown number. Then write an equation.

35. Subtract an unknown number from itself. What is the result?

36. An unknown number is multiplied by one. What is the number?

37. What is the result when an unknown number is divided by itself?

Ant Antics

The symbol *ACDB* describes an ant's trip from *A* to *B* along just three edges of the cube.

How many different trips are there from *A* to *B* along just
a. three edges of the cube?
b. four edges of the cube?
c. five edges of the cube?
d. seven edges of the cube?

It is agreed that in a trip no edge is to be used twice.

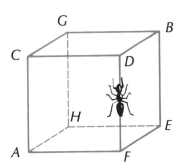

Order of Operations

An expression is simplified in a certain *order*.

Rule 1:

First: Evaluate exponents.
Next: Multiply and divide from left to right.
Finally: Add and subtract from left to right.

Number expressions simplified:

$27 + 5^2$
$= 27 + 25$
$= 52$

3×4^2
$= 3 \times 16$
$= 48$

$30 + 15 \div 5 - 4 \times 2$
$= 30 + 3 - 8$
$= 33 - 8$
$= 41$

Variable expressions simplified:

Let $a = 2$

$5a + 6$
$= 10 + 6$
$= 16$

$a^2 - 1^2$
$= 4 - 1$
$= 3$

$46 + a^3 - 5 \times 3$
$= 46 + 8 - 5 \times 3$
$= 46 + 8 - 15$
$= 54 - 15$
$= 39$

Rule 2:

First: Work inside the parentheses:
Next: Follow Rule 1.

Study the effects of parentheses:

$3 \times 2 + 6$
$= 6 + 6$
$= 12$

$3 \times (2 + 6)$
$= 3 \times 8$
$= 24$

$2 \times 9 + 3 - 15 \div 5 - 2$
$= 18 + 3 - 3 - 2$
$= 21 - 3 - 2$
$= 18 - 2$
$= 16$

$2 \times (9 + 3) - 15 \div (5 - 2)$
$= 2 \times 12 - 15 \div 3$
$= 24 - 5$
$= 19$

Let $n = 5$

$3n^2$
$= 3 \times 25$
$= 75$

$(3n)^2$
$= 15^2$
$= 225$

EXERCISES

Simplify. Work from left to right.

1. $3 + 18 + 9$
    $= 21 + 9$
    $= \blacksquare$

2. $84 - 35 + 21$

3. $96 \div 8 \div 4 \div 3$

Simplify. Remember to multiply and divide first.

4. $31 + 3 \div 3 \times 2$
    $= 31 + 1 \times 2$
    $= 31 + 2$

5. $13 + 3 \times 15 \div 2$

6. $62 - 8 \times 2 + 2$

Simplify. Remember to evaluate exponents first.

7. $27 + 3^3$
    $= 27 + 27$

8. $14 \div 1^9$

9. 9×6^2

Evaluate each expression. Suppose $n = 6$.

10. $9 + n^2$
    $= 9 + 36$

11. $2n + 5$

12. $4n - 3n$

13. $n - 2^5 \div 8$
    $= 6 - 32 \div 8$
    $= 6 - 4$

14. $n^2 + 3^3 \times 2$

15. $8^2 - 8n \div 4$

Simplify. Work inside the parentheses first.

16. $50 \div (9 - 4)$
    $= 50 \div 5$

17. $3 \times (27 + 0)$

18. $11 \times (5 + 6)$

19. $(7 + 3)^2$
    $= 10^2$

20. $(8 \div 2)^3$

21. $(9 - 8)^7$

Simplify using Rule 2. Then apply Rule 1.

22. $100 \div (2 - 1) \div 10$
    $= 100 \div 1 \div 10$
    $= 100 \div 10$

23. $80 - (9 + 3) + 2$

24. $420 \div (1 + 5) - 5$

25. $2^6 - (3 + 5) \times 2$
    $= 2^6 - 8 \times 2$
    $= 64 - 16$

26. $4^2 \times (12 - 9) - 40$

27. $6^2 - (2^2 - 1^2) \times 8$

Evaluate each expression. Suppose $a = 2$.

28. $45 \div (11 - a)$
    $= 45 \div 9$

29. $(3a)^2$

30. $12 \times (a^2 + a^3)$

Simplify.

1. $36 \div 9 \times 6$
2. $13 + 100 \div 100$
3. $162 - 75 + 23$
4. $17 \times (46 - 46)$
5. $21 - 2^4$
6. $75 - (0 \div 14)$
7. $41 - 16 + 2^3$
8. $(54 - 36) \div 9 \times 10$
9. $45 \div 3^2$
10. $27 - (7 \times 1 + 6)$
11. $3^2 + 4 - 5 + 5$
12. $12 \times (63 - 48) + 5$
13. $96 \div 2^4 - 105 \div 35 + 1^8 \times 4$
14. $500 - (29 + 11) \times 2^3 \times 5 \times 0$

Copy and complete. Use $<$, $=$, or $>$.

15. $120 \div 10 \div 5 \ \bullet \ 120 \div (10 \div 5)$
16. $16 \times 8 \times 10 \ \bullet \ 16 \times (8 \times 10)$
17. $59 - (27 - 14) \ \bullet \ (59 - 27) - 14$
18. $(6 \times 6)^2 \ \bullet \ 6 \times 6^2$
19. $(27 \div 9) \times 3 \ \bullet \ 27 \div (9 \times 3)$
20. $13 + 39 \div 3 \ \bullet \ (13 + 39) \div 3$

Rewrite with parentheses to make a true statement.

21. $36 - 12 \div 2^2 = 6$
22. $10 \times 2^3 - 5 = 30$
23. $19 + 6^2 \times 5 = 275$
24. $72 \div 2^2 + 5 = 8$
25. $6 \times 3^2 - 12 + 22 = 20$
26. $4 \times 1^5 + 3 \times 5 + 7 = 192$
27. $5^0 + 3 \times 6 - 4 = 7$
28. $17 - 3^2 - 4^0 + 3 = 4$
29. $12 \div 4 - 1 \times 2 = 8$
30. $4 \times 3 - 4 + 5 = 3$
31. $3^2 + 5 \times 2 + 4 = 39$
32. $4 + 2^4 - 3 \times 5 = 5$

Evaluate each expression. Suppose $w = 4$, $x = 12$, and $y = 20$.

33. $w + (x + y)$
34. $y + x \div w$
35. $(y - x) \div w$
36. $xy \div w$
37. $(x - w)^2$
38. $y^2 - (x^2 + w^2)$

Copy and complete.

39.

x	$x \div 4 \div 2$
40	
524	
3.6	
0.16	

40.

x	y	$3x + (y - 3)$
2	5	
100	200	
0.5	10	
1.2	3.4	

Match the number of each phrase with the letter of the expression.

41. 4 times the sum of a number and 12

42. 4 plus the difference between 12 and a number

43. 12 minus the product of 4 and a number

44. 12 more than a number divided by 4

45. 4 less than the sum of 12 and a number

a. $12 - 4n$

b. $4 \times (n + 12)$

c. $12 + n - 4$

d. $n \div 4 + 12$

e. $4 + (12 - n)$

Find an equation at the right for each problem. Then guess and test the solution.

46. Fifteen minus the product of 2 and an unknown number is 3. What is the number?

47. Twenty-four times the quotient of an unknown number divided by 4 is 120. What is the number?

48. Eleven plus the difference between 30 and an unknown number is 21. What is the number?

49. Seventy-two times the quotient of 157 divided by an unknown number is 72. What is the number?

50. Forty-eight minus the product of an unknown number and 27 is 48. What is the number?

$$11 + 30 \div n = 21$$

$$24 \times n \div 4 = 120$$

$$72 + 157 \div n = 72$$

$$15 \times 2n = 3$$

$$24 - n \div 4 = 120$$

$$48 - 27n = 48$$

$$11 + 30 - n = 21$$

$$15 - 2n = 3$$

$$48 + 27n = 48$$

$$72 \times 157 \div n = 72$$

Operation Signs

Complete each sentence with $+$, $-$, $\times$, or $\div$ to make a true statement.

a. $(36 \bullet 18) \bullet 6 = 3$
b. $50 \bullet 25 \bullet 5 = 55$
c. $(6 \bullet 9) \bullet 3 \bullet 7 = 12$
d. $(11 \bullet 11 \bullet 3) \bullet 4 = 11$

Problem Solving

The Pine Valley basketball team scored a total of 195 points in 3 successive games. In each game's first half, they scored 40 points. In each game's second half, they scored fewer points than the first half but always the same number. How many points did Pine Valley score in each game's second half?

Write an equation to solve the problem.

Decide.

1. Let n = the unknown number of points in each second half.

2. Write an equation. $3 \times 40 + 3n = 195$

3. Guess and test the solution.

1st guess and test:
Let $n = 20$
$3 \times 40 + 3 \times 20 = 180$

Too small!

2nd guess and test:
Let $n = 25$
$3 \times 40 + 3 \times 25 = 195$

Just right!

Pine Valley scored 25 points in each second half.

EXERCISES

Complete the equation for the problem.
Then guess and test the solution.

1. The area of a parallelogram is found by multiplying the base length by the height. What is the *height* of a parallelogram which has a base of 36 cm and an area of 900 cm²?

   ■ × h = ■

2. A book has an average of 8 words a line and 14 lines a page. Altogether there are 5600 words in the book. How many *pages* does the book have?

   ■ × ■ × p = ■

3. Six dances during a school year had a total of 1260 students attend. Four of the dances had 196 students attend. The same number of students attended the remaining two dances. How many *students* attended the two other dances?

   ■ × ■ + ■ × s = ■

Complete the equation for the problem.
Then guess and total the solution.

1. Ann Sperry paid $2700 for her home
    computer system. Included in the system
    was a printer, a monitor for $250, the
    computer for $1295, and a disk drive for
    $575. What was the cost of the *printer*?

    $p + ■ + ■ + ■ = ■$

2. A repairman replaced bathroom tiles in a
    rectangular area measuring 2700 cm². If the
    length of the rectangular area was 60 cm,
    what was the *width*?

    $■ × w = ■$

3. An auditorium has 256 seats in all. The
    seating is divided into 3 sections each
    having an equal number of rows. The
    middle section of the seating has 8 seats
    per row and each of the 2 side sections has
    4 seats per row. How many *rows* are in the
    auditorium?

    $r × (■ + ■ + ■) = ■$

4. Mary earned $19.25 baby-sitting last
    weekend. On Saturday, she baby-sat for 6 h
    and on Sunday for 5 h. How much *money*
    did Mary earn per hour?

    $(m × ■) + (m × ■) = ■$

5. Fifteen times the product of an unknown
    number and 8 is 6000. What is the *number*?

    $■ × (n × ■) = ■$

Compute. Use the properties.

1. 129 + 632 + 171	2. (25 × 24) × 8	3. 4 × (30 + 4)
4. (377 + 237) + 123	5. 7 × (100 − 4)	6. 80 × 32 × 50

Find the value of *y*.

7. $y^2 = 25$	8. $y × y × y = 64$	9. $y^4 = 81$
10. $y − 0 = 12$	11. $y^1 ÷ 25 + 14 = 15$	12. $7 × y × 6 = 0$

Simplify.

13. $21 × 9 ÷ 3^1$	14. $72 + 2^3 × 3^2$	15. $6^0 + (9 − 5) × 3$

Making a Flow Chart

A **flow chart** is a drawing of a sequence of events.

Special flow chart symbols:

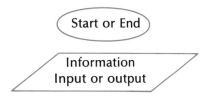

Start or End

Information Input or output

Statement

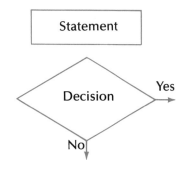

Decision

Yes

No

A flow chart showing the steps taken to play tennis:

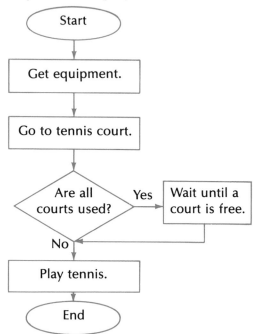

Start

Get equipment.

Go to tennis court.

Are all courts used? — Yes — Wait until a court is free.

No

Play tennis.

End

EXERCISES

Copy the flow chart. Write the events in the flow chart in order.

1. Participating in a bike-a-thon:

Ride home.

Reach destination.

Yes

No

Get bike.

Need air in tires?

Fill tires with air.

2. Adding a 1-digit and a 2-digit number:

Add tens.

Input 2 numbers.

Add ones.

Yes

No

Write down the ones carry the tens.

Is the sum > 9?

PRACTICE

Complete a flow chart for the problem.

1. A family of 5 is choosing a London hotel. They plan to stay there for 7 days. If they have $1500 saved for hotel expenses, can they afford a hotel charging $36 per person per day?

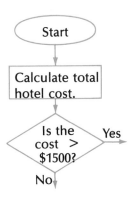

2. How is a one-digit number subtracted from a two-digit number?

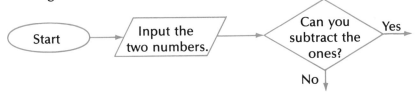

3. What steps are taken when a two-digit number is multiplied by a one-digit number?

4. Mr. & Mrs. Curran plan to rent a car for a trip to Nova Scotia. They have $300 saved for the car rental. If the trip lasts for 12 days, which type of car would they be able to rent?

GROUP	CAR TYPE OR SIMILAR	PER DAY
A	2-door	$22.00
B	4-door	$28.00
C	station wagon	$33.00

Charting the Flow

Copy and complete a flow chart for each situation.

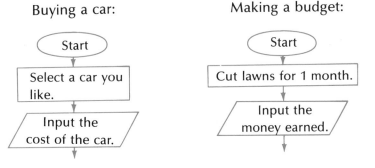

Computer Applications

Some computers use the symbol $\wedge$ to exponentiate.

$$2^3 = 2 \wedge 3 \qquad 4^2 = 4 \wedge 2$$

Computers are programmed to use the order of operations rules to evaluate expressions.

Input: Output:

```
PRINT 2*4^2                    32
```

What would be the computer output if the following PRINT statements were typed?

```
1.  PRINT 29 + 25/5 - 8*3
2.  PRINT 135 - 6^2 + 27/3
3.  PRINT 24/2 +(22 - 4^2)
4.  PRINT (75 - 39)*8 - 2^8
5.  PRINT (3 + 5*3)/6
6.  PRINT 4 + 8*2^3 - 4/2*2
```

Study each computer program. Then write the computer output if the program were RUN.

```
7.  10 LET A = 7          8.  10 PRINT "CANADA BECAME A NATION IN"
    20 LET B = 5              20 PRINT 2^10 + 20^2 + 10^2 + 7^3
    30 LET C = 3              30 END
    40 PRINT A*B^3
    50 END
```

```
9.  10 PRINT "WHAT HAPPENDED IN THE YEAR"
    20 PRINT (1*10^3) + (4*10^2) + (9*10^1) + 7;"?"
    30 PRINT "OR IN THE YEAR"
    40 PRINT (1*10^3) + (6*10^2) + 3;"?"
    50 END
```

```
10. 10 PRINT "SQUARING NUMBERS"    11. 10 PRINT "CUBING NUMBERS"
    20 FOR N = 1 TO 12                 20 FOR N = 1 TO 12
    30 PRINT N;"^2 =";N^2              30 PRINT N;"^3 =";N^3
    40 NEXT N                          40 NEXT N
    50 END                             50 END
```

```
12. 10 FOR N = 1 TO 12
    20 PRINT N;" TO THE 4TH POWER IS ";N^4
    30 NEXT N
    40 END
```

Calculator Exponents

Study the calculator expression for each numerical expression.

8^2 = $\boxed{8}$ $\boxed{\times}$ $\boxed{=}$ `64` $(6 + 4)^2$ = $\boxed{6}$ $\boxed{+}$ $\boxed{4}$ $\boxed{\times}$ $\boxed{=}$ `100`

8^3 = $\boxed{8}$ $\boxed{\times}$ $\boxed{=}$ $\boxed{=}$ `512` $(8 - 3)^3$ = $\boxed{8}$ $\boxed{-}$ $\boxed{3}$ $\boxed{\times}$ $\boxed{=}$ $\boxed{=}$ `125`

8^4 = $\boxed{8}$ $\boxed{\times}$ $\boxed{=}$ $\boxed{=}$ $\boxed{=}$ `4096` $(9 + 5)^4$ = $\boxed{9}$ $\boxed{+}$ $\boxed{5}$ $\boxed{\times}$ $\boxed{=}$ $\boxed{=}$ $\boxed{=}$ `38416`

Evaluate using a calculator. Record the key presses used.

a. 7^3 **b.** 9^4 **c.** $(5 + 2)^3$ **d.** $(12 - 6)^2$ **e.** $(24 \div 8)^5$

Calculator Memory

A calculator's memory keys can help you evaluate number expressions.

$\boxed{M+}$ Adds the number in the display to memory.

$\boxed{M-}$ Subtracts the number in the display from memory.

$\boxed{MR}$ Recalls the number in memory to the display.

$\boxed{MC}$ Clears only the memory.

Study how the expression is evaluated on a calculator.

$26 + 7^2 - 16 \div 2$ = $\boxed{2}$ $\boxed{6}$ $\boxed{M+}$ $\boxed{7}$ $\boxed{\times}$ $\boxed{=}$ $\boxed{M+}$ $\boxed{1}$ $\boxed{6}$ $\boxed{\div}$ $\boxed{2}$ $\boxed{M-}$ $\boxed{MR}$ `67`

| 26 is added to memory. | 7^2 is added to memory. | 16 ÷ 2 is subtracted from memory. |

Evaluate using a calculator's memory.

f. $6 + 7 \times 8$
$\boxed{6}$ $\boxed{M+}$ $\boxed{7}$ $\boxed{\times}$ $\boxed{8}$ $\boxed{=}$ $\boxed{M+}$ $\boxed{MR}$

g. $9 + 3 \times 5 - 12$
$\boxed{9}$ $\boxed{M+}$ $\boxed{3}$ $\boxed{\times}$ $\boxed{5}$ $\boxed{=}$ $\boxed{M+}$ $\boxed{1}$ $\boxed{2}$ $\boxed{M-}$ $\boxed{MR}$

h. $(8 + 9) - (9 - 2)$
$\boxed{8}$ $\boxed{+}$ $\boxed{9}$ $\boxed{=}$ $\boxed{M+}$ $\boxed{9}$ $\boxed{-}$ $\boxed{2}$ $\boxed{=}$ $\boxed{M-}$ $\boxed{MR}$

i. $(6^2 - 12) - (20 - 7)$
$\boxed{6}$ $\boxed{\times}$ $\boxed{=}$ $\boxed{-}$ $\boxed{1}$ $\boxed{2}$ $\boxed{=}$ $\boxed{M+}$ $\boxed{2}$ $\boxed{0}$
$\boxed{-}$ $\boxed{7}$ $\boxed{=}$ $\boxed{M-}$ $\boxed{MR}$

j. $(8 + 4)^3 \times (6^2 + 5)$
$\boxed{8}$ $\boxed{+}$ $\boxed{4}$ $\boxed{\times}$ $\boxed{=}$ $\boxed{=}$ $\boxed{M+}$ $\boxed{6}$ $\boxed{\times}$ $\boxed{=}$ $\boxed{+}$ $\boxed{5}$ $\boxed{=}$ $\boxed{\times}$ $\boxed{MR}$ $\boxed{=}$

k. $17 + 20 \div 4 - 3$ **l.** $(4 + 7) - (40 - 35)$ **m.** $(6 + 3^3) - (2^4 - 3)$

Find the value of n.

1. $89 + 105 = 105 + n$
2. $(27 \times 3) \times 14 = 27 \times 3n$
3. $18 + (m + 57) = (43 + 18) + 57$
4. $(100 - 2) \times 6 = 100n - 2n$

Evaluate.

5. $385 + (495 + 215)$
6. $4 \times (40 + 5)$
7. $(6 \times 9) \times 5$
8. $8 \times (100 - 5)$
9. $12 + 43 + 18 + 57 + 8$
10. $25 \times (7 \times 8)$
11. 9^2
12. 2^5
13. 10^1

Write in expanded form using powers of 10.

14. 754
15. 2739
16. $60\ 245$

Evaluate.

17. $16^1 + 0$
18. $56^0 \times 1$
19. $62 + (81 \div 81)$
20. $(4 + 0) - 4$
21. $5 + (18 - 18)$
22. $(17 \div 17) + 17^1$

Evaluate each expression. Suppose $c = 4$, $d = 8$, and $e = 3$.

23. $(cd)e$
24. $e + d \div c$
25. $d - (c + e)$
26. $(d + e)^2$
27. $c^0 + d^1$
28. $d^2 \div c^2 + e^2$

Simplify.

29. $2^5 - 5 \times (3 + 1)$
30. $7^2 - 39 + (16 + 14) \div 6$
31. $48 \div (15 - 3) \times 6^2$
32. $2^4 + (6 + 3^3) \div 3$
33. $(38 - 25) \times 10^1 - 45$
34. $2^8 - (9^2 + 3^3) - 12^2$

Solve.

35. Six times the sum of an unknown number and 8 is 90. What is the number?

36. Mary paid $1.97 for toothpaste and a bar of soap using a discount coupon. If the toothpaste cost $1.29 and the soap cost 83¢, what was the value of the discount coupon?

37. Bernie spent $12.73, including sales tax, for two records on sale. If the records were $5.95 each, how much did Bernie spend on sales tax?

Multiplication and Division

Find the product.

1. $98 \div 100$
2. $2.6 \div 10$
3. $4 \div 1000$

Estimate the product.

4. 218
   $\times\ 78$

5. 7942
   $\times\ \ 31$

6. 94.2
   $\times 6.85$

7. $48.75
   $\times\ \ \ 112$

Multiply.

8. 26
   $\times 57$

9. 374
   $\times\ 65$

10. 9302
    $\times\ 218$

11. 7029
    $\times\ 507$

12. 0.7
    $\times 0.5$

13. 8.45
    $\times\ 2.5$

14. $63.25
    $\times\ \ \ \ \ 32$

15. 2164
    $\times 0.005$

Divide.

16. $8\overline{)416}$
17. $4\overline{)2148}$
18. $6\overline{)137.4}$
19. $9\overline{)\$32.04}$

20. $38 \div 10$
21. $276 \div 10\ 000$
22. $9.5 \div 10$
23. $0.04 \div 1000$

Estimate the quotient.

24. $19\overline{)658}$
25. $42\overline{)2145}$
26. $78\overline{)736.5}$
27. $6.2\overline{)302}$

Divide.

28. $68\overline{)544}$
29. $35\overline{)\$58.45}$
30. $0.56\overline{)13.72}$
31. $7.4\overline{)166.5}$

Divide. Round the quotient to one decimal place.

32. $5\overline{)38.26}$
33. $1.3\overline{)8999}$
34. $0.48\overline{)776.5}$

35. $0.4\overline{)2616}$
36. $7.9\overline{)707.84}$
37. $3.25\overline{)2827.5}$
38. $0.06\overline{)576}$

Evaluate each expression. Suppose $m = 60$, $n = 0.1$ and $o = 2$.

39. $6n$
40. $\dfrac{95}{n}$
41. mn
42. $\dfrac{m}{o}$

Guess and test the solution for each equation.

43. $8a = 56$
44. $\dfrac{x}{14} = 3$
45. $25b = 400$

Write an equation. Then guess and test its solution.

46. When a number is divided by 5 the quotient is 24. What is the number?

Unit 4 Problem Solving I

Choosing the Operation

Certain words can be misleading when you are choosing the operation to solve a problem. The two problems below use the same key word, **more**. Yet, the operations needed are different.

Mr. Tonelli travelled 856 km to Calgary by plane. He then continued onward by train for 354 km **more**. How far has he travelled?

Add.

856 + 354 = 910
Mr. Tonelli travelled 910 km.

Rita has started to read a book with 856 pages. She has 354 **more** pages to read. How many pages has she already read?

Subtract.

856 − 354 = 502
Rita has already read 502 pages.

EXERCISES

Choose the operations needed to solve the problems. Be careful of words which might mislead.

1. At a pizza party, 12 pizzas were **divided** into 6 pieces each. Every person had 4 pieces. How many people were at the party?

2. Nine 2 L bottles of pop were **divided** equally among 24 children. How much did each child get?

3. For a school musical, students were **divided** into singing, dancing, and instrumental groups. There were 8 singers, 12 dancers, and 24 instrumentalists. How many more students were in the instrumental groups than in the other two groups?

4. Fifteen people organized a car wash one weekend. They **divided** their $210 profit equally. How much money did each person get?

PRACTICE

Choose the operations needed to solve the problems.

1. In 1860, the **average** mass of a human brain was 1372 g. By 1980, the **average** mass of a brain had increased by 52 g. What was the mass of an **average** brain in 1980?

2. One of the world's largest bank buildings is the 72-story Bank of Montreal in Toronto. If each story has an **average** height of 4.96 m, about how tall is the building?

3. In a recent hockey season, the Quebec Nordiques scored 356 goals in 80 games. What was their **average** number of goals per game?

4. On the **average**, Bernie scores on 0.7 of his foul shots in basketball. How many foul shots should he be expected to make in 40 attempts?

5. Suppose your **average** time for running the 100 m dash is 15 s. What time could you reasonably expect to run in 400 m? (How do you feel after running a fast 100 m?)

Estimating a Reasonable Solution

Using rounded numbers helps you find a **reasonable** solution to a problem.

Charles Lindbergh was the first man to fly solo across the Atlantic. In 1927, he flew from Long Island, New York to Paris, France in 33.5 h. His average speed was 173.4 km/h. About how long was the trip?

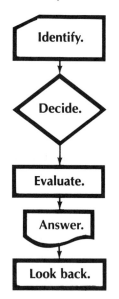

Identify.

Speed: 173.4 km/h
Time: 33.5 h

Decide.

Round and estimate.
Speed × Time = Distance
173.4 × 33.5 = Distance

200 × 30

Evaluate.

200 × 30 = 6000

Answer.

Lindbergh flew about 6000 km.

Look back.

6000 km is a reasonable distance.

EXERCISES

Estimate a reasonable solution using rounded numbers.

1. Mrs. Halberg caught a record-sized coho salmon in Cowichan Bay, Vancouver Island. The salmon had a mass of 14.06 kg. At a cost of $7.85/kg, about what would Mrs. Halberg's catch be worth?

2. Super Save Stores, Inc. is a large grocery chain. Super Save has 2477 stores and employs an average of 63.5 persons per store. About how many employees does Super Save have?

3. The average mass of a Siberian tiger is 190 kg. In 1967, a 388.7 kg tiger was found. About how much heavier was this tiger than the average?

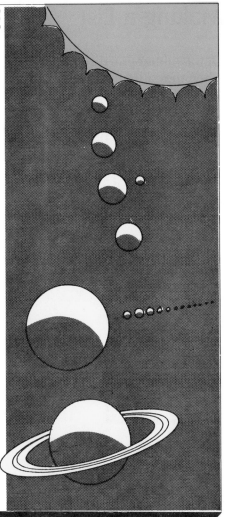

Estimate a reasonable solution.

1. It takes 499.012 s for the light of the Sun to reach the Earth. About how many minutes does it take?

2. The Earth is almost, but not quite, a sphere. The distance around the Earth at the equator is 40 007.903 km. The distance around the Earth through the North and South Poles is 40 075.06 km. About how much farther would a trip around the poles be than a trip around the equator?

3. The diameter of the Earth is 12 756.289 km. The Moon's diameter is 3476.27 km. About how much greater is the diameter of the Earth than the diameter of the Moon?

4. The Earth seems to be standing still, but it is actually speeding in its orbit around the Sun at a rate of 29.789 km/s. About how far does the Earth travel in one hour?

5. The planet Mercury is closer to the sun than the Earth and travels even faster than the Earth. Its orbital speed is 47.878 km/s. About how much farther will Mercury travel in one minute than the Earth?

Extraterrestrial

A. Suppose *E.T.* and his family were taking a holiday on the planet Neptune and invited you to join them. Neptune is about 4 690 235 000 km from Earth. If you could travel at a rate of 99 999.99 km/h, about how long would it take you to get there?

B. Suppose *Darth Vader* is planning to destroy the Earth from the planet Pluto which is about 7 473 773 000 km from Earth. If you direct a laser beam at *Darth Vader* at a rate of 299 337 km/h, how long will it be before you vaporize *Darth Vader*?

Making a List

Of the numerals 0 through 9, only 0, 1, and 8 look exactly the same when they are turned upside-down. How many numerals less than 100 look the same when they are turned upside-down?

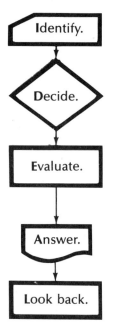

Use only the digits 0, 1, and 8.
The numerals must be less than 100.

Make an organized list of the numerals.

1-digit numerals:	2-digit numerals:	
0	10	80
1	11	81
8	18	88

There are 9 numerals less than 100 which look the same upside-down.

The list appears to be complete.
All combinations of 0, 1, and 8 have been used.

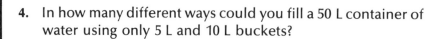

1. How many numerals less than 200 will look exactly the same when each digit is turned upside-down?

2. What are all of the 3-digit whole numbers that can be made with the numerals 1, 2, and 3? Each numeral may be used only once in the 3-digit number.

3. An amoeba is placed in an empty jar. After one minute, the amoeba splits into two amoebas. After another minute, the two amoebas split in the same way. How many amoebas will be in the jar after 6 min? 10 min?

4. In how many different ways could you fill a 50 L container of water using only 5 L and 10 L buckets?

94

1. List the different ways in which the product of two whole numbers equals 48.

2. Mark has a yellow, a blue, and a tan sweater which he wears with his brown and his blue pants. How many different combinations are possible?

3. How many different rectangles are there with a perimeter of 48 if you assume that the length of the sides can only be whole numbers?

4. Suppose you have a quarter, a dime, a nickel, and a penny. How many differently-priced items could you buy using exact change?

5. If a 10 m log were to be cut into three pieces with each piece having a length in a whole number of metres, how many different three piece groups would be possible?

6. In how many different ways can you combine coins to make 25¢?

The King's Reward

A wealthy king was once saved from drowning by a poor farm boy. To reward the boy, the king offered to pay him sums of money in 14 installments. But he offered the boy a choice of 2 plans of payment.

Under plan 1, the king would pay $100 the first day, $200 the second day, $300 the third day, and so on; the payment increasing by $100 each day.

Under plan 2, the king would pay $1 the first day, $2 the second day, $4 the third day, and so on; the payment doubling each day.

Which plan is the better reward?

Using a Calculator

A calculator can be used to test the accuracy of an estimate.

A male child born in Canada can expect to live for 69 a. About how many hours can the infant male expect to live?

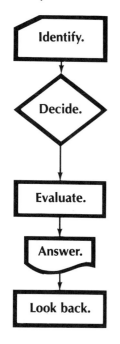

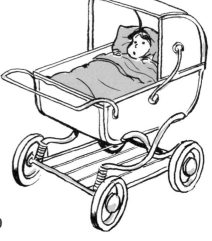

Identify.

Expected life is 69 a.
1 a is 365 d.
1 d is 24 h.

Decide.

Estimate the hours lived.
69 × 365 × 24
↓ ↓ ↓
70 × 400 × 20

Evaluate.

70 × 400 × 20 = 560 000

Answer.

The infant male is expected to live about 560 000 h.

Look back.

Use a calculator to test the accuracy of the estimate.

| 6 | 9 | × | 3 | 6 | 5 | × | 2 | 4 | = |

604 440

The estimate is reasonable.

EXERCISES

Estimate the answer. Then use a calculator to find the *exact* answer.

1. A female born in Canada can expect to live for 76 a.

   a. About how many hours can the infant female expect to live?
   b. About how many more hours can the female expect to live than a male?

2. During a weekend sale, a department store sold 19 television sets at $479.95 and 23 sets at $289.95. About how much money was taken in on sales of television sets?

PRACTICE

Estimate the answer. Then use a calculator to find the *exact* answer.

1. At a hockey game, 14 789 fans paid an average ticket price of $9.75. About how much money was paid in all for hockey tickets?

2. A bee hummingbird can have a mass as little as 1.6 g. An ostrich can have a mass as great as 1565 kg. About how many bee hummingbirds would it take to have a mass equal to that of a large ostrich?

3. About how much money would be left from $500 after buying three airline tickets costing $151.65?

4. A DC-10 has a fuel capacity of 138 500 L and uses about 9990 L/h. About how long could a DC-10 fly if it used all but 10 000 L of its fuel?

5. The maximum take-off mass for a Boeing 747 is 352 531 kg. If all 442 seats are filled and there are 12 additional crew members, about how much mass is left for cargo and fuel? Assume a mass of 65 kg per person.

Strokes

Unscramble the keystrokes for each problem.

a. $(3 \times 2) + (7 \times 4)$

| 2 | 3 | 4 | 7 | × | × | M+ | M+ | MR |

b. $10 \div (5 - 3)$

| 0 | 1 | 3 | 5 | ÷ | − | = | M+ | MR |

c. $[8 \div (2 \div 2)]$

| | 2 | 2 | 8 | ÷ | ÷ | = | M+ | MR |

d. $8 \div 2 \times (4 + 3)$

| = | 2 | 3 | 4 | 8 | ÷ | × | + | M+ | MR |

e. $9 - 12 \div 3 + 21$

| 1 | 1 | 2 | 2 | 3 | 9 | − | + | ÷ | = | M+ | MR |

Making Diagrams

The town of Lockjaw lies on the same road as the towns of Cupcake and Aardvark, which are 100 km from each other. Cupcake is west of Aardvark. Lockjaw is 20 km west of Cupcake. Wolf Hollow, on the same road, is 30 km east of Aardvark. How far is it from Wolf Hollow to Lockjaw?

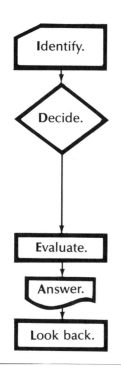

All towns are on the same road.
Cupcake is 100 km west of Aardvark.
Lockjaw is 20 km west of Cupcake.
Wolf Hollow is 30 km east of Aardvark.

Draw a diagram to show the positions of the towns.

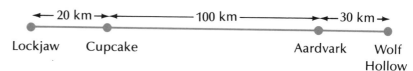

The total distance can be found by adding.

$$20 + 100 + 30 = 150$$

Wolf Hollow is 150 km from Lockjaw.

The answer of 150 km makes sense because Lockjaw and Wolf Hollow are farther apart than 100 km.

EXERCISES

1. Solve the problem above, but this time assume Cupcake is *east* of Aardvark.

2. In a race, Beth finished ahead of Sam but behind Hilda. Inge finished behind Lars but ahead of Hilda. In what position did each racer finish?

3. Four squares can be put together edge to edge to form 5 different figures. Use grid paper to find these 5 figures. (One example is shown at the right. The two figures are the same.)

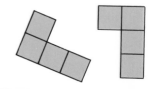

PRACTICE

1. A commuter train stops in 5 towns daily. The Paxton stop is 40 km north of the Oak Glen stop and 60 km south of the Sommerset stop. The Trent stop is 20 km south of the Oak Glen stop. The Sommerset stop is 35 km north of the Valley Woods stop. How far is it between the Paxton stop and the Valley Woods stop?

2. Suppose you are allowed to walk north, south, east, or west through several city blocks. You must walk 4 different lengths, 2 blocks, 3 blocks, 4 blocks, and 5 blocks, but not necessarily in that order. Use grid paper to find different paths you could take. Can you find a path that returns you to the starting point?

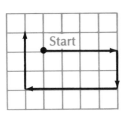

3. Centimetre cubes are stacked in 12 layers with one cube on the top layer, two cubes in the second layer, three cubes in the next layer, and so on. How many cubes will be in the stack altogether?

4. There are 20 different figures having a perimeter of 12 units which can be formed from squares. Use grid paper to see how many you can find.

5. On grid paper, make a square which is 8 cm on each side. Mark the midpoints of each side. Connect these midpoints forming another square. Now your figure has 5 regions. Mark the midpoints of the inner square and form another square. Continue until your figure contains 6 squares. How many regions does it have?

Graph Storytelling

Cindy ran some water into the tub and took a bath.
Use the graph below to help you write a story about what happened.

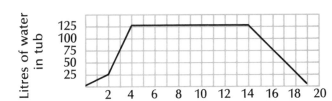

99

Problems

Use the table below to answer questions 1–3.

Canadian Lakes

Lake	Area (km²)	Length (km)	Depth (m)
Great Bear	31 328	306	413
Winnipeg	24 396	426	18
Ontario	19 011	311	244
Athabasca	7 938	322	122

1. Which one of the lakes is:
   a. the longest?
   b. the deepest?

2. Which lake is twice as deep as another?

3. Which lake is about 3 times smaller than Lake Winnipeg?

4. When a certain pair of numbers is added, the sum is 29. When the numbers are multiplied, the product is 120. What are the two numbers?

5. A whole number has two digits. The second digit is four times the first digit. The sum of the digits is 10. What is the number?

6. Pam shopped all afternoon after she got off the bus. She walked 2 blocks east to the first store and 3 blocks north to the second store. Next, she walked 4 blocks west to the third store. Finally, she walked 3 blocks south to the fourth store.
   How far was she from the bus stop?
   In what direction should she proceed to get the bus?

7. Ralph had 6 sticks of gum. He traded each stick for 5 peanuts. He traded each peanut for 3 jelly beans. How many jelly beans did Ralph get?

8. Using only the numerals 4, 5, and 6, how many different 3-digit whole numbers can you write? Each numeral is to be used exactly once in each 3-digit whole number.

9. What *even* 3-digit numbers can be made from 2, 3, 4, and 5?

10. How many ways can you obtain three dollars worth of stamps using only 60¢ and 30¢ stamps?

11. How can you make a dollar using exactly 25 coins?

100

REVIEW

Solve.

1. On the average, Maryann spells 0.8 of the words on her spelling tests correctly. Which operation would you use to find how many correct spellings she could expect to have on a 25-word test?

2. Dave Dowdle of England ran a distance of 274.48 km in 24 h. Estimate his average rate per hour.

3. Estimate the change from $10 after buying 3 hot dogs at $1.25 each and 3 orders of fries at $0.85 each.
Now find the *exact* answers with a calculator.

4. Adult tickets for a movie cost $5 and children's tickets cost $3.50. Mr. Garcia bought twice as many children's tickets as adult tickets. Altogether he spent $60. How many children's tickets did he buy?

5. Eagle's Wing Airlines has 6 planes. Some of the planes have 2 engines, and the rest have 3 engines. Altogether there are 14 engines on all of the planes. How many planes have 2 engines?

6. Mrs. Lee wants to plant rose bushes around the edge of her triangular garden, which is 5 m on each side. She wants the rose bushes to be 1 m apart. How many rose bushes will she need?

7. Four boys are lined up in front of the room. Brad is standing to Tim's right, Joe is standing to Al's left. Al is standing between Tim and Joe. Which boys are standing at the ends of the line?

8. How many times will the digit 2 be written if you write down all the numerals from 1 to 99?

9. At a local refreshment stand, hamburgers and hot dogs are sold with a choice of one of four kinds of toppings: catsup, mustard, pickle relish, and cheese. How many different sandwich combinations are possible?

10. Mr. Sloan, Mr. Ali, Mr. Wiemer, and Mr. Tung are introduced to each other. Each man shakes the others' hands only once. How many handshakes take place?

Choose the operations which would solve the problems.

1. Donalda caught three brook trout having a total mass of 1.56 kg. What was the average mass of the trout?
   a. multiply   b. divide   c. multiply and divide

2. Carl bought three records at $5.98 each. The sales tax came to 36¢. How much change should he get from $20?

   a. multiply and   b. multiply and   c. multiply, add,
      subtract   add   and subtract

Estimate a reasonable answer.

3. The Bible contains 3 566 480 letters. The average word has 4.6 letters. About how many words are in the Bible?

4. An aircraft carrier can cruise at 56 km/h for 25 892 h before it needs refueling for its nuclear power. About how far could the aircraft carrier go before it needs to refuel?

Estimate the answer. Then use a calculator to find the *exact* answer.

5. In 1978, James Warnock of Cantley, Quebec made a house of cards 353 cm high. He used 3650 cards. How many 52-card decks did he use?

6. Mercury travels around the sun at the rate of 47.878 km/h. The Earth moves more slowly at a rate of 29.789 km/h. In 10 h, how much farther does Mercury go than the Earth?

Solve.

7. Ted, Ned, and Red run a 100 m race. Find the total number of different orders in which the runners could finish the race.

8. How many different ways can you obtain 60¢ worth of stamps using only 5¢ and 10¢ stamps?

9. When Ms. Fabian uses a car pool to go to work, she travels 2 km north, 3 km east, 1 km south, 1 km east, and 1 km south. How many kilometres, and in what direction, would Ms. Fabian travel if she drove directly to work without any passengers?

BACK

Copy and complete using = or ≠. Do not calculate.

1. $(26.15 + 31.84) + 12.52 \bullet 26.15 + (31.84 + 12.52)$

2. $1835 \div 620 \bullet 620 \div 1835$

3. $6.4 \times (30 + 6) \bullet (6.4 \times 30) + (6.4 \times 6)$

4. $36.52 - (14.04 - 6.95) \bullet (36.52 - 14.04) - 6.95$

5. $4.2 \times (5 \times 7.4) \bullet (4.2 \times 5) \times 7.4$

Evaluate.

6. $9 + 7 + 4 + 3 + 1$

7. $8 \times (70 + 3)$

8. $12 \times (5 \times 7)$

9. $30 \times (100 - 5)$

10. $672 + (128 + 356)$

11. $26 + 22 + 74 + 15 + 88$

12. 12^2

13. 3^3

14. 2^6

15. $5^4 + 75$

16. $2^0 - 1$

17. $100^1 - 1^{15}$

Evaluate each expression. Suppose $p = 5$, $q = 9$, and $r = 3$.

18. $q \times (p - r)$

19. $p + q \div r$

20. $pq \div r$

21. $(p + r)^2$

22. $pqr + 50$

23. $p^2 + q^2 \div r^2$

Simplify.

24. 15×5^2

25. $(3 + 7) \times 4 - 16 \div 2^1$

26. $74 - 8 \times 4^0 \div 2 + 5$

27. $2^2 + 10^3 \div 5^3$

28. $8^2 \div (16 - 7 \times 2) - 10^1$

29. $(7 + 8)^2 \div (8 - 5)^2$

Solve.

30. Fourteen plus the product of an unknown number and five is 44. What is the number?

31. Jane put some stamps in packages of 6 to sell at a garage sale. She has 89 stamps in all, but wishes to keep 5 stamps for herself. How many packages of stamps did Jane have to sell?

32. The sum of seventy-three and an unknown number times four is 312. What is the number?

UNIT 5   Measurement

Measuring Length

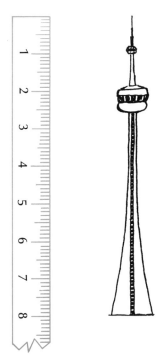

Prefix	Meaning	Unit	Symbol
kilo	1000	kilometre	km
hecto	100	hectometre	hm
deca	10	decametre	dam
Basic Unit		metre	m
deci	0.1	decimetre	dm
centi	0.01	centimetre	cm
milli	0.001	millimetre	mm

In the drawing, the CN Tower is 8 cm tall.

Actually, the CN Tower is 55 300 cm, or 553 m, or about one half kilometre tall.

km	hm	dam	m	dm	cm	mm
0.553	5.53	55.3	553	5530	55 300	553 000

Which unit is appropriate? Use **km**, **m**, **cm**, or **mm**.

1. length of a pencil

2. thickness of a nail

3. width of a door

4. length of a ski trail

5. length of skis

6. air distances between cities

7. Copy and complete.

km	hm	dam	m	dm	cm	mm
	0.86	8.6	86	860		
4						
					342	
						9550
6.2						

Write the metric prefix which means:

1. 1000

2. 0.01

3. 100

4. 0.001

Which unit is appropriate? Use **km**, **m**, **cm**, or **mm**.

5. length of Lake Winnipeg

6. length of a room

7. thickness of a wire

8. height of a flower

Copy and complete.

9. 345 cm = ■ m

10. 76 mm = ■ cm

11. 5000 mm = ■ m

12. 0.5 m = ■ mm

13. 0.5 km = ■ cm

14. 0.5 cm = ■ mm

Bookworms

Two books stand on a shelf. A bookworm starts at page 1 of one book and chews a straight path to the last page of the other book.

If the thickness of each book cover is 3 mm and each book's pages is 3.5 cm, how far did the bookworm travel?

105

Polygon Perimeters

How much ribbon is needed to go
around the perimeter of each figure?

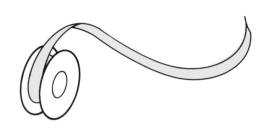

The **perimeter** of any polygon is the sum of the
lengths of its sides.

square:

2.5 cm

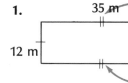

Perimeter = sum of sides
P = 4 × length of side
P = 4s
P = 4 × 2.5
P = 10 cm

triangle:

1.5 cm   2.5 cm

3 cm

Perimeter = sum of sides
P = 2.5 + 1.5 + 3
P = 8 cm

rectangle:

1.7 cm

3 cm

Perimeter = sum of sides
P = 2 × length + 2 × width
P = 2l + 2w
P = (2 × 3) + (2 × 1.7)
P = 9.4 cm

or

P = 2 × (l + w)
P = 2 × (3 + 1.7)
P = 9.4 cm

EXERCISES

Find the perimeter of each polygon.

1.

35 m

12 m

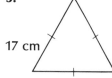

Matching
marks indicate
sides of equal
length.

2.

11.1 cm

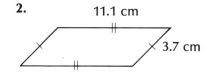

3.7 cm

3.

17 cm

4.

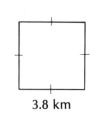

3.8 km

5.

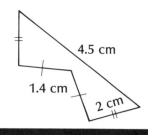

4.5 cm

1.4 cm

2 cm

Find the perimeter of each polygon.

1.

7.8 m

4 m

2.

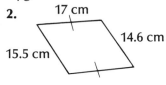

17 cm

14.6 cm

15.5 cm

3.

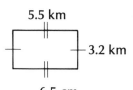

5.5 km

3.2 km

6.5 cm

4.

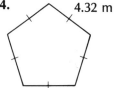

4.32 m

5.

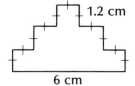

1.2 cm

6 cm

6.

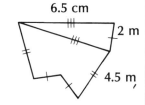

2 m

4.5 m

The perimeter of each polygon is 50.5 cm.
What is the length of the side QR in each?

7.

Q   R

5 cm

S   T

8.

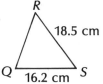

R

18.5 cm

Q   16.2 cm   S

9.

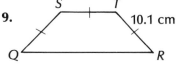

S   T

10.1 cm

Q   R

Solve.

10. Fencing is needed for a flower garden planted in the centre of a yard. The yard is 20 m long and 16 m wide. Five metres of grass surround the garden on all sides. How much fencing is needed to enclose the flower garden?

Perimeter Graphing

Join the coordinates on a centimetre grid in the order given.
What is the perimeter of the figure?

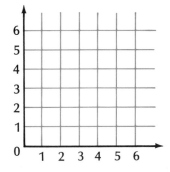

(1,1) (1,6) (4,6) (4,5) (2,5) (2,4)

(3,4) (3,3) (2,3) (2,2) (4,2) (4,1) (1,1)

Measuring Circles

What are some ways to measure this record?

Measure its **diameter** (d).

30 cm
diameter

The distance from edge to edge, through centre, is called the *diameter.*
The record's diameter is 30 cm.

diameter = 2 × radius
$d = 2r$
$d = 2 \times 15$
$d = 30$ cm

Measure its **radius** (r).

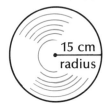

15 cm
radius

The distance from the centre to the edge is called the *radius.*
The record's radius is 15 cm.

radius = diameter ÷ 2
$r = \dfrac{d}{2}$
$r = \dfrac{30}{2}$
$r = 15$ cm

Measure its **circumference** (C). The distance around the edge (its perimeter) is called the *circumference.*

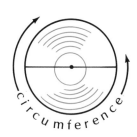

circumference

The circumference is *about* 3 times greater than the diameter.

circumference ≈ 3 × diameter
$C \approx 3d$
$C \approx 3 \times 30$
$C \approx 90$ cm

More accurately, the circumference is π (≈ 3.14) times greater than the diameter.

circumference = π × diameter
$C = \pi d$
$C \approx 3.14 \times 30$
$C \approx 94.2$ cm

Did you know?

The Greek symbol π (called pi) is 3.141 592 653 589 793 238 . . .
It is often rounded to two decimal places: 3.14.

EXERCISES

Find the **diameter**.

1.

12 m

$d = 2r$
$d = 2 \times 12$
$d = \blacksquare$

2.

28 cm

3.

3 km

4.

6.9 m

5.

58.6 cm

6.

0.48 km

7.

0.05 mm

Find the **radius**.

8.

30 cm

$r = \dfrac{d}{2}$
$r = \dfrac{30}{2}$
$r = \blacksquare$

9.

350 m

10.

9 km

11.

46.5 cm

12.

1.25 m

13.

7.4 km

14.

8.7 m

Estimate π using the measurements given.

15.

7 cm
21.98 cm

$\pi = \dfrac{c}{d}$
$\pi = \blacksquare$

16.

25 m
78.5 m

17.

12 km
37.68 km

Find the circumference.

18.

18 m

$c = \pi d$
$c = 3.14 \times \blacksquare$
$c = \blacksquare$

19.

84 cm

20.

3.5 km

21.

4 m

22.
20 cm

23.

1 km

24.
3.7 m

PRACTICE

Estimate the circumference. Use $C \approx 3d$.

1.

96 cm

2.

5.9 km

3.
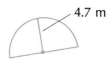
2.2 m

What is the diameter? Use 3.14 for π.

4.

78 cm

5.

109.9 cm

6.

4.7 m

What is the radius? Use 3.14 for π.

7.

15 km

8.

36 cm

9.

15.7 km

What is the circumference? Use 3.14 for π.

10.
40 m

11.
11 m

12.
3.5 km

What is the perimeter? Use 3.14 for π.

13.

8 m

14.
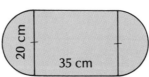
20 cm
35 cm

15.
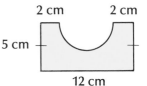
2 cm   2 cm
5 cm
12 cm

16. Measure the circumference and diameter of 4 circular objects. Then copy and complete the table at the right. What can you say about $C \div d$?

Circumference	Diameter	$C \div d$

17. What is the diameter and circumference of each Canadian coin?

110

Computer Circumference

The BASIC computer program below will calculate the circumference of a circle.

Each step of the program is represented on a flow chart.

Try the program on a computer.

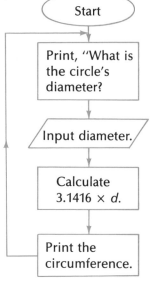

```
10 PRINT "WHAT IS THE
   CIRCLE'S DIAMETER? "
20 INPUT D
30 LET C = 3.1416 * D
40 PRINT "THE CIRCLE'S
   CIRCUMFERENCE IS ";C
50 GOTO 10
60 END
```

The computer waits for you to type in a diameter.

The computer goes into an **infinite** loop back to line 10. It never reaches the end statement.

Read your computer manual for instructions on how to stop or "break" the program to get out of the infinite loop.

Calculator Perimeter

The perimeter of the rectangle can be found by using a calculator's memory.

$P = 2l + 2w$

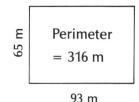

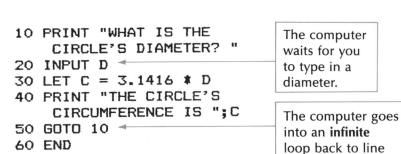

Use a calculator's memory to find the perimeter.

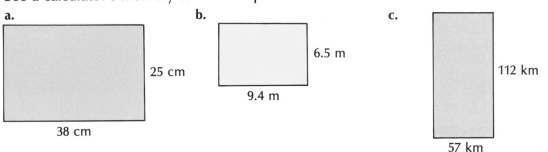

a. 38 cm, 25 cm

b. 9.4 m, 6.5 m

c. 57 km, 112 km

111

Estimating Measurements

A tree has a circumference of 118 cm.
Estimate the tree's diameter.

118 cm *rounds up* to 120 cm.

$$\text{diameter} \approx \frac{\text{circumference}}{3}$$

$$d \approx \frac{120}{3}$$

$$d \approx 40 \text{ cm}$$

The tree's diameter is *about* 40 cm.

A tree's height can be estimated using your height as a benchmark.

My height is about 2 m. The tree is about 3 times taller, or 6 m high.

EXERCISES

Estimate the length, *AB*, in centimetres.
Use the width of your index finger as a benchmark for 1 cm.

1. A ———————————————————— B

2. A ———————————————————— B

3. A ———————————————————— B

Estimate the length of each in metres.
Use the length of your pace as a benchmark for 1 m.

4. school hallway   5. classroom   6. school cafeteria

Estimate the diameter.

7. 17.3 cm

8. 6.5 m

9. 35.8 cm

Estimate the circumference.

10. 91.4 cm

11. 135.2 cm

12. 5.92 m

Estimate the diameter.

1. 6.4 m

2.  56.9 m

3.  27.25 cm

Estimate the circumference.

4. 12.75 m

5. 4.3 cm

6.  24.85 cm

Estimate to the nearest centimetre.
Use the width of your index finger as a benchmark for 1 cm.

7. The length from *X* to *Y.*

a.

b.

8. The perimeter.

a.

b.

c.

9. The diameter.

a.

b.

c.

Estimate the length of each to the nearest metre. Use a benchmark
of your own choice.

10. telephone pole

11. compact car

12. lunch table

13. bus

14. school gym

15. flag pole

Measuring the Earth and Moon

Use the data given on the *circumference* of
the earth and moon to estimate and compare
their *diameters* and *radiuses*.

	Earth	Moon
Circumference	40 077 km	10 905 km

Area

The **area** of a figure is a measure of the surface it covers.

Area (*A*) can be found by counting the squares on a surface.

A = 7 square units

A = 4.5 square units

Area is often measured in **square centimetres (cm²), square metres (m²),** and **square kilometres (km²).**

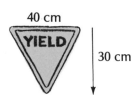
40 cm
YIELD
30 cm

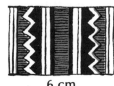
5 m
6 cm

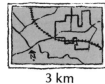
2 km
3 km

The sign's area is **600 cm².**

The rug's area is **30 m².**

The geographical area is **6 km².**

Farmlands are often measured in large squares called **hectares.**

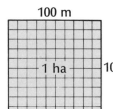
100 m
1 ha
100 m

1 ha = 10 000 m²

EXERCISES

Which unit is appropriate? Use **cm², m²,** or **km².**

1. a desk top
2. Québec
3. a living room floor
4. a barbecue grill
5. the earth's surface
6. a potato field

Count squares to find the area.

7.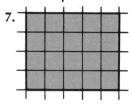
8.
9.
10.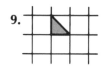

PRACTICE

Count squares to find the area.

1. 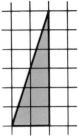 **2.** 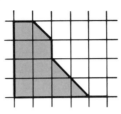 **3.** 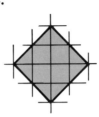 **4.**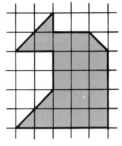

5. a. How many square centimetres?
   b. How many square metres?

100 cm

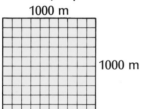

100 cm

6. a. How many square metres?
   b. How many square hectares?

100 m

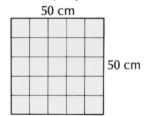

100 m

7. a. How many square metres?
   b. How many square kilometres?

1000 m

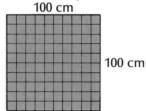

1000 m

8. a. How many square centimetres?
   b. How many square metres?

50 cm

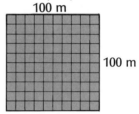

50 cm

Copy and complete.

9. 1 ha = ■ m²
   10 ha = ■ m²

10. 1 m² = ■ cm²
   50 m² = ■ cm²

11. 1 km² = ■ m²
   25 km² = ■ m²

Solve.

12. Which is larger, a 100 cm² surface or a surface that is 0.5 m²?

13. A square surface has an area of 400 m².
   What is the length of each side?

Block Letter Areas

Write your name in block letters on a piece of grid paper. How many square units are in your name?

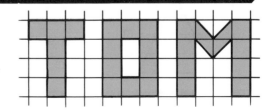

Computing Area

The area (A) of a polygon can be computed by using a formula.

Rectangle:

Area = length × width
$A = lw$ $A = 30\ m^2$

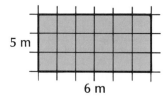

5 m

6 m

Square:

Area = sides squared
$A = s^2$ $A = 4^2$ $A = 16\ cm^2$

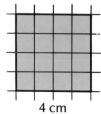

4 cm

Parallelogram:

Area = base × height
$A = bh$ $A = 21\ m^2$

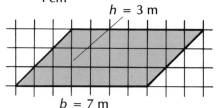

$h = 3\ m$

$b = 7\ m$

Triangle:

Area = $\dfrac{\text{base} \times \text{height}}{2}$
$A = \dfrac{bh}{2}$ $A = \dfrac{4 \times 3}{2}$ $A = 6\ cm^2$

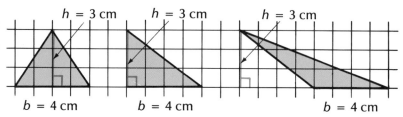

$h = 3\ cm$ $h = 3\ cm$ $h = 3\ cm$

$b = 4\ cm$ $b = 4\ cm$ $b = 4\ cm$

EXERCISES

Find the area.

1.

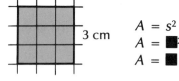

2 m

6 m

$A = lw$
$A = \blacksquare \times \blacksquare$
$A = \blacksquare$

2.

3 cm

$A = s^2$
$A = \blacksquare^2$
$A = \blacksquare$

3.

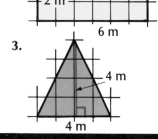

4 m

4 m

$A = \dfrac{bh}{2}$

$A = \dfrac{\blacksquare \times \blacksquare}{2}$

$A = \blacksquare$

4.

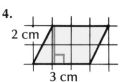

2 cm

3 cm

$A = bh$
$A = \blacksquare \times \blacksquare$
$A = \blacksquare$

Find the area.

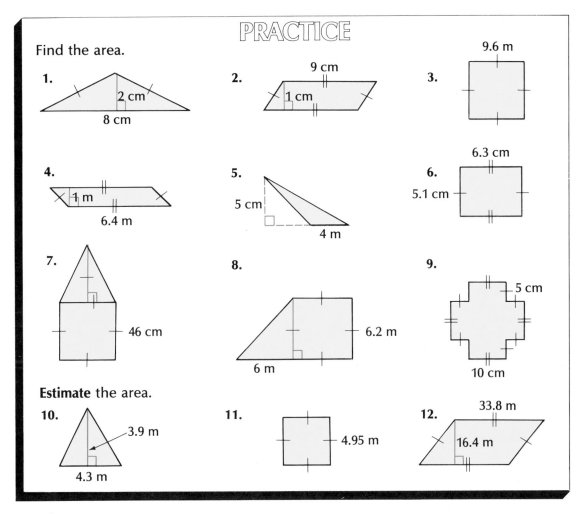

1.
2 cm
8 cm

2.
9 cm
1 cm

3.
9.6 m

4.
1 m
6.4 m

5.
5 cm
4 m

6.
6.3 cm
5.1 cm

7.
46 cm

8.
6.2 m
6 m

9.
5 cm
10 cm

Estimate the area.

10.
3.9 m
4.3 m

11.
4.95 m

12.
33.8 m
16.4 m

Surface Area

How much self-adhesive paper is needed to resurface each box?
Remember each box has 6 surfaces:

    1. top   **2.** bottom
    3. right   **4.** left
    5. front   **6.** back

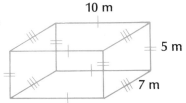

You must add the areas of all 6 surfaces.

a.
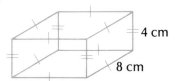
4 cm
8 cm

b.
10 m
5 m
7 m

c.
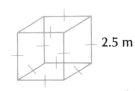
2.5 m

117

Area of a Circle

Mrs. Bosley wants to put a circular rug on her dining room floor. The rug has a diameter of 4 m. How much of the floor would be covered by the rug?

Estimate by counting squares.

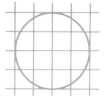

About 12 m² of the floor will be covered.

The area of the rug can be more accurately computed using a formula.

Area = *pi* × radius squared

A = πr^2
A = 3.14 × 2^2
A = 3.14 × 4
A = 12.56 m²

The circular rug will cover 12.56 m² of the floor.

EXERCISES

Estimate the areas of the circles by counting squares.

1.

2.
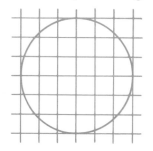

3.
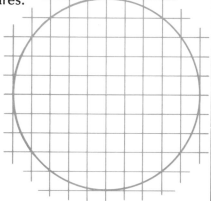

Calculate the area of a circle with each radius.

4.
4 cm

5.
3 cm

6.
6 cm

7.
10 m

$A = \pi r^2$
$A = 3.14 \times 4^2$
$A = \blacksquare$

8.

20 m

9.

30 m

10.

2.5 cm

Find the area of each.

1. 8 cm

2. 9 m

3. 12 cm

4. 18 cm

5. 30 m

6. 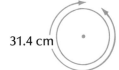 31.4 cm

7. a long-playing record with a *radius* of 15 cm

8. a swimming pool with a *diameter* of 3.6 m

9. a cake plate with a *circumference* of 125.6 cm

Copy and Complete.

1. 937 cm = ■ m

2. 7.2 km = ■ m

3. 985 mm = ■ m

Find the perimeter.

4. 2.5 m

5. 5 cm 7.6 cm

6. 16.2 m 7.5 m

Find the circumference of a circle with the given measurement.

7. diameter = 8 cm

8. diameter = 55 cm

9. radius = 12 m

Estimate the perimeter.

10. 17.9 cm

11. 12.6 cm 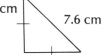 6.3 cm

12. 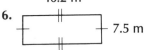 5 cm

Copy and complete.

13. $1 \text{ m}^2 = $ ■ cm^2

14. $1 \text{ km}^2 = $ ■ m^2

15. $1 \text{ cm}^2 = $ ■ mm^2

Find the area.

16. rectangle:
    length = 7 m
    width = 3.2 m

17. triangle:
    base = 5.5 cm
    height = 4 cm

18. parallelogram:
    base = 8.7 m
    height = 3.4 m

19. circle:
    radius = 4 cm

20. circle:
    radius = 13 m

21. circle:
    diameter = 24 cm

119

Volume

The **volume** (*V*) of a solid is a measure of the space it occupies.
Volume can sometimes be found by counting cubes.

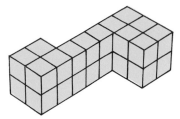

V = 26 cubic units

Volume is often measured in **cubic centimetres (cm³)** and **cubic
metres (m³)**

The volume of
the can is 339 cm³.

The volume of
the coal car is
48 m³.

EXERCISES

Which unit is appropriate? Use **cm³** or **m³**.

1. a can of soup

2. an aquarium

3. a large swimming pool

Count cubes to find the volume.

4.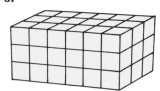

5.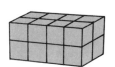

6.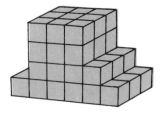

7.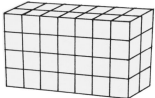

8.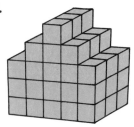

9.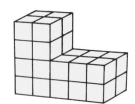

What is the volume in cubic units?

1.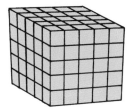

2.

3.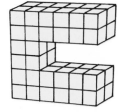

4.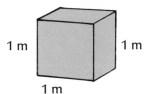

5.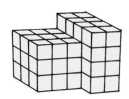

6.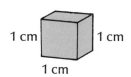

7. **a.** How many cubic metres?
   b. How many cubic centimetres?

8. **a.** How many cubic centimetres?
   b. How many cubic millimetres?

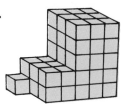

1 m   1 m

1 m

1 cm   1 cm

1 cm

Copy and complete.

9. $1 m^3 = \blacksquare cm^3$ 10. $1 cm^3 = \blacksquare mm^3$ 11. $1 m^3 = \blacksquare mm^3$

   $4 m^3 = \blacksquare cm^3$ $50 cm^3 = \blacksquare mm^3$ $3 m^3 = \blacksquare mm^3$

Solve.

12. The earth's volume is $1.083\,230 \times 10^6\ km^3$.
    Write the volume in standard form.

Cubic Patterns

A 3 cm × 3 cm × 3 cm cube is painted and cut into
centimetre cubes.

a. How many centimetre cubes were made?

b. How many vertices does it have? edges?
faces?

c. What is the fewest number of cuts made?

d. How many centimetre cubes have 3 sides
painted? 2 sides painted? 1 side painted?

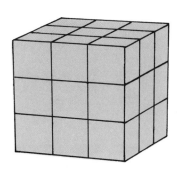

Computing Volume

Volume (*V*) can be computed using a formula.

Rectangular Prism:

Volume = area of base × height
$V = (4 \times 2) \times 3$
$V = 8 \times 3$
$V = 24$ cm³

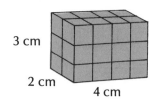

3 cm
2 cm
4 cm

Triangular Prism:

Volume = area of base × height
$V = \dfrac{8 \times 3}{2} \times 4$
$V = 12 \times 4$
$V = 48$ cm³

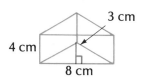

3 cm
4 cm
8 cm

Cylinder:

Volume = area of base × height
$V = (3.14 \times 6^2) \times 10$
$V = 113.04 \times 10$
$V = 1130.4$ cm³

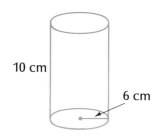

10 cm
6 cm

EXERCISES

Find the volume.

1. area of base: 48 cm²
    height: 5 cm

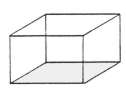

2. area of base: 20 cm²
    height: 6 cm

3. area of base: 314 cm²
    height: 35 cm

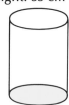

4.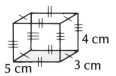

    4 cm
    5 cm   3 cm

5.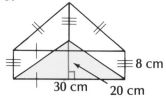

    8 cm
    30 cm   20 cm

6.

    25 cm
    18 cm

122

Find the volume.

1.

18 cm

25 cm

2.

40 cm

7 cm

15 cm

3.

5 cm

7.8 cm

9 cm

4.

3 cm

5 cm

5.

15 cm

8 cm

6.

1.5 m

6 m

7.

0.5 m

1.2 m

2.5 m

8.

20 cm

30 cm

9.

8.4 cm

7.2 cm

Estimate the volume.

10.

2 m

2.8 m

4 m

11.

90 cm

45 cm

70 cm

12.

10.8 m

7.2 m

PETROCAN

13. Draw 2 different rectangular prisms having a volume of 48 cm³.

14. Draw 2 different triangular prisms having a volume of 60 cm³.

Stacking Bricks

How many bricks measuring
21 cm × 9 cm × 6 cm will
fit inside the carton?

Draw a diagram of your solution.

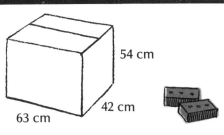

54 cm

42 cm

63 cm

Measuring Capacity

Capacity is a measure of how much liquid a container holds.

The **litre (L)** is the basic unit of capacity.

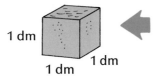 Both contain 1 dm³ of liquid.
Both have a capacity for 1 L.

The **millilitre (mL)** is used to measure small amounts of liquid.

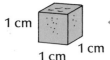   Both contain 1 cm³ of liquid.
Both have a capacity for 1 mL.

The **kilolitre (kL)** is used to measure large amounts of liquid.

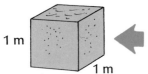 Both contain 1 m³ of liquid.
Both have a capacity for 1 kL.

1 L = 1000 mL	1 kL = 1000 L
1 mL = 0.001 L	1 L = 0.001 kL

EXERCISES

Which unit is appropriate? Use **L**, **mL**, or **kL**.

1. a mug of coffee
2. oil storage tank
3. a washing machine
4. a lake
5. a sprinkling can
6. nose drops
7. a tube of toothpaste.
8. a swimming pool

Copy and complete.

9. 5 L = ■ mL
10. 1.2 L = ■ mL
11. 850 mL = ■ L
12. 700 L = ■ kL
13. 9525 L = ■ kL
14. 0.5 kL = ■ L
15. ■ mL of liquid fills a volume of 1 cm³.
16. ■ L of liquid fills a volume of 1 dm³.
17. ■ kL of liquid fills a volume of 1 m³.

Copy and complete.

1. 3 L = ▉ mL
2. 0.6 kL = ▉ L
3. 573 mL = ▉ L
4. 15 kL = ▉ L
5. 214 L = ▉ kL
6. 34 L = ▉ mL

What is the capacity of each container in millilitres?

7.  909 cm³

8. 284 cm³

9. 300 cm³

10. 15 cm, 16 cm

11. 30 cm, 45 cm, 60 cm

12. 80 cm, 95 cm

Solve.

13. A bathtub measures 15.2 dm × 8 dm × 4 dm. How many litres of water will fill the tub to a depth of 2 dm?

14. A 250 mL carton of whipping cream is whipped in a cylindrical bowl having a radius of 4.5 cm and a height of 9 cm. After whipping, the cream completely fills the container. How much whipped cream is made?

Cake Batter Matters

Decide which cake pans to use for 1.8 L of cake batter. To allow room for rising, the pan (or pans) should be only half full.

one oblong pan?   **or**   two round pans?

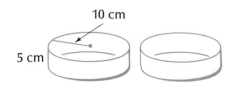

22 cm   33 cm   5 cm   10 cm   5 cm

Measuring Mass

Mass is the amount of matter in an object.

The **kilogram (kg)** is the basic unit for mass.

The **gram (g)** is used to measure small masses.

A **tonne (t)** is used to measure very large masses.

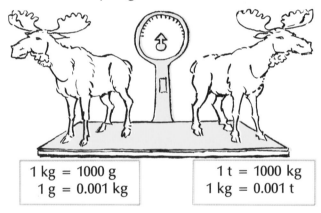

| 1 kg = 1000 g | 1 t = 1000 kg |
| 1 g = 0.001 kg | 1 kg = 0.001 t |

EXERCISES

Which unit is appropriate? Use **kg**, **g**, or **t**.

1. a pig
2. a handful of raisins
3. a football player
4. a planet
5. a penny
6. a blue whale

Copy and complete.

7. 7 kg = ■ g
8. 12.5 kg = ■ g
9. 350 g = ■ kg
10. 3 t = ■ kg
11. 0.5 t = ■ kg
12. 2900 kg = ■ t
13. 3 t + 4000 kg = ■ t
14. 1 kg + 1000 g = ■ kg
15. 16 t + 5500 kg = ■ t
16. 2 t + 200 kg = ■ t

PRACTICE

Copy and complete. Use <, >, or =.

1. 3256 g ● 3.26 kg
2. 5.48 kg ● 547 g
3. 8270 g ● 8.27 kg
4. 0.423 kg ● 42.3 g
5. 3768 kg ● 37.68 g
6. 6.47 t ● 6476 kg
7. 576.7 kg ● 0.576 t
8. 0.73 t ● 73 kg

Copy and complete.

9. 4 kg + 375 g = ■ kg
10. 1 kg + 42 g = ■ kg
11. 7 kg + 7 g = ■ kg
12. 8 t + 812 kg = ■ t
13. 5 t + 35 kg = ■ t
14. 11 t + 57 kg = ■ t
15. 7.3 kg = ■ t + ■ kg
16. 6.08 kg = ■ kg + ■ g
17. 0.875 kg = ■ kg + ■ g
18. 6.4 t = ■ t + ■ kg
19. 2 t = ■ g
20. 3.2 t = ■ g

Solve.

21. A nickel has a mass of about 5 g.
    How many nickels would have a mass of:
    a. 250 g?   b. 2 kg?   c. 0.45 kg?   d. 1 t?

22. One hundred grams of boiled ham sells for $1.29. How much would 1 kg cost?

23. A loaf of bread which has a mass of 680 g is cut into 25 equal slices. What is the mass of the slices needed to make one sandwich?

24. A full-grown moose has a mass of about 0.5 t. Jerry's mass is 40 kg. How many times greater is the moose's mass?

Mighty Masses

The mass of the earth is about 5.9×10^{21} t.

The mass of the moon is about 7.28×10^{19} t.

Write these masses in standard form.

Volume, Capacity, and Mass

In the metric system, volume, capacity, and mass are related for water measured at 4°C.

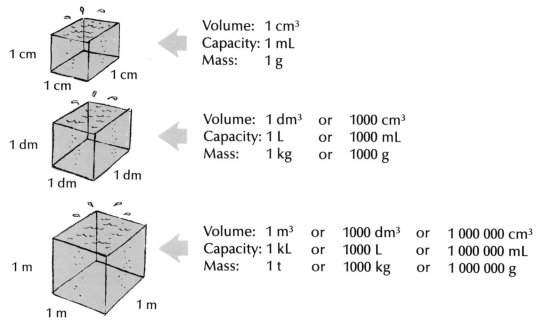

Volume: 1 cm³
Capacity: 1 mL
Mass: 1 g

Volume: 1 dm³   or   1000 cm³
Capacity: 1 L   or   1000 mL
Mass: 1 kg   or   1000 g

Volume: 1 m³   or   1000 dm³   or   1 000 000 cm³
Capacity: 1 kL   or   1000 L   or   1 000 000 mL
Mass: 1 t   or   1000 kg   or   1 000 000 g

EXERCISES

Copy and complete.

	Volume of Water	Capacity	Mass
1.	1 cm³	■ mL	■ g
2.	45 cm³	■ mL	■ g
3.	1 dm³	■ L or ■ mL	■ kg or ■ g
4.	53.5 dm³	■ L or ■ mL	■ kg or ■ g
5.	1 m³	■ kL or ■ L or ■ mL	■ t or ■ kg or ■ g
6.	7.2 m³	■ kL or ■ L or ■ mL	■ t or ■ kg or ■ g

7. 4 L of water has a mass of ■ kg and a volume of ■ dm³.

8. 50 L or water has a mass of ■ kg and a volume of ■ dm³.

9. 3 kg of water has a volume of ■ dm³ and a capacity of ■ L.

10. 8 t of water has a volume of ■ m³ and a capacity of ■ kL.

Copy and complete the chart for water at 4°C.

	Volume			Capacity			Mass		
	cm³	dm³	m³	mL	L	kL	g	kg	t
1.			1						
2.						4			
3.									9

What is the volume, capacity, and mass of water if each container is half-filled?

4.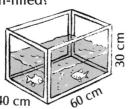
40 cm   60 cm   30 cm

5.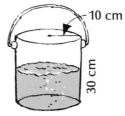
10 cm   30 cm

6.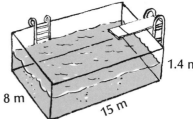
1.4 m   8 m   15 m

Copy and complete.

1. $1 \text{ cm}^3 = \blacksquare \text{ mm}^3$

2. $7 \text{ cm}^3 = \blacksquare \text{ mm}^3$

3. $1 \text{ m}^3 = \blacksquare \text{ cm}^3$

Find the volume.

4.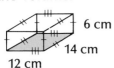
6 cm   14 cm   12 cm

5.
20 cm   27.7 cm   32 cm

6.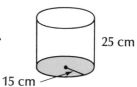
25 cm   15 cm

Copy and complete.

7. $7 \text{ mL} = \blacksquare \text{ L}$

8. $0.9 \text{ kL} = \blacksquare \text{ L}$

9. $3.4 \text{ L} = \blacksquare \text{ mL}$

10. $40 \text{ kg} = \blacksquare \text{ g}$

11. $65 \text{ kg} = \blacksquare \text{ t}$

12. $680 \text{ g} = \blacksquare \text{ kg}$

13. 1 cm^3 of water has a capacity of $\blacksquare$ mL and a mass of $\blacksquare$ g.

14. 1 m^3 of water has a capacity of $\blacksquare$ kL and a mass of $\blacksquare$ t.

Making Predictions

You can make a **prediction** once you have *listed the facts* and *looked for patterns*.

Make boxes with increasing heights, as shown below, out of centimetre grid paper. Note the surface area and volume of each box.

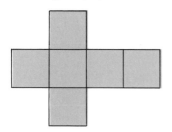

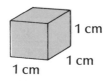

height: 1 cm

surface area: 6 cm²
volume: 1 cm³

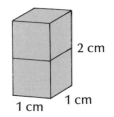

2 cm

1 cm 1 cm

height: 2 cm

surface area: 10 cm²
volume: 2 cm³

Continue increasing the height by 1 cm.
Record the facts in a table.

Predict the surface area and volume of a similar box with a height of 15 cm.

Height	Surface Area	Volume
1 cm	6 cm²	1 cm³
2 cm	10 cm²	2 cm³
3 cm		
4 cm		
5 cm		

A *pentomino* is a figure made up of 5 squares touching edge to edge. The pentomino below has had each side made 2 times greater.

Now make the pentomino 3 times, 4 times, and 5 times greater on grid paper. Record the perimeters and areas in a table.

Predict the perimeter and area of the pentomino if it were made 20 times greater.

Times greater	P	A
1 time	12 cm	5 cm²
2 times	24 cm	20 cm²
3 times		
4		

Computer Volume

The BASIC computer program below will calculate the volume of a rectangular prism.

Try the program on a computer.

```
10 PRINT "VOLUME OF A RECTANGULAR PRISM "
20 PRINT "=(LENGTH X WIDTH) X HEIGHT "
25 PRINT
30 PRINT "WHAT IS THE LENGTH? "
40 INPUT L
45 PRINT
50 PRINT "WHAT IS THE WIDTH? "
60 INPUT W
65 PRINT
70 PRINT "WHAT IS THE HEIGHT? "
80 INPUT H
90 LET V = (L * W) * H
100 PRINT "THE VOLUME IS ";V
105 PRINT
110 PRINT "IF YOU WISH TO STOP, "
120 PRINT "PRESS -1, OTHERWISE PRESS 0. "
130 INPUT C
140 IF C = -1 THEN 160
150 GOTO 10
160 PRINT "THE END"
170 END
```

The GOTO statement in line 150 creates a loop beginning at line 10.

Lines 110 and 120 tell you to press −1 when you wish to stop using the program.

The IF … THEN statement in line 140 requires the computer to study the input, −1 or 0, and decide to go to line 160 and END or not.

The IF … THEN statement is a way to get out of an endless loop.

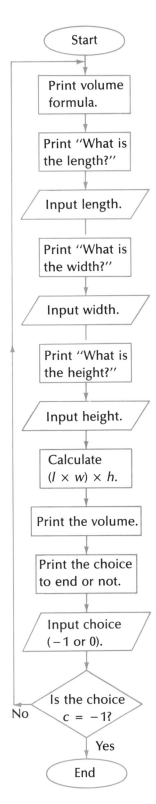

131

TEST   UNIT 5

Copy and complete.

1. 4.3 m = ■ cm

2. 650 mm = ■ m

3. 12 km = ■ m

Find the perimeter.

4.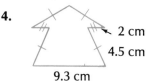
2 cm
4.5 cm
9.3 cm

5.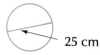
18.5 km
6 m

6.
36.2 cm

Find the circumference.

7.
4 cm

8.
25 cm

9.
9 m

Estimate the perimeter to the nearest centimetre.

10.

11.

12.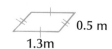

Find the area.

13.

14.
8 cm
5.5 cm

15.
0.5 m
1.3m

16.
16 cm
33.2 cm

17.
5 cm

18.
9.1 m

Find the volume.

19. 1 m³ has a volume of ■ cm³

20. 1 cm³ has a volume of ■ mm³

21. rectangular prism: length = 3.9 cm, width = 4.2 cm, height = 2 cm

22. triangular prism: triangle base = 42 cm, triangle height = 36.4 cm, prism height = 20 cm

23. cylinder: radius of base = 12 cm, height = 8 cm

Copy and complete.

24. ■ mL = 8.2 L

25. 17 kL = ■ L

26. 95 L = ■ kL

27. 3.5 t = ■ kg

28. 4800 g = ■ kg

29. 0.5 kg = ■ g

30. 1 m³ of water has a capacity of ■ and a mass of ■.

LOOKING BACK

Problem Solving

Choose the operations which would solve the problem.

1. Ann Zachary drove 240 km in 3 h.
   Then she drove 180 km in 2 h.
   How far did she travel?

   a. Add and divide.   **b.** Add only.   **c.** Divide only.

2. Fifteen pizzas were divided into 5 pieces
   each. Each person was given 3 pieces. How
   many pieces were made?

   a. Divide only.   **b.** Multiply only.   **c.** Multiply and divide.

Estimate a reasonable solution.

3. Astro Airways has 26 planes with 2 engines each; 18 planes with
   3 engines each; and 12 planes with 4 engines each. About how
   many engines do Astro Airways have altogether?

4. Recently, the average weekly wages in the Western provinces
   were:

   > Manitoba: $329.64
   > Saskatchewan: $352.92
   > Alberta: $412.99
   > British Columbia: $431.31

   Approximately what was the difference in wages between the
   highest and lowest weekly average?

Estimate the answer. Then use a calculator to find the *exact* answer.

5. The Boeing B-767 has a fuel capacity of
   84.95 kL. It consumes fuel at a rate of
   5450 L/h. How long can it fly before it is
   completely out of fuel?

Solve.

6. The sum of Mr. and Mrs. Elliott's masses is 129 kg. Mr. Elliott's
   mass is 15 kg more than Mrs. Elliott's mass. What is the mass of
   Mr. Elliott and Mrs. Elliott?

UNIT 6   Basic Geometry

Plane Figures

A **point** has an exact position.
It is shown by a dot on the page.
See *J* and *K*.

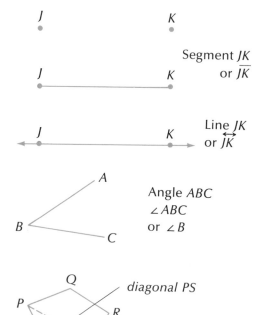

J   K

When *J* and *K* are joined, a (line) **segment** is
formed. *J* and *K* are its **endpoints.**

Segment *JK*
or $\overline{JK}$

J   K

If $\overline{JK}$ is extended indefinitely in both directions,
a **line** is formed.

Line *JK*
or $\overleftrightarrow{JK}$

J   K

An **angle** is formed by segments *BA and BC*.
Point *B* is the **vertex** of the angle. $\overline{BA}$ and $\overline{BC}$
are its **arms.**

Angle *ABC*
∠*ABC*
or ∠*B*

A
B
C

A **polygon** is a *closed* figure made up of segments
called sides. A segment joining two vertices of
a polygon is called a **diagonal**.

Q
diagonal *PS*
P   R
Polygon *PQRST*
T   S

Points, segments, lines, angles, and polygons are
called **plane figures**. They lie in a flat surface.

134

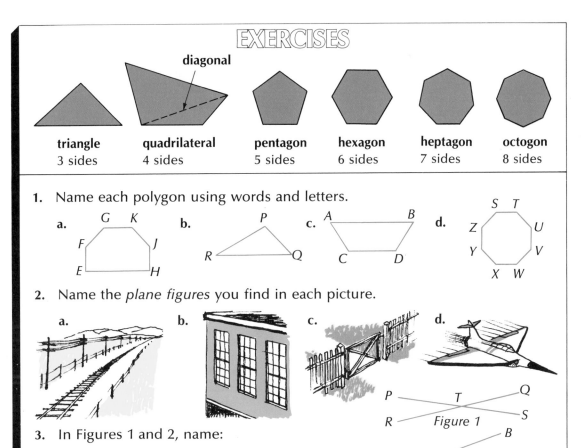

EXERCISES

diagonal

triangle	quadrilateral	pentagon	hexagon	heptagon	octogon
3 sides	4 sides	5 sides	6 sides	7 sides	8 sides

1. Name each polygon using words and letters.

   a. G K F J E H

   b. P R Q

   c. A B C D

   d. S T Z U Y V X W

2. Name the *plane figures* you find in each picture.

   a.   b.   c.   d.

   P   T   Q
   R   S
   Figure 1

3. In Figures 1 and 2, name:

   a. all segments.
   b. the intersection point of the segments.
   c. all angles.

   A   B C D
   Figure 2

PRACTICE

Draw a triangle, quadrilateral, pentagon, hexagon, heptagon, and octagon. Draw all diagonals of each polygon.
Copy and complete the table.

Polygon	Vertices	Angles	Sides	Diagonals	Sum of Sides and Diagonals
triangle	3	3	3	0	3
quadrilateral	4	?	?	2	6
pentagon	?	?	5	?	?

135

Size of an Angle

The blades of a pair of scissors form angles of different sizes.

The size of an angle is measured in degrees. It tells the amount of turn from one arm of an angle to the other arm.

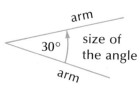

A protractor is used to measure the size of an angle in degrees.

obtuse angle
> 90°
< 180°

acute angle
90°   < 90°

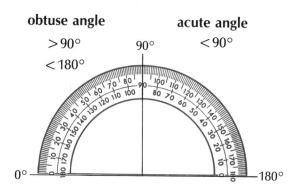

right angle
The size is 90°.

straight angle
The size is 180°.

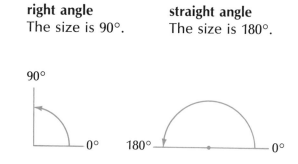

EXERCISES

1. Classify each angle as acute, right, obtuse, or straight.

a.   b.   c.   d.

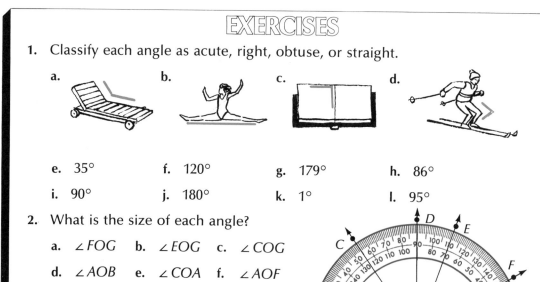

e. 35°   f. 120°   g. 179°   h. 86°

i. 90°   j. 180°   k. 1°   l. 95°

2. What is the size of each angle?

a. ∠FOG   b. ∠EOG   c. ∠COG

d. ∠AOB   e. ∠COA   f. ∠AOF

g. ∠DOG   h. ∠AOG   i. ∠DOA

j. ∠EOF   k. ∠EOB   l. ∠FOD

1. Construct angles with the given sizes using a protractor.

   a. 30°   **b.** 150°   **c.** 76°   **d.** 125°

2. Trace each angle. Lengthen the arms. What is the size of each angle?

   a.   **b.**   **c.**   **d.**

3. Draw a line segment *AB*.
   Use a protractor to construct right angles at *A* and *B*.

4. Draw two segments that intersect.
   Measure the size of each angle formed.
   Compare the size of *opposite angles* (∠1 and ∠3, ∠2 and ∠4).

   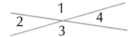

5. Draw four different, large triangles.
   Measure the three angles in each triangle.
   Copy and complete the table.

Triangle	∠1	∠2	∠3	Sum of 3 angles
1				
2				
3				
4				

Clock Hands Puzzler

a. At 12:30, how many degrees has each clock hand moved from 12:00?

b. At 7:10, how many degrees has each clock hand moved from 7:00?

c. It is between 12:00 and 12:15. The hands of a clock form an angle of 55°. What time is it?

d. It is between 9:00 and 10:00. At what time do the hands of a clock form an angle of 35°?

e. How often during a day do the clock hands form a right angle? List six of the approximate times?

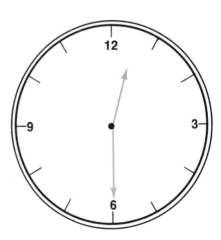

Congruent Figures

Two plane figures are **congruent** if they have the same shape and the same size.

 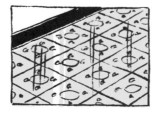 

Which figures at the right are congruent?

You can use tracing paper to test for congruence. Try to fit tracings of the figures onto each other.

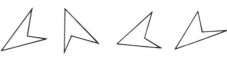

Figure 1   Figure 2   Figure 3   Figure 4

Figure 2 is congruent to Figure 3.

≅ means **is congruent to**.

$\angle A \cong \angle F$ $\overline{AB} \cong \overline{GF}$
$\angle B \cong \angle G$ $\overline{DB} \cong \overline{GI}$
$\angle C \cong \angle H$ $\overline{DC} \cong \overline{IH}$
$\angle D \cong \angle I$ $\overline{AC} \cong \overline{FH}$

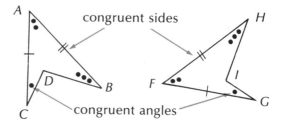

congruent sides

congruent angles

EXERCISES

1. Use tracing paper to find the congruent figures.

   a. 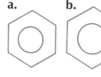 b.  c.   d.   e.   f.   g.   h.

2. Test each pair of figures for congruency. Name all congruent segments and angles.

 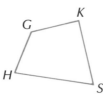 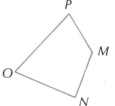

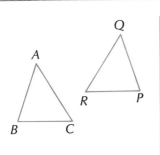

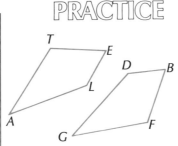

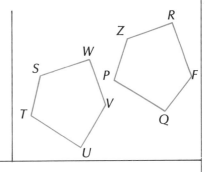

For each pair of figures:

1. Test for congruency using tracing paper.
   Then write a congruency statement for congruent figures.
   For example, triangle *ABC* ≅ ■.

2. Write congruency statements for the congruent angles.

3. Write congruency statements for the congruent sides.

Draw two intersecting segments.
Label the angles as shown.
Trace the angles to test for congruency.

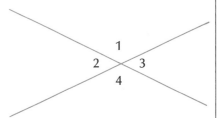

4. Write congruency statements for the congruent angles.

5. What do you conclude about the **opposite angles** in the figure?

6. Measure the size of each angle.

7. What is the sum of the four angles?

Congruency In Art

The Dutch artist, M.C. Escher (1898-1972) used congruent figures in his work.

Make a tracing of the man. Show that all figures in the design are congruent.

Constructions I

We can use a ruler and a compass to construct geometric figures.

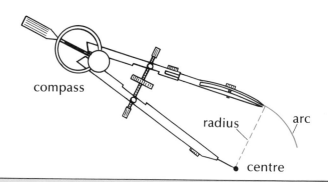

compass
radius
arc
centre

Congruent Segments

Given: segment *AB*
Construct: segment *CD* congruent to segment *AB*

A •————————————————• B

1. Draw segment *CX* longer than segment *AB*.

C •————————————————————• X

2. With the centre at *C*, draw an arc cutting $\overline{CX}$ at *D*.
   $\overline{CD} \cong \overline{AB}$

C •——————————————————• X
                    D

Congruent Angles

Given: angle *ABC*
Construct: angle *DEF* congruent to angle *ABC*

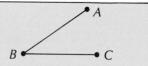

E •————————• F

1. Draw segment *EF*.

2. With centre *B*, draw an arc cutting the arms of ∠*ABC* at *Q* and *P*.

   With centre *E* and the same radius, draw an arc cutting $\overline{EF}$ at *R*.

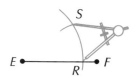

3. Make the radius equal to *QP*.

   With the centre at *R* and the same radius, draw an arc to intersect the other arc at *S*.

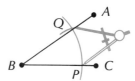
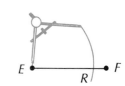

4. Draw $\overline{ED}$ through points *E* and *S*.
   ∠*DEF* ≅ ∠*ABC*

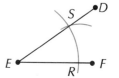

EXERCISES

Draw each figure.
Then use a compass for the constructions.

1.
X •———————• Y

Construct $\overline{AB} \cong \overline{XY}$.

2.
R •———————————————• S

Construct $\overline{BD} \cong \overline{RS}$.

3.
C •———————————————• D

Construct $\overline{TR} \cong \overline{CD}$.

4.

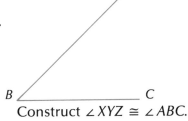

Construct $\angle XYZ \cong \angle ABC$.

5.

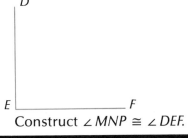

Construct $\angle MNP \cong \angle DEF$.

PRACTICE

1. Construct segments with these lengths using a ruler and a compass.
  a. 7 cm   **b.** 10 cm   **c.** 5 cm   **d.** 65 mm

2. $\overline{AB}$ means segment AB. AB stands for the length of segment AB. Write each statement in words.
  a. $AB = CD$ **b.** $\overline{AB} \cong \overline{CD}$ **c.** $\angle ABC = \angle DEF$ **d.** $\angle ABC \cong \angle DEF$

3. Construct a figure congruent to the intersecting line segments at the right. (Start by drawing a segment congruent to $\overline{KL}$.)

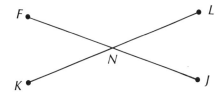

4. Construct triangle PQR with sides 5 cm, 3 cm, and 4 cm. (First draw side PQ 5 cm long.)

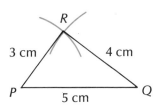

5. Construct a rectangle congruent to the one enclosing this Practice section.

6. Construct triangle XYZ with the base $\overline{XY} = 6$ cm, $\angle XYZ = 30°$, and $\angle XZY = 110°$.

Protractor Constructions

Congruent Angles

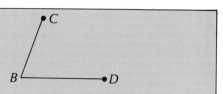

Given: angle *CBD*
Construct: angle *WXY* congruent to angle *CBD*

Measure the size of ∠*CBD*.

Construct ∠*WXY* the same size.

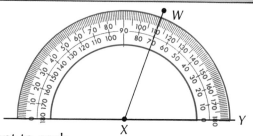

Use a protractor to construct an angle congruent to each.

a.

b.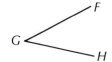

c.

Given: △*ABC*
Construct: ∠*D*, ∠*E*, and ∠*F*, as shown below
so that ∠*D* ≅ ∠*A*, ∠*E* ≅ ∠*B*,
and ∠*F* ≅ ∠*C*

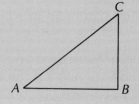

What is the size of ∠A + ∠B + ∠C?

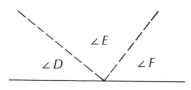

Polygons

Draw a circle with your protractor.
Starting at any point *A*, mark points every 40°.
Draw 9 congruent segments connecting the
points to make a nonagon.

Use your protractor to make other polygons
with congruent sides.

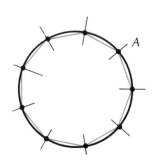

Tracing Paper Constructions

Tracing paper can also be used to construct congruent figures.

Congruent segments:

Given: $\overline{MN}$
Construct: $\overline{RS} \cong \overline{MN}$

1. Trace points *M* and *N*.

2. Turn over the tracing paper and press the tracing onto paper. Label the new points *R* and *S*.

3. Draw $\overline{RS}$.

Congruent angles:

Given: $\angle BXA$
Construct: $\angle KRG \cong \angle BXA$

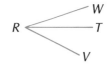

1. Trace points *B*, *X*, and *A*.

2. Turn over the tracing paper and press the tracing onto paper.

3. Label the new points *K*, *R*, and *G*.

4. Draw $\overline{RK}$ and $\overline{RG}$.

REVIEW

1. Name all segments

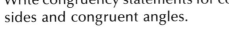

2. Name all angles.

3. Construct an angle of the given size with a protractor.

a. 20°   b. 100°   c. 160°   d. 90°   e. 65°

4. Write congruency statements for congruent sides and congruent angles.

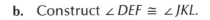

5. Draw a segment and an angle. Then use tracing paper to make the constructions.

a. Construct $\overline{XY} \cong \overline{AB}$.

b. Construct $\angle DEF \cong \angle JKL$.

143

Reflection

Reflection in geometry resembles reflection in a flat mirror of our everyday world.

In geometry, a straight line represents the flat mirror. It is called a **reflection line**.

The reflection image in line *m* of triangle *ABC* can be drawn with a *MIRA* or tracing paper.

Where is the *image* of △*ABC*?

reflection line

EXERCISES

Try the methods below for drawing a reflection image of △*ABC*.

Method 1: Tracing Paper

1. Mark a point *P* on line *m*.

2. Place tracing paper on △*ABC*. Mark the position of *P*, *A*, *B*, and *C*.

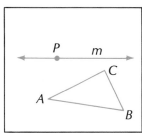

3. Flip the tracing paper over, so that the tracing of line *m* fits on line *m* and the tracing of *P* fits on *P*.

4. Mark the positions of the tracing of *A*, *B*, and *C*. Label them *A'*, *B'*, and *C'*.

5. Draw △*A'B'C'*.

Method 2: *MIRA*

1. Place the *MIRA* with its *MIRA* line on line *m*.

2. Reach behind the *MIRA* with a pencil. Mark the positions of the images of point *A*, *B*, and *C*.

3. Label these points *A'*, *B'*, and *C'*.

4. Draw △*A'B'C'* as a reflection image △*ABC*.

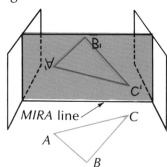

MIRA line

PRACTICE

1. Draw a reflection image of each figure.
   Begin by drawing a reflection line *m* for each figure.

   a.   b.   c.   d.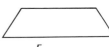

2. Triangle *DEF* is the reflection image of
   triangle *ABC* in line *m*.
   a. Name the images of points *A*, *B*, and *C*.
   b. Name the images of $\overline{AB}$, $\overline{BC}$, and $\overline{AC}$.
   c. Name the images of ∠*A*, ∠*B*, and ∠*C*.

   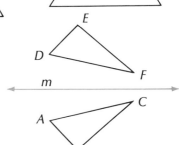

3. Triangles *ABC* and *FGH* are reflection images
   of each other in line *m*.

   a. Name all pairs of congruent sides.
   b. Name all pairs of congruent angles.

   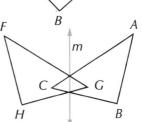

4. Draw figures like these, only larger. Using tracing paper, draw
   the reflection image of each figure in line *m*. Use a *MIRA* to check.

   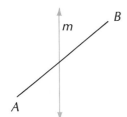   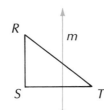   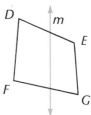

Reading Reflections

a. What time is it?

b. Which way is the car going to turn?

145

Line Symmetry

A tracing of some figures, like this maple leaf, will fold so that one half fits exactly on the other half.

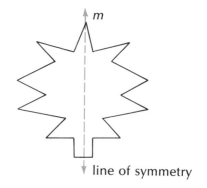

The fold line is a **line of symmetry**.
The picture of the leaf has line symmetry.

line of symmetry

You can use a *MIRA* to reflect one half of the leaf exactly on the other half.

The *MIRA* line is the line of symmetry.

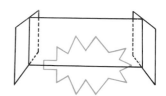

EXERCISES

1. Test each figure for line symmetry. Use tracing paper or a *MIRA*.

a.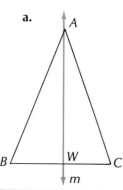

b.

c.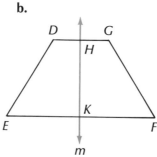

d.

e.

f.

g.

h.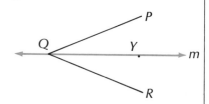

2. Name all congruent segments and angles in each figure. Line *m* is a line of symmetry of each figure.

a.

A

B *W* *C*

m

b.

D *G*

H

K

E *F*

m

c.

P

Q *Y* *m*

R

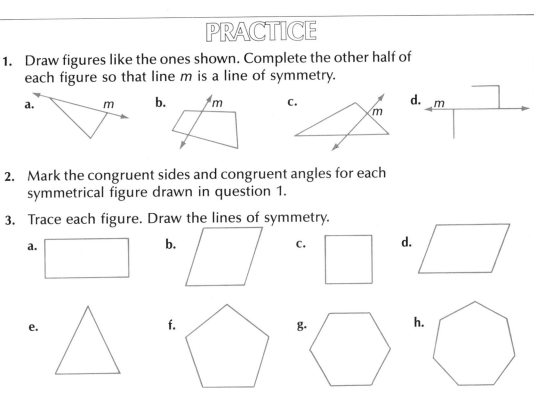

PRACTICE

1. Draw figures like the ones shown. Complete the other half of each figure so that line *m* is a line of symmetry.

   a.   b.   c.   d.

2. Mark the congruent sides and congruent angles for each symmetrical figure drawn in question 1.

3. Trace each figure. Draw the lines of symmetry.

   a.   b.   c.   d.

   e.   f.   g.   h.

   i.   j.   k.   l.

Indian Art

The art of the Canadian Pacific Northwest-coast Indians uses line symmetry.
Trace the designs. Draw the lines of symmetry.

Ram

Frog

Eagle

147

Perpendicular Lines

The Leaning Tower of Pisa is famous for not being *perpendicular* to the ground.

Perpendicular lines form 90° angles when they intersect.

$\overline{AB}$ and $\overline{CD}$ are perpendicular.
Write: $\overline{AB} \perp \overline{CD}$.

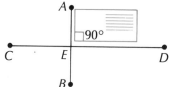

Since *opposite angles* are equal, $\angle AED = \angle CEB$ and $\angle AEC = \angle DEB$. All four angles are equal to 90°.

Here are some ways to draw perpendicular line segments.

Method 1: Protractor

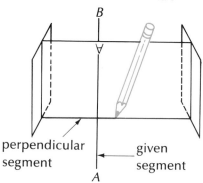

given segment

perpendicular segment ⟶

Method 2: *MIRA*

perpendicular segment

given segment

EXERCISES

1. Which objects are perpendicular to the ground?

a.

b.

c.

2. Draw $\overline{AB}$.
   Mark a point X in $\overline{AB}$.
   Draw a segment through X perpendicular to $\overline{AB}$.

3. Draw $\overline{CD}$.
   Mark a point Y not in $\overline{CD}$.
   Draw a segment through Y perpendicular to $\overline{CD}$.

PRACTICE

Refer to the figure at the right to answer true or false.

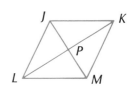

1. ∠DEH = ∠FEJ
2. $\overline{HJ} \perp \overline{DG}$
3. ∠DEF = 90°
4. ∠IFG = ∠EFK
5. $\overline{IK} \perp \overline{DG}$
6. ∠EFK = 90°

Name the perpendicular segments in each figure.

7.
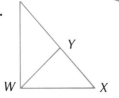

8.
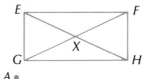

9.
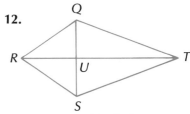

10.
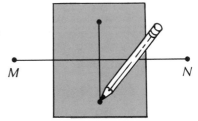

11.

12.

13. Draw $\overline{MN}$.
Fold tracing paper into four congruent parts.
Use the perpendicular fold lines to draw a segment perpendicular to $\overline{MN}$.

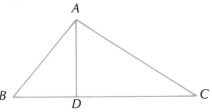

14. Trace an example of two well-known streets which are perpendicular to each other from a map of your city.

Altitude of a Triangle

An **altitude** of a triangle is a segment from a vertex *perpendicular* to the opposite side (or an extension of the opposite side).

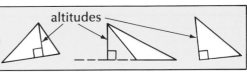

altitudes

Draw the triangle at the right (only larger).

a. Draw altitude *AD* of △*ABC*.
$\overline{AD} \perp \overline{BC}$, with *D* in $\overline{BC}$.

b. Draw the other altitudes of △*ABC*.
How many altitudes does a triangle have?

c. Draw several triangles and their altitudes.
What special property do the altitudes seem to have?

149

Bisectors

A *line of symmetry* divides a figure into two congruent parts.
In other words, it **bisects** the figure.

line of symmetry   bisector

A figure can be bisected with a *MIRA*.

To bisect an angle:

1. Reflect one arm exactly onto the other arm.

2. Draw the *MIRA* line. It is the *angle bisector.*

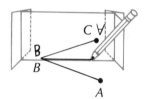

To bisect a segment with a perpendicular line:

1. Reflect one endpoint exactly onto the other endpoint.

2. Draw the *MIRA* line. It is the *perpendicular bisector.*

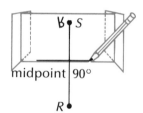

EXERCISES

Complete.

1. ∠*ABC* = 50°
   $\overrightarrow{AD}$ bisects ∠*ABC*.
   ∠*ABD* = ■°

2. ∠*KLH* = 130°
   $\overrightarrow{LN}$ bisects ∠*HLM*.
   ∠*HLN* = ■°

3. $\overline{AC}$ = 6 cm
   $\overline{FG}$ is the perpendicular bisector of $\overline{AB}$.
   The midpoint of $\overline{AB}$ is ■.
   ∠*ACG* = ■°
   $\overline{AB}$ = ■ cm

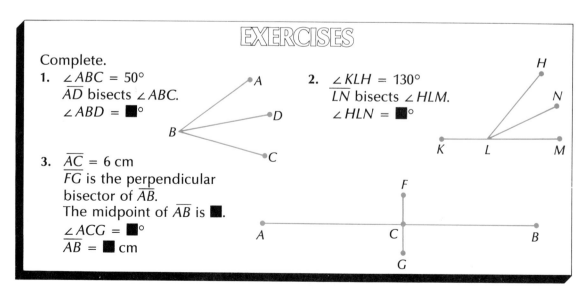

PRACTICE

1. Draw angles like the following. Lengthen the arms.
   Then bisect the angles with a *MIRA*.

   a.   **b.**   **c.**   **d.**

2. Draw two segments, 6 cm and 10 cm in length.
   Draw the perpendicular bisector of each segment with a *MIRA*.

3. An angle can also be bisected with
   a protractor.
   Use a protractor to draw and bisect
   the given angles.

   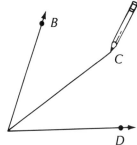

   a. 64°   **b.** 110°   **c.** 90°

   d. 125°   **e.** 180°   **f.** 45°

4. Draw a few triangles like △*ABC*, only larger.
   a. Bisect each angle of the triangles.
      What seems to be true for the three
      angle bisectors of each triangle?

   b. Draw the perpendicular bisector of each
      side. What seems to be true for the
      three perpendicular bisectors of the
      sides of the triangles?

   B

   A   *C*

Drawing an Octagon

Follow the steps below to draw an equal-sided
octagon.

1. Draw a circle.

2. Draw a diameter *AE*.

3. Draw the perpendicular bisector of $\overline{AE}$ to
   meet the circle at *C* and *G*.

4. Bisect the 4 angles formed to meet the circles
   at *B*, *D*, *F*, and *H*.

5. Join the endpoints, as shown.

What other polygons can be made from this figure?

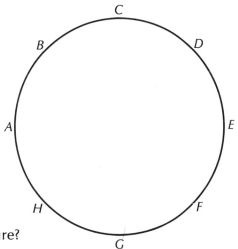

Constructions II

A draftsman often uses a compass and a straightedge to design structures or equipment precisely.

We can use a compass and ruler to construct **bisectors**. A bisector divides a figure into two congruent parts.

Constructing an angle bisector

Given: angle ABC
Construct: $\overline{BF}$ to bisect angle ABC

1. With B as centre, draw an arc cutting $\overline{BA}$ at D and $\overline{BC}$ at E.

2. Using D and E as centres and with a suitable radius, draw two arcs to intersect at F.

3. Draw $\overline{BF}$.
   BF bisects ∠ABC.
   ∠ABF ≅ ∠FBC.

Constructing a perpendicular bisector

Given: segment AB
Construct: segment CD as the perpendicular bisector of $\overline{AB}$

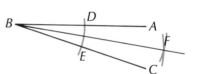

1. Using A and B as centres and a suitable radius, draw arcs to intersect.

2. Draw $\overline{CD}$.
   $\overline{CD}$ is the perpendicular bisector of $\overline{AB}$.
   $\overline{AX} \cong \overline{XB}$

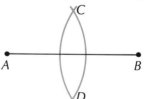

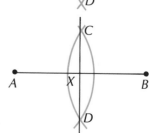

EXERCISES

Draw angles like the following. Lengthen their arms.
Use a compass to construct the angle bisectors of each angle.

1.

2.

3.

4.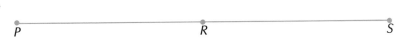

Draw line segments like the following.
Use a compass to construct the perpendicular bisector of each
segment.

5.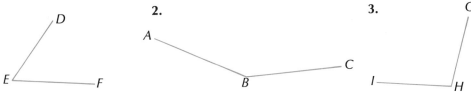
6.
7.

Draw angles with the sizes shown using a protractor.
Construct the angle bisector of each angle using a compass.

8. 55°

9. 115°

10. 90°

Construct a perpendicular bisector for each segment below with a
compass.

11. 2 cm segment

12. 4 cm segment

13. 8 cm segment

14. Test the accuracy of each construction in questions 7 to 12,
using a *MIRA* or tracing paper.

15. Draw each figure below with a ruler. Then use a compass to
divide the figure into four congruent parts.

    a. a line segment   **b.** an obtuse angle   **c.** a straight angle

16. Trace each line segment below. Then use a compass to measure
each segment in centimetres.

    a. |————|————
        1 cm

    b. |————————————|

    c. |————————|

153

1. Draw an equilateral triangle.
   Use a compass to bisect one angle.

   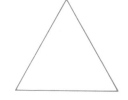

   a. Does the angle bisector become a
      perpendicular bisector of the opposite
      side?

   b. Is this true for all angle bisectors of
      the triangle?

2. Draw a triangle with sides of three different
   lengths. Bisect the angles.

   Do the angle bisectors become perpendicular bisectors of the opposite sides?

   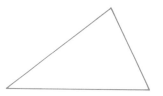

3. Draw intersecting segments like the ones at
   the right, only larger.

   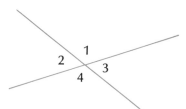

   a. Bisect ∠1 and ∠2 with a compass.
      Are the bisectors perpendicular to each
      other?

   b. Draw other different pairs of intersecting segments.
      Do the angle bisectors always form perpendicular lines?

4. Draw a 15 cm line segment. Divide the segment into four
   congruent parts using a compass.

5. Construct a 45° angle with a compass (not a protractor).

6. For each compass construction, $\overline{OP}$ bisects ∠XOY. What is the
   size of ∠XOP?

   a.

   b.

   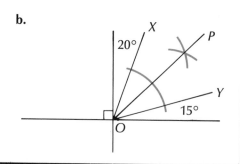

Compass Designs

A circle can be cut into six congruent arcs with a compass. Start at any point in the circle. Use the circle's radius for each arc.
Study the compass and ruler construction.

Use the construction to make these and other designs.

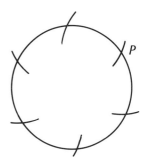

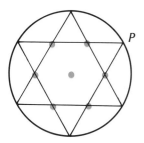 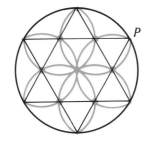 

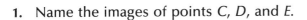

REVIEW

Triangle *FGH* is the reflection image of triangle *CDE* in line *m*.

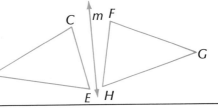

1. Name the images of points *C*, *D*, and *E*.

2. Name all pairs of congruent sides.

3. Draw the figure shown, only larger. Complete the figure so that line *m* is a line of symmetry.

4. Name all perpendicular segments.

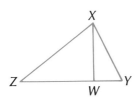

5. Complete.
   ∠*ABC* = 58°

   $\overline{BP}$ bisects ∠*ABC*
   ∠*PBC* = ■°

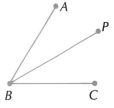

6. Draw a 90° angle. Use a compass to bisect it.

7. Draw a 6 cm segment. Use a compass to construct a perpendicular bisector of it.

Classifying Triangles

Triangles can be classified by their angles, sides, or lines of symmetry.

A N G L E S A N D	acute	right	obtuse
S I D E S	3 angles <90°	1 angle = 90°	1 angle >90°
	isosceles	equilateral	scalene
S Y M M E T R Y	2 equal sides or 2 equal angles	3 equal sides or 3 equal angles	0 equal sides or 0 equal angles
	1 line of symmetry	3 lines of symmetry	0 lines of symmetry

EXERCISES

Classify each triangle as isosceles, equilateral, or scalene.

1.

2.

3.
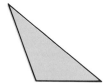

4.
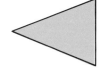

Classify each triangle as acute, right, or obtuse.

5.

6.

7.

8.

156

PRACTICE

On grid paper, draw a triangle that is:

1. isosceles
2. scalene
3. acute
4. right
5. obtuse
6. obtuse isosceles
7. right isosceles
8. right scalene
9. equilateral

What kind of triangle has these angle sizes?

10. 30°, 70°, 80°
11. 15°, 60°, 105°
12. 40°, 50°, 90°
13. 10°, 20°
14. 17°, 78°
15. 45°, 45°

What kind of triangle has:

16. 2 equal sides?
17. no equal sides?
18. 1 line of symmetry?
19. 3 lines of symmetry?
20. no line of symmetry?
21. 2 lines of symmetry?

What kinds of triangles do you see in each picture?

22.
23.
24.
25.

26. Measure each angle in an equilateral triangle.
    What is their sum?

27. Measure each angle in an isosceles triangle.
    What is their sum?

28. Measure each angle in a scalene triangle.
    What is their sum?

Triangle Search

Find all possible different-sized right isosceles triangles on a 5 by 5 dot array or geoboard.

One possibility is shown at the right.

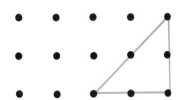

157

Constructions III

Constructing a triangle

Equipment: **compass** and **ruler**
Given: $\overline{AB}$, $\overline{AC}$, and $\overline{BC}$ with length 2.5 cm
Construct: equilateral triangle ABC

1. Draw $\overline{BC}$.

2. With radius 2.5 cm and centre at B and at C, draw two arcs to intersect at A.

3. Draw $\overline{AB}$ and $\overline{AC}$.
   △ABC is equilateral.

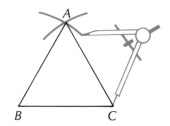

Equipment: **MIRA** and **ruler**
Given: altitude AD with 3 cm in length, base BC with 4 cm in length.
Construct: isosceles triangle ABC

1. Draw $\overline{BC}$ 4 cm in length.

2. Draw the perpendicular bisector of $\overline{BC}$ to meet $\overline{BC}$ at D by reflecting B onto C.

3. Locate A so that $\overline{AD}$ has the length of 3 cm.

4. Draw △ABC.
   △ABC is isosceles.

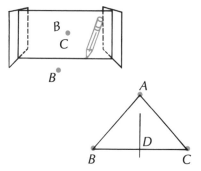

Equipment: **protractor** and **ruler**
Given: $\overline{KL}$ with length 2 cm, ∠JKL and ∠JLK both equal to 60°
Construct: equilateral triangle JKL

1. Draw $\overline{KL}$ 2 cm in length.

2. With the protractor vertex at K and at L, draw a 60° angle.
   △JKL is equilateral.

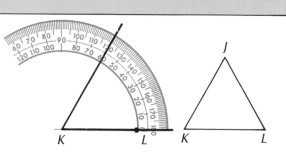

EXERCISES

Construct each triangle with the equipment shown.

1.

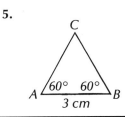

2.

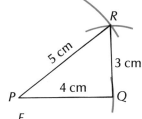

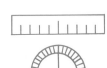

3.

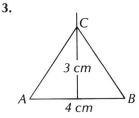

4.

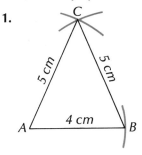

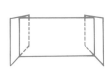

5.

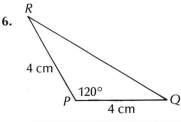

6.

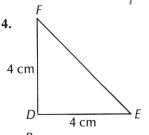

PRACTICE

First make a *sketch* of the triangle with approximate measurements.
Then *construct* the triangle. List the equipment used.

1. △ABC: AB and AC = 3.7 cm; BC = 4.5 cm

2. △XYZ: all sides = 4 cm

3. Right isosceles △DEF: ∠E = 90°; DE = 4.2 cm

4. △PQR: ∠R = 90°; QR = 4 cm; PR = 3 cm

5. △RST: RS = 2 cm; RT = 3 cm; ST = 4 cm

6. △MNO: MN and MO = 2.5 cm; ∠M = 90°

7. △FGH: all sides = 5.5 cm

8. Isosceles △HKL: KL = 4.4 cm; altitude HM = 3.5 cm

Parallel Lines

Two segments drawn on opposite sides of a ruler are **parallel**.

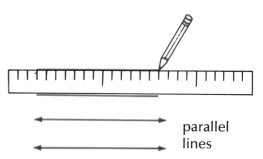

No matter how far you extend these segments, they will never intersect.

They are always the same distance apart.

parallel lines

Construct a segment through a point *P* **parallel** to segment *AB*.

Method 1: *MIRA*

1. Stand the *MIRA* perpendicular to $\overline{AB}$.

2. Mark the image of *P*. Label it *Q*.

3. Draw line *PQ*. $\overline{PQ}$ is parallel to $\overline{AB}$.

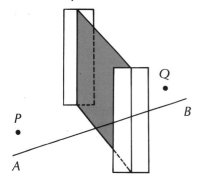

Method 2: Tracing paper

1. Trace point *P* and $\overline{AB}$.

2. Turn the tracing paper over. Fit the tracing of $\overline{AB}$ onto $\overline{AB}$.

3. Mark the tracing of *P*. Label it *Q*.

4. Draw $\overline{PQ}$. $\overline{PQ}$ is parallel to $\overline{AB}$.

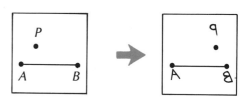

EXERCISES

1. Describe the parallel segments you see in your classroom.

Draw segment *XY* with length 5 cm and point *Z*.

• Z

2. Use a *MIRA* to construct segment *ZS* parallel to segment *XY* through point *Z*.

X   Y

Draw segment *FG* with length 8 cm and point *H*.

3. Use tracing paper to construct segment *HD* parallel to segment *FG* through point *H*.

F   G

• H

160

PRACTICE

Make diagrams like the ones at the right (only larger).

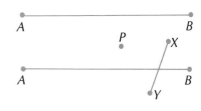

1. Construct a segment through C parallel to $\overline{AB}$.

2. Construct two segments through P:
   a. one parallel to $\overline{AB}$;
   b. the other parallel to $\overline{XY}$.

3. Construct two segments perpendicular to $\overline{CD}$.
   Are the two segments parallel?

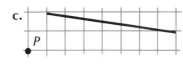

4. Construct $\overline{PQ}$ perpendicular to $\overline{RS}$.
   Construct $\overline{XY}$ perpendicular to $\overline{PQ}$.
   Is $\overline{XY}$ parallel to $\overline{RS}$?

Draw each figure below on grid paper.

5. Draw a parallel segment through point P for each.

   a. 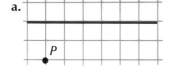   b. 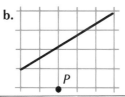   c.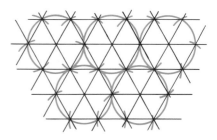

A box has 6 **faces** and 8 **edges.**
The faces intersect in edges.

---

6. a. How many pairs of parallel edges are in each face of a box?
   b. How many pairs of parallel faces are in a box?
   c. How many pairs of parallel edges are in a box?

An Equilateral Grid

Can you figure out how to construct an equilateral grid using a compass and a ruler?

Hint: Start by drawing a circle and dividing it into 6 congruent arcs.

Parallelograms

The rectangle, rhombus, and square are special kinds of parallelograms.

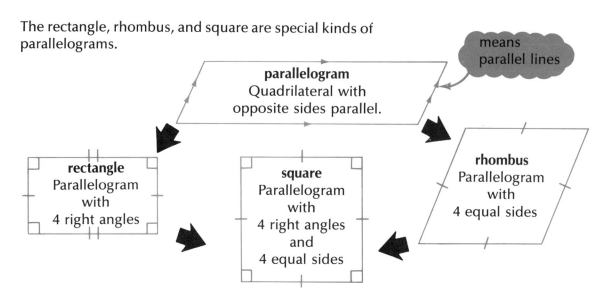

parallelogram
Quadrilateral with opposite sides parallel.

means parallel lines

rectangle
Parallelogram with 4 right angles

square
Parallelogram with 4 right angles and 4 equal sides

rhombus
Parallelogram with 4 equal sides

EXERCISES

Name each figure.

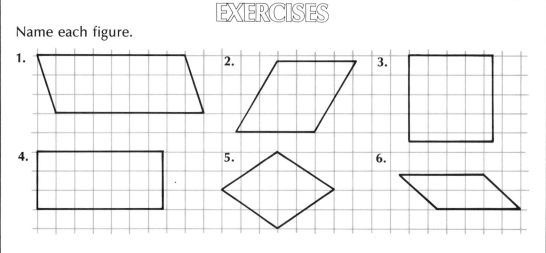

1.

2.

3.

4.

5.

6.

On grid paper, draw two different examples of a rectangle, a square, a parallelogram, and a rhombus.

7. Mark on each figure:
   a. the parallel sides (⟶, ⟶⟶).
   b. the right angles (⌐).
   c. the equal sides (╫, ╪).

8. How many diagonals are in each figure?

9. How many lines of symmetry are in each figure?

PRACTICE

True or False?

1. A square is a rhombus.
2. A square is a rectangle.
3. A parallelogram is a rectangle.
4. A rhombus is a parallelogram.
5. A rectangle is a square.
6. A square is a parallelogram.
7. A quadrilateral is a rectangle.
8. A rhombus is a square.

Copy and complete the table with yes or no.

Properties of Parallelograms

	Property ╲ Name	Parallelogram	Rectangle	Rhombus	Square
9.	opposite sides parallel				
10.	opposite sides equal				
11.	opposite angles equal				
12.	diagonals bisect each other				
13.	four equal sides				
14.	four 90° angles				
15.	perpendicular diagonals				
16.	number of lines of symmetry				

The Mystery Vertex

A, B, and C are three vertices of a parallelogram.
Where is the fourth vertex?
There are three possibilities.

A   C

B

163

Constructions IV

Parallel Lines

Equipment: Compass and ruler
Given: $\overline{AB}$ and point P
Construct: segment PQ parallel to $\overline{AB}$ through P.

1. Draw an arc above B having a radius of AP and centre at B.

2. With centre P and radius AB, draw an arc cutting the first arc at Q.

3. Draw segment PQ.
   $\overline{PQ}$ is parallel to $\overline{AB}$.

Parallelograms

Equipment: MIRA and ruler
Given: segment AB and segment BC
Construct: parallelogram $ABCD$

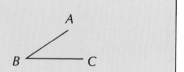

1. Stand MIRA perpendicular to $\overline{BC}$.

2. Mark the image of A.
   Label it A'.

3. Draw line AA' parallel to $\overline{BC}$.

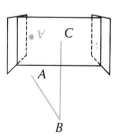
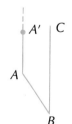

4. Stand MIRA perpendicular to $\overline{AB}$ (extended).

5. Mark the image of C.
   Label it C'.

6. Draw line CC' parallel to $\overline{AB}$.

7. Line AA' and line CC' meet at D to form parallelogram $ABCD$.

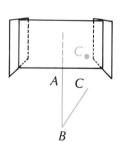
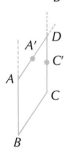

1. Draw segment *XY* and point *A* as shown at the right.
   Use a compass to construct a line parallel to $\overline{XY}$ through *A*.

2. Draw angle *ABC* as shown at the right.
   Use a *MIRA* to:
   a. construct a line parallel to $\overline{BC}$ through *A*.
   b. construct a line parallel to $\overline{BA}$ through *C*.

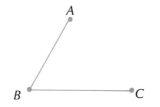

PRACTICE

Draw a diagram like the ones at the right.

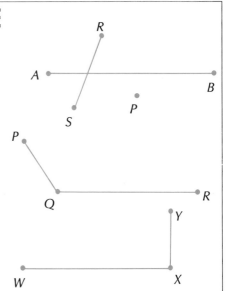

1. Use a compass to:
   a. construct a line parallel to $\overline{AB}$ through *P*.
   b. construct a line parallel to $\overline{RS}$ through *P*.

2. Use a *MIRA* to construct parallelogram *PQRS*.

3. Use a *MIRA* to construct rectangle *WXYZ*.

A Test for Parallel Lines

A *MIRA* can be used to test parallel lines.

Test the parallel lines in your constructions above with a *MIRA*.

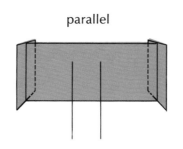

parallel

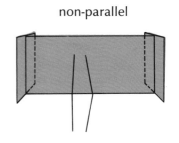

non-parallel

Rigid and Non-Rigid Polygons

1. Use congruent cardboard strips and paper fasteners to construct:
   a. an equilateral triangle. b. an isosceles triangle. c. a scalene triangle.

   d. a rhombus. e. a parallelogram. f. pentagon.

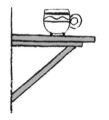 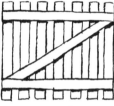

2. Which polygons are **rigid** (one fixed shape)?

3. Which polygons are *non-rigid*?

4. How can the non-rigid polygons be made rigid?

5. Explain the role of the triangle in each object.

   a.   b.  c.

   d.  e.  f.

6. Explain the role of the parallelogram or rhombus in each.

   a.  b.  c.

166

Creating Line Designs

Try making these designs and then create your own.
Start by constructing an equilateral triangle and marking equal
units of length on all segments.

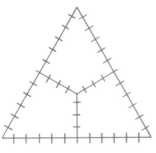

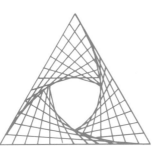

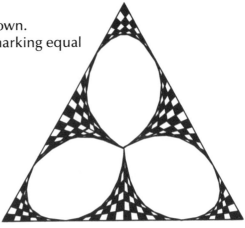

1. Draw two segments, *MN* and *OP*, to intersect at point *Q*.
   Name each angle formed at vertex *Q*.
   Name six segments in the figure.

2. Construct an angle of the given size with a protractor.

   a. 75° **b.** 165° **c.** 90° **d.** 10° **e.** 62°

3. Write congruency statements for the congruent sides and the congruent angles.

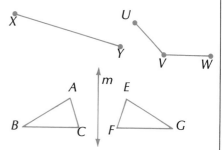

4. Draw a segment and an angle. Use a compass to construct a congruent segment and a congruent angle.

5. Triangle *EFG* is the reflection image of triangle *ABC* in line *m*.
   a. Name the image points of *A*, *B*, and *C*.
   b. Name all pairs of congruent sides.
   c. Name all pairs of congruent angles.

6. Draw two figures which have line symmetry.

7. Draw a segment *JK*.
   Draw a segment perpendicular to $\overline{JK}$.

8. Draw the bisector of an acute angle *PYR*.

9. What kind of triangle has these angle sizes?

   a. 15°, 55°, 110° **b.** 30°, 120° **c.** 90°, 45°

10. Construct △*DEF* with *DE* = 3.5 cm, *EF* = 3.5 cm, and ∠*E* = 55°.

11. Draw a segment *RS* and point *T*. Construct line *TV* parallel to $\overline{RS}$.

12. Draw an example of a rhombus, a rectangle, a square, and a parallelogram.

13. Draw an angle *DEF*.
    Construct parallelogram *DEFG*.

BACK

Copy and complete.

1. 3.5 m = ■ mm
2. 75 m = ■ km
3. 12.8 m = ■ cm

4. ■ mL = 45 L
5. 96 kL = ■ L
6. 25 L = ■ kL

7. 14 t = ■ kg
8. 6500 g = ■ kg
9. 7.2 kg = ■ g

10. 1 cm³ of water has a capacity of ■ and a mass of ■.

11. 1 dm³ of water has a capacity of ■ and a mass of ■.

12. 1 m³ of water has a capacity of ■ and a mass of ■.

Find the perimeter.

13.
2.5 cm
7.5 cm

14.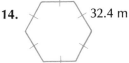
32.4 m

15.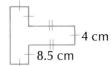
4 cm
8.5 cm

Find the area.

16.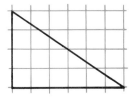

17.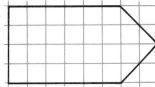

18.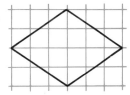

19.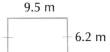
9.5 m
6.2 m

20.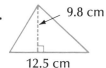
9.8 cm
12.5 cm

21.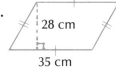
28 cm
35 cm

22.
40 cm

23.
8.2 m

24.
98 cm

Find the volume.

25.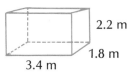
2.2 m
1.8 m
3.4 m

26.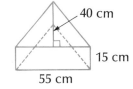
40 cm
15 cm
55 cm

27.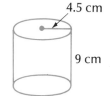
4.5 cm
9 cm

169

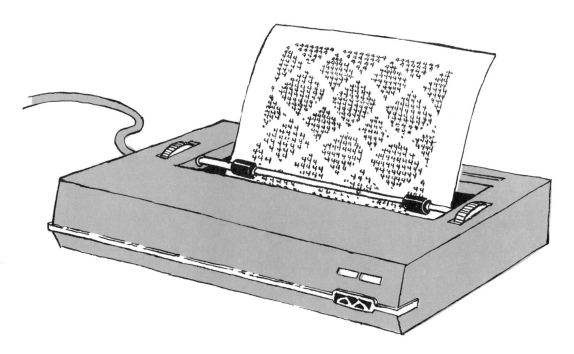

Divisibility Rules

By 2.	The number is even. It ends in 0, 2, 4, 6, or 8.	$\dfrac{34}{2)\overline{68}}$	
By 3.	The sum of the number's digits is divisible by 3.	$\dfrac{19}{3)\overline{57}}$	5 + 7 = 12
By 4.	The last two digits of the number are divisible by 4.	$\dfrac{31}{4)\overline{124}}$	
By 5.	The last two digits of the number is 5 or 0.	$\dfrac{97}{5)\overline{485}}$	
By 6.	The number is even and divisible by 3.	$\dfrac{13}{6)\overline{78}}$	7 + 8 = 15
By 9.	The sum of the number's digits is divisible by 9.	$\dfrac{86}{9)\overline{774}}$	7 + 7 + 4 = 18
By 10.	The last digit of the number is 0.	$\dfrac{77}{10)\overline{770}}$	

1. a. What is the sum of the digits in 4386?
   b. Is 4386 divisible by 3?
   c. Is 4386 divisible by 9?

2. a. What are the last two digits of 7836?
   b. Is 7836 divisible by 4?
   c. Is 7836 divisible by 10?

Which is evenly divisible? Find the quotient.

3. by 2: 683 or 386
4. by 3: 111 or 538
5. by 4: 726 or 536
6. by 5: 723 or 375
7. by 6: 223 or 312
8. by 9: 675 or 874
9. by 9: 7911 or 3669
10. by 10: 3500 or 3005

PRACTICE

Copy the table. Find the even quotients.

Divisible		by 2	by 3	by 4	by 5	by 6	by 9	by 10
1.	282							
2.	8398							
3.	20 736							
4.	237 654							
5.	6177							

Answer *yes* or *no*.

6. Can all 52 cards in a standard playing deck be dealt to 5 people so that every one has the same number of cards?

7. Can Mr. Fitch plant 342 cabbages in 6 rows of equal numbers of cabbages? 4 rows?

Divisibility Detective

Think of a divisibility rule for 8.
Look closely at the clues.

Clue 1: Evaluate $(46 \times 100) + 16$.
Why is it sensible that 4616 is divisible by 4?

Clue 2: Evaluate $(32 \times 100) + 64$.
Why is it sensible that 3264 is divisible by 4?

Clue 3: Evaluate $10 \div 8$; $100 \div 8$; and $1000 \div 8$.

Look for patterns.

Factors

The courtyard of Willowbrook school will be a rectangle that can be paved with 24 large, square tiles, each 1 m on a side. What dimensions could the courtyard be?

Make an organized list.

Possible dimensions	
width	length
1 m × 24 m	
2 m × 12 m	
3 m × 8 m	
4 m × 6 m	

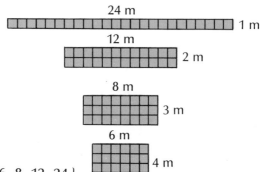

The **set of factors** of 24 is {1, 2, 3, 4, 6, 8, 12, 24.}

Each number in the set is a **divisor** or **factor** of 24.

EXERCISES

Answer *yes* or *no*.

1. Is 6 a factor of 30?   2. Is 9 a factor of 48?

3. Is 7 a factor of 57?   4. Is 4 a factor of 100?

Guess and test to find the missing factor.

5. $40a = 40$ 6. $7b = 63$ 7. $15p = 60$

8. $\dfrac{36}{x} = 4$ 9. $\dfrac{72}{m} = 24$ 10. $\dfrac{47}{w} = 1$

Write the set of factors for each.

11. factors of 72 = {1, 2, ■, 4, 6, ■, 9, ■, ■, 24, ■, 72}

12. factors of 102 = {■, 2, ■, ■, 17, ■, ■, 102}

13. factors of 6 = {■, ■, ■, ■}

14. factors of 10 = {■, ■, ■, ■}

15. factors of 15   16. factors of 57

17. factors of 36   18. factors of 54

172

PRACTICE

1. Write the numbers which are factors of 60.   1, 2, 3, 4, 5, 6, 7, 8, 9, 10
2. Write the numbers which are factors of 28.   2, 4, 6, 8, 10, 14, 16, 18, 20

Guess and test to find the missing factor.

3. $7b = 140$

4. $19e = 57$

5. $\dfrac{150}{a} = 10$

6. $\dfrac{68}{4} = n$

7. $8c \times 5 = 120$

8. $3z \times 7 = 105$

Write the set of factors for each number.

9. 96   10. 75   11. 43   12. 100   13. 8

14. 64   15. 200   16. 29   17. 49   18. 500

Solve using an organized list.

19. There are 52 cards in a standard playing deck. To what different numbers of people could you deal the cards equally with no cards left over?

20. Numbers usually have an *even* number of factors. Which numbers between 1 and 25 have an *odd* number of factors?

21. Find the three dimensions of all possible rectangular solids you can build with 30 cubes.

22. The number 6 is called a *Perfect Number*. If you add all the factors of 6, except 6, the sum is 6. $1 + 2 + 3 = 6$

    a. There is a second perfect number between 20 and 30.
    b. Perfect numbers are usually far apart. The third perfect number is between 495 and 500. What is it?

Magic Multiplication Square

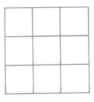

Use the numbers 1, 2, 3, 4, 6, 9, 12, 18, and 36 to fill in the cells of the grid so that each row, column, and diagonal has the same product.

Prime and Composite Numbers

The graph below shows all of the factors for each whole number <21.

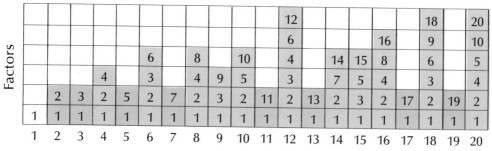

Whole numbers, like 5, which have *only 2 factors* are called **prime numbers.**

Whole numbers, like 12, which have *more than 2 factors* are called **composite numbers.**

EXERCISES

Use the graph above to answer the question.

1. Which numbers <21 have *only 2 factors* and are *prime*?

2. Which numbers <21 have *more than 2 factors* and are *composite*?

3. Which number <21 is neither prime nor composite? Why?

4. Which composite numbers <21 have 4 factors?

5. There is only one even prime number. What is it?

Write the set of factors for each number.
Then state whether the number is prime or composite.

6. 22 = {■, ■, ■, ■}

7. 29 = {■, ■}

8. 24 = {■, ■, ■, ■, ■, ■, ■, ■}

9. 34 = {■, ■, ■, ■}

10. 23 = {■, ■}

11. 37 = {■, ■}

12. 40

13. 45

14. 43

15. 42

16. 49

17. 31

PRACTICE

Is the number prime or composite?

1. 9   2. 15   3. 17   4. 25   5. 29

6. 38   7. 51   8. 59   9. 62   10. 65

11. 71   12. 73   13. 79   14. 89   15. 99

16. Which numbers at the right have 3 for a factor?

17. List the prime numbers shown at the right.

18. Which two numbers at the right are neither prime nor composite?

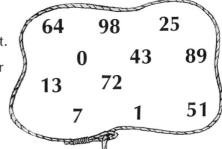

64   98   25   0   43   89   13   72   7   1   51

19. Write the prime numbers <80 and >70.

20. Write the composite numbers <37 and >29.

21. In 1742, a mathematician named Christian Goldbach believed that every number larger than 4 could be expressed as the sum of two primes. Write each of the following numbers as the sum of two primes:

 a. 16   b. 28   c. 46   d. 60   e. 82

22. Goldbach also believed that every odd number large than 7 could be written as the sum of three odd primes. Test this idea by writing each number as the sum of three odd primes.

 a. 9   b. 13   c. 21   d. 57   e. 99

Sieve of Eratosthenes

A method of making a list of prime numbers was devised by an ancient Greek scholar, Eratosthenes, in the third century B.C. The method consists of taking a 100 chart and circling the first five primes 2, 3, 5, 7, and 11. Then all numbers divisible by 2, 3, 5, 7, and 11 are crossed out. The prime numbers <100 will become visible as they will not be crossed out.

Use the sieve of Eratosthenes to find all of the prime numbers <100.

	(2)	(3)	4	(5)	6	(7)	8	9	10
(11)	12	13	14	15	16	17	18	19	20
21	22	23	24	25	26	27	28	29	30
31	32	33	34	35	36	37	38	39	40
41	42	43	44	45	46	47	48	49	50
51	52	53	54	55	56	57	58	59	60
61	62	63	64	65	66	67	68	69	70
71	72	73	74	75	76	77	78	79	80

Prime Factors

The set of factors of 84 = {1, 2, 3, 4, 6, 7, 12, 14, 21, 28, 42, 84}
Only the factors 2, 3, and 7 are **prime** numbers.
The set of **prime factors** of 84 = {2, 3, 7}

The prime factors of a number can be found using a factor tree.

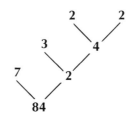

A number can be written as a product of its prime factors.

$$84 = 2 \times 2 \times 3 \times 7$$
$$= 2^2 \times 3 \times 7$$

The prime factors can be multiplied to find all other factors of a number.

Prime factors: Factors:

$$84 = \boxed{2 \times 2 \times 3 \times 7} = 1 \times 84$$
$$= \boxed{2} \times 2 \times 3 \times 7 = 2 \times 42$$
$$= 2 \times 2 \times \boxed{3} \times 7 = 3 \times 28$$
$$= \boxed{2 \times 2} \times 3 \times 7 = 4 \times 21$$
$$= 2 \times \boxed{2 \times 3} \times 7 = 6 \times 14$$
$$= 2 \times 2 \times 3 \times \boxed{7} = 7 \times 12$$

EXERCISES

Write the prime factors in each set of factors.

1. 21: {1, 3, 7, 21}   **2.** 18: {1, 2, 3, 6, 9, 18}   **3.** 64: {1, 2, 4, 8, 16, 32, 64}

Rewrite using exponents.

4. $5 \times 5 \times 7 = 175$ **5.** $2 \times 3 \times 3 \times 3 \stackrel{?}{=} 54$ **6.** $2 \times 2 \times 7 \times 7 = 196$

Write each as a product of prime factors using exponents.

7. 16 = ■■   **8.** 28 = ■■ × ■   **9.** 12 = ■■ × 3

Find all factors of each number.

         prime factors: factors: prime factors: factors:

10. $20 = 2 \times 2 \times 5 = 1 \times 20$ **11.** $99 = 3 \times 3 \times 11 = $ ■ × ■
          $= 2 \times 2 \times 5 = $ ■ × ■ $= 3 \times 3 \times 11 = $ ■ × ■
          $= 2 \times 2 \times 5 = $ ■ × ■ $= 3 \times 3 \times 11 = $ ■ × ■

What is the product?

1. $2^2 \times 5$ **2.** 2×3^3 **3.** $2^2 \times 11$

4. $3^2 \times 13$ **5.** $2^4 \times 3$ **6.** $2^3 \times 17$

Draw two different factor trees for these numbers.
Are the top branches of each the same?

7. 24   **8.** 36   **9.** 48   **10.** 60   **11.** 144

Write each number as a product of prime factors using exponents.

12. 8   **13.** 72   **14.** 50   **15.** 35   **16.** 52

17. 18   **18.** 42   **19.** 55   **20.** 45   **21.** 250

22. 108   **23.** 196   **24.** 475   **25.** 117   **26.** 1000

For each equation, guess and test to find the missing prime factor.

27. $3n \times 5^2 = 150$ **28.** $3f = 57$ **29.** $2 \times s^2 = 98$

30. $m^2 \times 5 \times 19 = 380$ **31.** $x^4 = 625$ **32.** $g^5 \times 5^2 = 800$

Find all factors of each number.

33. $70 = 2 \times 5 \times 7$ **34.** $30 = 2 \times 3 \times 5$ **35.** $36 = 2 \times 2 \times 3 \times 3$

36. Some computers use the symbol $\wedge$ to exponentiate and the symbol $*$ to multiply. What is each product?

    a. 2^3*7   **b.** 2^2*5^2

    c. 5*11^2   **d.** 2*3^2*5^2

Napoleon's Palindrome

Napoleon Bonaparte was once exiled to the isle of Elba. When he first saw this Island he made a statement which is a *palindrome*.

Write each number in the statement as the product of prime factors. Then use the code box to decipher Napoleon's statement.

510   154   19   117   19   154   510

A = 2, B = 5, E = 3, I = 19
L = 17, R = 13, S = 7, W = 11

GCF

Gerry and Tina need to tile a rectangular area, 24 cm by 18 cm, with square tiles. What are the largest-size square tiles they could use?

Gerry and Tina could compute the **greatest common factor (GCF)** of 24 and 18 to solve the problem.

Method 1: Listing all factors

24 = {**1, 2, 3, 4, 6,** 8, 12, 24}
18 = {**1, 2, 3, 6,** 9, 18}

Common factors: 1, 2, 3, 6.
GCF = 6

Possible tile sizes:

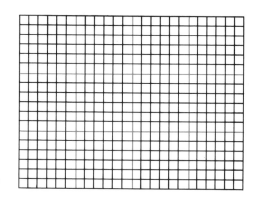

1 × 1   2 × 2   3 × 3   6 × 6

Method 2: Writing products of prime factors

24 = 2 × 2 × **2 × 3**
18 =   **2 × 3** × 3

Common factors: 2 × 3
GCF = 6

A 6 × 6 tile is the largest size they could use.

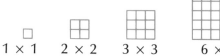

EXERCISES

Use Method 1 to find the GCF.

1. 24 and 36
24 = {■, ■, ■, ■, ■, ■, ■, ■}
36 = {■, ■, ■, ■, ■, ■, ■, ■, ■}
GCF = ■

2. 12, 18, and 20
12 = {■, ■, ■, ■, ■, ■}
18 = {■, ■, ■, ■, ■, ■}
20 = {■, ■, ■, ■, ■, ■}
GCF = ■

3. 45 and 75   **4.** 39 and 49   **5.** 4, 10, and 12

Use Method 2 to find the GCF.

6. 81 and 72
81 = 3 × 3 × 3 × 3
72 = 2 × 2 × 2 × 3 × 3
GCF = ■

7. 40, 56, and 64
40 = 2 × ■ × ■ × ■
56 = 2 × ■ × ■ × ■
64 = 2 × ■ × ■ × ■ × ■ × ■
GCF = ■

8. 105 and 140   **9.** 96 and 240   **10.** 90, 120, and 150

PRACTICE

Find the GCF.

1. 25 and 26
2. 42 and 28
3. 49 and 105
4. 28 and 36
5. 130 and 195
6. 180 and 270
7. 18, 24, and 36
8. 16, 40, and 56
9. 26, 52, and 65
10. 44, 88, and 110
11. 135, 162, and 189
12. 128, 160, and 192

Solve.

13. Carla wishes to cut her birthday cake into the largest square pieces possible. If the cake is 30 cm by 42 cm, what is the *largest* size square piece she can cut?

14. The students in a school crafts club have 120 red beads and 180 green beads for making Christmas ornaments. What is the *greatest* number of ornaments they could make if the ornaments contain equal numbers of red and green beads?

15. The Coverall Paint Company wants to sell paint in can sizes that most people would use up completely. The company has found that most people paint wall surfaces of 300 m^2, 450 m^2, or 600 m^2. How many square metres of wall surface should the paint in their *largest* can cover?

REVIEW

Is 582 462 divisible by:

1. 2?
2. 5?
3. 9?
4. 4?
5. 6?

Write the set of factors for each.

6. 42
7. 84
8. 90
9. 65
10. 110

Is the number prime or composite?

11. 27
12. 19
13. 51
14. 71
15. 85

Express each as a product of prime factors using exponents.

16. 48
17. 21
18. 126
19. 189
20. 1300

Find the GCF.

21. 24 and 32
22. 15 and 37
23. 84 and 126
24. 99, 132, 165

Multiples

A **multiple** of any number is the product of the number and any other factor.

The set of multiples of 5 = {0, 5, 10, 15, 20, . . .}

$0 \times 5 = 0$, $1 \times 5 = 5$, $2 \times 5 = 10$, $3 \times 5 = 15$, $4 \times 5 = 20$, . . .

> A set of multiples is *infinite*.

The BASIC computer program below prints the multiples of 5. The program is represented on a flowchart.

Input:
```
10 LET F = 0
20 LET M = F * 5
30 PRINT M,
40 LET F = F + 1
50 GOTO 20
60 END
```

Output:

0	5	10
15	20	25
30	35	40
45	50	55
60	65	70
75	80	85

and so on.

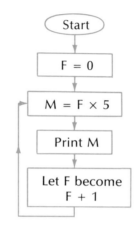

EXERCISES

Write the set of the first six multiples for each.

1. 2 = {0, 2, 4, ■, ■, ■, . . .}   2. 6 = {0, 6, 12, ■, ■, ■, . . .}

3. 8 = {■, ■, ■, ■, ■, ■, . . .}   4. 12 = {■, ■, ■, ■, ■, ■, . . .}

5. 20 = {■, ■, ■, ■, ■, ■, . . .}   6. 15 = {■, ■, ■, ■, ■, ■, . . .}

7. 4   8. 7

9. 11   10. 30

11. 25   12. 75

Write the numbers in the set which are multiples of the given number.

13. 6 {16, 21, 40, 48}   14. 3 {21, 40, 60, 38}

15. 7 {36, 35, 29, 38}   16. 10 {85, 95, 120, 200}

17. 9 {42, 45, 78, 108}   18. 2 {60, 44, 700, 150}

19. 40 {40, 150, 320, 1200}   20. 25 {70, 400, 675, 120}

180

Write the set of the first 5 multiples for each.

1. 3	**2.** 8	**3.** 11	**4.** 30	**5.** 16
6. 25	**7.** 18	**8.** 9	**9.** 50	**10.** 100
11. 45	**12.** 36	**13.** 75	**14.** 33	**15.** 13

Write the numbers in the set which are multiples of the given number.

16. 2 {3, 8, 15, 23, 8061, 2572, 3945, 3624}   **17.** 25 {525, 610, 9055, 257, 850, 675}

18. 8 {94, 334, 815, 532, 208, 392}   **19.** 12 {32, 96, 75, 540, 252, 307}

20. 10 {4086, 3750, 20 576, 39 050, 271 566, 385 210}

Solve.

21. The Hole-in-One donut shop sells donuts only in groups of 6. Can you buy 78 donuts? 162 donuts? 198 donuts?

22. What number is a multiple of every number? Why?

23. Explain the relationship between the factors of a number and the multiples of a number.

Computer Multiples

This BASIC computer program will print the first 50 multiples of any number you input.

```
10 PRINT "TO FIND THE FIRST 50 ";
20 PRINT "MULTIPLES OF A NUMBER."
30 PRINT "TYPE THAT NUMBER AND THEN ";
40 PRINT "PRESS THE RETURN KEY."
50 INPUT N
60 PRINT "THE FIRST 50 MULTIPLES ";
70 PRINT "OF ";N;" ARE..."
80 FOR F = 0 TO 49
90 LET M = F * N
100 PRINT M
110 NEXT F
120 END
```

How would you change the program so that it would print the first 100 multiples?

LCM

Jody and Paul jog together at the YMCA. Jody can complete a lap in 60 s, but it takes Paul 80 s. They agree to stop for a rest every time they meet one another at the end of a lap. After how many seconds do they first meet and rest?

Jody and Paul could compute the **least common multiple (LCM)** of 60 and 80 to solve the problem.

Method 1: Listing Multiples
60 = {60, 120, 180, **240**, 300, 360, 420, **480** . . .}
80 = {80, 160, **240**, 320, 400, **480**, . . .}

Common multiples: {240, 480, . . .}
LCM = 240

	Lap 1	Lap 2	Lap 3	Lap 4
Jody	60s	120s	180s	240s
Pat	80s	160s	240s	320s

Method 2: Writing Products of Prime Factors
$$60 = 2 \times 2 \qquad \times 3 \times 5$$
$$80 = 2 \times 2 \times 2 \times 2 \qquad \times 5$$
$$LCM = 2 \times 2 \times 2 \times 2 \times 3 \times 5$$
$$LCM = 240$$

They first meet and rest after 240 s.

EXERCISES

Use Method 1 to find the LCM.

1. 16 and 12
16 = {■, ■, ■, ■, ■, . . .}
12 = {■, ■, ■, ■, ■, . . .}
LCM = ■

2. 4, 6, and 8
4 = {■, ■, ■, ■, ■, ■, . . .}
6 = {■, ■, ■, ■, ■, ■, . . .}
8 = {■, ■, ■, ■, ■, ■, . . .}
LCM = ■

3. 16 and 20

4. 15 and 25

5. 6, 10, and 15

Use Method 2 to find the LCM.

6. 24 and 64
24 = $2^3 \times$ ■
64 = $2^■$
LCM = ■

7. 16, 36, and 48
16 = $2^■$
32 − $2^■ \times$ ■■
48 = $2^■ \times$ ■
LCM = ■

8. 55 and 25

9. 15, 25, and 10

10. 12, 15, and 18

PRACTICE

Find the LCM.

1. 16 and 24	**2.** 80 and 30	**3.** 25 and 35
4. 60 and 50	**5.** 50 and 75	**6.** 21 and 28
7. 35 and 14	**8.** 15 and 18	**9.** 21 and 30
10. 36 and 28	**11.** 27 and 54	**12.** 98 and 28
13. 6, 12, and 15	**14.** 8, 10, and 16	**15.** 9, 12, and 24
16. 25, 20, and 50	**17.** 18, 24, and 30	**18.** 32, 12, and 40

19. 2×5^2 and $2^2 \times 3$

20. $3^2 \times 7$ and 2×3^2

Find:

21. GCF (4, 6); LCM (4, 6)

22. GCF (8, 12); LCM (8, 12)

23. GCF (12, 16); LCM (12, 16)

24. GCF (10, 15); LCM (10, 15)

25. GCF (9, 12); LCM (9, 12)

26. GCF (12, 20); LCM (12, 20)

Solve.

27. A soft drink company wants to ship its pop in cartons containing multiples of 12, 15, and 20 bottles. What is the least number of bottles it should ship in a carton?

28. The lights in front of a downtown movie theatre are wired so that one half of them momentarily goes off every 10 s. The other half of the lights goes off momentarily every 18 s. After how many seconds do *all* of the lights momentarily go off?

29. What is the LCM of any 2 prime numbers. Why?

Jazzy!

The members of the Sparkville Jazz Ensemble have the following practice schedule:

Andy practises every day.
Bob practises every second day.
Petra practises every third day.
Dorothy practises every fifth day.

If they all practise on October 1, on what date do they all practise together next?

Problems and Applications

Divisibility rules, factors, prime numbers, the GCF, and the LCM are useful in solving the problems.

Suppose you have two sizes of square tiles: 12 cm and 15 cm. What is the smallest square surface that can be evenly covered by either of these two sizes of tiles?

Find the LCM of 12 and 15.
$$12 = 2^2 \times 3$$
$$15 = \qquad 3 \times 5$$
$$\text{LCM} = 2^2 \times 3 \times 5 = 60$$

The smallest square surface which can be covered by either 12 cm or 15 cm tiles is 60 cm by 60 cm.

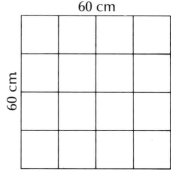

 12 cm tiles  15 cm tiles

 EXERCISES

You may use lists, tables, or diagrams to help you solve the problems.

1. How many different ways can 42 people be grouped into teams of equal numbers of players?

TEAMS	PLAYERS
2	?
3	?
?	?
?	?

2. Can 357 oranges be shared equally by 3 people? 6 people? 9 people?

3. How many different ways can 90 square tiles be arranged into rectangular shapes?

4. What is the greatest number of people among whom 28 cookies, 42 cupcakes, and 70 donuts may be shared equally?

5. There are 30 students in a gym class. How many ways can the students be divided to make teams of equal numbers?

PRACTICE

You may use lists, tables, or diagrams to help you solve the problems.

1. It takes 3 m of material to make a Batik print. Can Suzy use all of a 35 m piece of material to make Batik prints? If Suzy were to use all of the material, how much material would each Batik print have to take?

2. Peter has two rolls of newsprint. One roll is 130 m long and the other is 78 m long. He wants to cut each roll so that he has pieces of equal length. What is the length of the longest piece that he can cut from each roll and have no newsprint left over?

3. On the railway line between Axton and Bonnyville, a freight train takes 45 h to make a round trip. The express freight train makes the same journey in only 36 h. On Monday, both trains left Axton together. If the trains run continually, how long will it take before they are in Axton together again?

4. The Universal Pipe Company is laying a water pipe and a gas line pipe side by side. The water pipe comes in 16 m lengths. The gas line pipe comes in 10 m lengths.

   Each time the two pipes have a joint in the same place, a brace must be installed. How many braces must be installed when 200 m of both pipes are layed? (Do not count the start or end of the pipes.)

5. The Willowbrook Little Theatre Company is building scenery panels. The panels must span widths of 12 m, 18 m, and 24 m. What should the largest width of each panel be?

6. Donald had almost 3 dozen cookies. He had enough so that he could share them equally with his 4 friends and himself.

   After his sister had eaten one of his cookies, Donald found that no matter how many friends he had, he could not evenly share more than one cookie with them.

   How many cookies did Donald originally have?

7. An aircraft engine requires servicing of its fuel system after every 36 h in flight. The engine needs its electrical system checked after 15 h of flight. After how many hours of flight will the fuel system and the electrical system both be serviced at the same time?

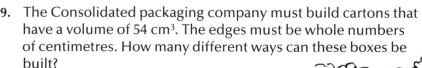

8. Rectangular blocks measuring 8 cm by 15 cm by 10 cm are to be packed in a cube-shaped carton. What are the dimensions of the smallest possible carton?

9. The Consolidated packaging company must build cartons that have a volume of 54 cm³. The edges must be whole numbers of centimetres. How many different ways can these boxes be built?

10. A City Hall courtyard measuring 30 m by 20 m is to be paved with large, cement, square blocks.
   a. What are the possible sizes of cement square blocks which could be used?
   b. What is the largest possible cement square block that could be used?

Patterns

Write the next four numbers in each sequence.
a. {38, 36, 34, 32, 30, 28, . . .}

b. {2, 3, 5, 7, 11, 13, . . .}

c. {16, 20, 24, 28, 32, 36, . . .}

d. {57, 54, 51, 48, 45, 42, . . .}

e. {4, 6, 8, 9, 10, 12, . . .}

f. {117, 126, 135, 144, 153, 162, . . .}

g. {41, 43, 47, 53, 59, 61, . . .}

h. {152, 156, 160, 164, 168, 172, . . .}

i. {77, 78, 80, 81, 82, 84, . . .}

Pascal's Triangle

Pascal, a 17th century French Mathematician, devised the triangle below. There are many number patterns to be found in Pascal's triangle.

Get 4 copies of the triangle from your teacher. Fill in all numbers in each copy.

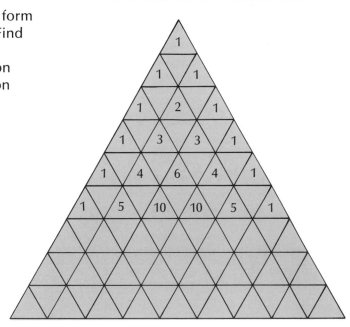

1. Find the hexagons made up of 6 small triangles. What pattern do you find for the numbers in the hexagons?

2. The multiples of 2, 3, 4, and 5 form patterns in Pascal's triangle. Find these multiple patterns by colouring the multiples of 2 on one copy, the multiples of 3 on another copy, and so on.

3. Describe the pattern formed by the sum of the digits in each row. If the triangle were extended one more row, what would be the sum of the digits?

4. Describe any other patterns that you can find.

REVIEW

Write the set of the first six multiples for each.

1. 4	**2.** 9	**3.** 12	**4.** 17	**5.** 25
6. 60	**7.** 35	**8.** 130	**9.** 75	**10.** 150

Find the LCM.

11. 9 and 12

12. 12 and 30

13. 16 and 14

14. 15 and 45

15. 10, 21, and 35

16. 15, 39, and 65

Ancient Numerals and Numbers

EGYPTIAN

The ancient Egyptians devised a number system 5000 years ago using these numerals:

stroke:	heel bone:	scroll:	lotus flower:	pointing finger:	tadpole:	astonished man:
$\mid$	$\cap$	φ				
1	10^1	10^2	10^3	10^4	10^5	10^6

The earliest evidence of the Egyptian number system is found on a ceremonial stone mace which belonged to king Menes. The numerals on the stone mace show how many oxen, goats, and prisoners Menes captured on a successful military campaign.

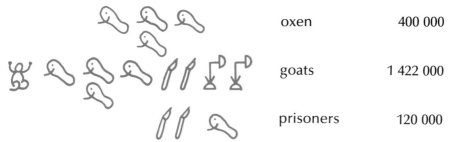

oxen	400 000
goats	1 422 000
prisoners	120 000

The Egyptians used an additive system for writing numbers. Order did not matter.

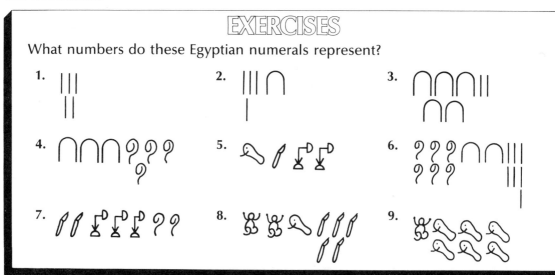

EXERCISES

What numbers do these Egyptian numerals represent?

1.
2.
3.
4.
5.
6.
7.
8.
9.

What numbers do these Egyptian numerals represent?

1.

2.

3.

4.

5.

6.

Chinese-Japanese

The number system of the ancient Chinese-Japanese, dating back as early as 300 B.C., used the numerals at the right.

The Chinese-Japanese used a *multiplicative, base 10*, grouping system for writing numbers vertically. The largest powers of 10 were written first.

1	一	十	10^1
2	二	百	10^2
3	三	千	10^3
4	四		
5	五		
6	六		
7	七		
8	八		
9	九		

四百 } 4×10^2

二十 } 2×10^1

五 } 5

$$(4 \times 10^2) + (2 \times 10^1) + 5 = 425$$

What numbers do these Chinese-Japanese numerals represent?

1. 四十三

2. 九百八

3. 六千七十

4. 二百四十五

Is 54 162 divisible by the number?

1. 2   **2.** 3   **3.** 4   **4.** 6   **5.** 9

Is 703 950 divisible by the number?

6. 3   **7.** 4   **8.** 5   **9.** 9   **10.** 10

11. Which of the following numbers have 14 as a factor?
   a. 7   **b.** 14   **c.** 114   **d.** 140   **e.** 1040

Write the set of factors for each number.

12. 12   **13.** 43   **14.** 20   **15.** 38   **16.** 100

Identify the number as prime or composite.

17. 2   **18.** 14   **19.** 57   **20.** 71   **21.** 97

Write each as a product of prime factors.

22. 56   **23.** 98   **24.** 108   **25.** 240   **26.** 350

Find the GCF.

27. 36 and 42   **28.** 28 and 56   **29.** 32, 48, and 96

30. Which of the following are multiples of 6?

   a. 0   **b.** 1   **c.** 6   **d.** 60   **e.** 150

Write the set of the first six multiples for each.
31. 3   **32.** 7   **33.** 14   **34.** 18   **35.** 24

Find the LCM.

36. 8 and 24   **37.** 14 and 35   **38.** 16, 22, and 32

Solve.

39. Barb has the oil changed in her car every 6000 km and has the engine tuned every 15 000 km. How far will Barb have to drive before she has the oil changed and the engine tuned at the same time?

LOOKING BACK

Use a protractor and ruler to help answer these questions.

True or false?

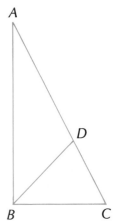

1. ∠ABD and ∠DBC have the same vertex.
2. △ABC is a right isosceles triangle.
3. $\overline{BD}$ bisects ∠ABC.
4. △DBC is equilateral.
5. $\overline{AB} \cong \overline{AC}$.
6. ∠A + ∠B + ∠C = 180°.
7. $\overline{AB} \perp \overline{BC}$.

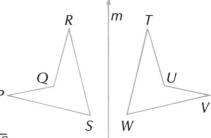

8. The figures have line symmetry.
9. Point S is the reflection image of point W.
10. $\overline{TV} \cong \overline{UV}$.
11. ∠P ≅ ∠V.
12. Point R is the reflection image of point V.
13. PQRS is the reflection image of TUVW in $\overline{RS}$.
14. $\overline{PS} \cong \overline{UV}$.

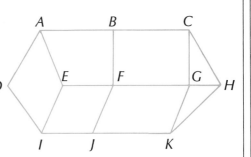

15. Figure ABFE is a square.
16. Figure BCHF is a parallelogram.
17. ∠JFG = 90°.
18. Figure ADIE is a rhombus.
19. Figure FGKJ has 2 sets of parallel sides.
20. Figure EFJI is a rhombus.
21. Figure ACHKID is a hexagon.

UNIT 8 Fractions I

Meanings of Fractions

There are several ways to illustrate fractions.

$\frac{3}{4}$ of the *figure*
is shaded.

$\frac{5}{18}$ of the *set* of fish
are swordtails.

$$\frac{0}{5} \quad \frac{1}{5} \quad \frac{2}{5} \quad \frac{3}{5} \quad \mathbf{\frac{4}{5}} \quad \frac{5}{5}$$

$\frac{4}{5}$ is shown on a
number line.

The **numerator** of a fraction tells how many parts are being considered.
The **denominator** of a fraction tells how many parts there are in all.

---

numerator → 5 ← parts considered
denominator → 18 ← parts in all

192

What fraction of each *figure* is shaded?

1.   **2.**  **3.**   **4.**

What fraction of each *set* is shaded?

5. **6.** **7.** **8.**

Name each lettered point on the number lines.

9.
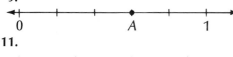
0   A   1

10.
0   B   1

11.
0   C   1

12.
0   D   1

What fraction of each is shaded?

1. 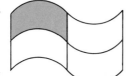 **2.**   **3.**   **4.**

Name each lettered point on the number lines.

5.

0   M   1

6.
0   N   1

7.
0   X   1

8.
0   Y   1

Solve.

9. Luigi is making a pizza for his friends. For the topping, he uses 8 slices of salami, 6 slices of onion, 5 slices of green pepper, 9 slices of tomato, and 12 slices of cheese. What fractional part of the topping is each ingredient?

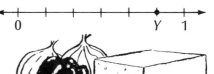

Equivalent Fractions

There are 20 members on the track team.
Three fifths of the team are girls.
How many members are girls?

One way to solve this is by finding an **equivalent fraction.**

> To find an equivalent fraction, multiply both the numerator and denominator by the *same* number.

$$\frac{3}{5} = \frac{3}{5}\boxed{\begin{array}{c}\times\,4\\\times\,4\end{array}} = \frac{12}{20}$$

$\frac{3}{5}$ is *equivalent* to $\frac{12}{20}$.

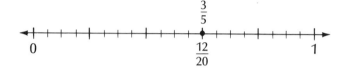

There are 12 girls on the track team.

EXERCISES

Copy and complete to find the equivalent fractions.

1. $\frac{2}{5} = \frac{2\times 2}{5\times 2} = \frac{\blacksquare}{\blacksquare}$

2. $\frac{2}{5} = \frac{2\times 3}{5\times 3} = \frac{\blacksquare}{\blacksquare}$

3. $\frac{2}{5} = \frac{2\times 4}{5\times 4} = \frac{\blacksquare}{\blacksquare}$

4. $\frac{3}{8} = \frac{3\times 3}{8\times 3} = \frac{\blacksquare}{\blacksquare}$

5. $\frac{4}{5} = \frac{4\times 4}{5\times 4} = \frac{\blacksquare}{\blacksquare}$

6. $\frac{3}{7} = \frac{3\times 8}{7\times 8} = \frac{\blacksquare}{\blacksquare}$

7. $\frac{5}{9} = \frac{\blacksquare}{36}$

8. $\frac{7}{8} = \frac{42}{\blacksquare}$

9. $\frac{4}{7} = \frac{\blacksquare}{35}$

10. $\frac{5}{6} = \frac{20}{\blacksquare}$

11. $\frac{2}{3} = \frac{\blacksquare}{24}$

12. $\frac{1}{12} = \frac{\blacksquare}{24}$

13. $\frac{7}{10} = \frac{49}{\blacksquare}$

14. $\frac{3}{4} = \frac{36}{\blacksquare}$

Name 2 equivalent fractions for each point.

15. $\frac{3}{4} = ?$

16. $\frac{1}{5} = ?$

17.

18.

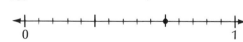

194

PRACTICE

Copy and complete to find the equivalent fractions.

1. $\frac{2}{3} = \frac{\blacksquare}{12}$

2. $\frac{4}{5} = \frac{16}{\blacksquare}$

3. $\frac{5}{6} = \frac{\blacksquare}{30}$

4. $\frac{3}{4} = \frac{\blacksquare}{16}$

5. $\frac{1}{2} = \frac{\blacksquare}{14}$

6. $\frac{3}{7} = \frac{\blacksquare}{21}$

7. $\frac{7}{10} = \frac{28}{\blacksquare}$

8. $\frac{5}{12} = \frac{15}{\blacksquare}$

9. $\frac{7}{8} = \frac{\blacksquare}{80}$

10. $\frac{5}{9} = \frac{45}{\blacksquare}$

11. $\frac{9}{11} = \frac{72}{\blacksquare}$

12. $\frac{8}{15} = \frac{32}{\blacksquare}$

13. $\frac{1}{3} = \frac{\blacksquare}{6} = \frac{3}{\blacksquare} = \frac{\blacksquare}{12} = \frac{\blacksquare}{15}$

14. $\frac{2}{5} = \frac{4}{\blacksquare} = \frac{\blacksquare}{15} = \frac{8}{\blacksquare} = \frac{10}{\blacksquare} = \frac{\blacksquare}{30}$

Find an equivalent fraction to help you answer each problem.

15. $\frac{3}{10}$ of 100

16. $\frac{3}{4}$ of 16

17. $\frac{2}{5}$ of 35

18. $\frac{7}{8}$ of 72

Name 2 equivalent fractions for each diagram.

19.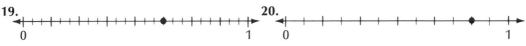

20.

21.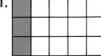

22.

23.

24.

Solve by finding an equivalent fraction.

25. There are 12 clarinet players in the orchestra. Two thirds of them are male. How many male clarinet players are in the orchestra?

26. An apple orchard has 120 trees. Three fourths of the trees are Northern Spies. How many of the trees are Northern Spies?

Cutting the Cake

A baker cuts his cakes in such a way that his customers can buy a whole cake, half a cake, a third of a cake, or a quarter of a cake without his having to cut the cake again. Into how many equal-sized pieces does he cut his cakes?

Simplifying Fractions

At the all-city track meet, $\frac{18}{24}$ of the medals won by the Richmond Rockets were for first place. Can you replace $\frac{18}{24}$ with an *equivalent fraction* in **simplest terms**?

Method 1:
Simplify a fraction by dividing the numerator and denominator by a **common factor**.

2 is a common factor of 18 and 24.

$$\frac{18}{24} = \frac{18 \div 2}{24 \div 2} = \frac{9}{12}$$

3 is a common factor of 9 and 12.

$$\frac{9}{12} = \frac{9 \div 3}{12 \div 3} = \frac{3}{4}$$

Method 2:
Simplify a fraction by dividing the numerator and denominator by the greatest common factor (**GCF**).

The GCF of 18 and 24 is 6.

$$\frac{18}{24} = \frac{18 \div 6}{24 \div 6} = \frac{3}{4}$$

In simplest terms, $\frac{18}{24} = \frac{3}{4}$.

EXERCISES

Find the GCF of each pair of numbers.
Then write the fraction in simplest terms.

1. GCF (6, 10) = ■

$\frac{6}{10} = \frac{■}{■}$

2. GCF (12, 20) = ■

$\frac{12}{20} = \frac{■}{■}$

3. GCF (10, 25) = ■

$\frac{10}{25} = \frac{■}{■}$

Write each fraction in simplest terms.

4.  $\frac{2}{6} = \frac{■}{■}$

5. 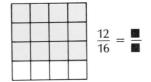 $\frac{12}{16} = \frac{■}{■}$

6. 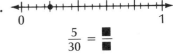 $\frac{5}{30} = \frac{■}{■}$

7. $\frac{6}{8}$

8. $\frac{5}{10}$

9. $\frac{15}{20}$

10. $\frac{16}{24}$

11. $\frac{8}{12}$

12. $\frac{27}{36}$

13. $\frac{13}{26}$

14. $\frac{60}{80}$

15. $\frac{300}{500}$

16. $\frac{17}{17}$

Write each fraction in simplest terms.

1. $\frac{12}{18}$ **2.** $\frac{15}{20}$ **3.** $\frac{16}{40}$ **4.** $\frac{36}{45}$ **5.** $\frac{7}{15}$

6. $\frac{28}{36}$ **7.** $\frac{48}{80}$ **8.** $\frac{24}{100}$ **9.** $\frac{21}{105}$ **10.** $\frac{30}{135}$

Write the fraction shown by the diagram in simplest terms.

11.   **12.**   **13.**

14.    **15.**

The fractions below are written as products of prime factors.
Write each fraction in simplest terms by using the prime factors.

EXAMPLE: $\frac{30}{42} = \frac{2 \times 3 \times 5}{2 \times 3 \times 7} = \frac{5}{7}$

16. $\frac{45}{63} = \frac{3 \times 3 \times 5}{3 \times 3 \times 7}$ **17.** $\frac{70}{110} = \frac{2 \times 5 \times 7}{2 \times 5 \times 11}$ **18.** $\frac{77}{143} = \frac{7 \times 11}{11 \times 13}$

19. $\frac{70}{385} = \frac{2 \times 5 \times 7}{5 \times 7 \times 11}$ **20.** $\frac{182}{91} = \frac{2 \times 7 \times 13}{7 \times 13}$ **21.** $\frac{437}{589} = \frac{19 \times 23}{19 \times 31}$

Write the solutions in simplest terms.

22. Of the 24 medals won by the Rockets at the track meet, 3 were won by the senior boys, 8 by the senior girls, 9 by the junior boys, and 4 by the junior girls. What fraction of the medals was won by each group?

23. During the 1500 m road race, David had completed 900 m in 5 min 43 s. What fraction of the race had David completed? What fraction of the race had he left to finish?

Getting Punchy

a. What fraction of the recipe is soda water? sugar? orange juice? lemon juice?

b. Double the recipe for fruit punch. What fraction of the recipe is each ingredient? What pattern do you notice? Can you explain why?

Fruit Punch
250 mL sugar
250 mL water
750 mL orange juice
125 mL lemon juice
125 mL pineapple juice
1000 mL soda water

Comparing Fractions

Which is more, $\frac{2}{3}$ of an hour or $\frac{3}{5}$ of an hour?

To solve the problem, rewrite each fraction with the same denominator. Then it is easier to compare the fractions.

$$\frac{2}{3} = \frac{2}{3}\boxed{\frac{\times 5}{\times 5}} = \frac{10}{15} \qquad \frac{3}{5} = \frac{3}{5}\boxed{\frac{\times 3}{\times 3}} = \frac{9}{15}$$

$$\frac{10}{15} > \frac{9}{15} \quad \text{so} \quad \frac{2}{3} > \frac{3}{5}$$

Two thirds of an hour is more than $\frac{3}{5}$ of an hour.

It is $\frac{1}{15}$ (or 4 min) more.

> Compare fractions by finding equivalent fractions with the *same denominator*.

EXERCISES

Copy and compare. Use > or <.

1. $\frac{3}{8} \bullet \frac{5}{8}$ 2. $\frac{7}{9} \bullet \frac{5}{9}$ 3. $\frac{2}{5} \bullet \frac{4}{5}$ 4. $\frac{4}{7} \bullet \frac{3}{7}$

5.

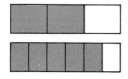

6.

$\frac{2}{3} = \frac{\blacksquare}{6}$ so $\frac{2}{3} \bullet \frac{5}{6}$

$\frac{3}{4} = \frac{\blacksquare}{8}$ so $\frac{3}{4} \bullet \frac{5}{8}$

7. $\frac{1}{2} \bullet \frac{7}{10}$ 8. $\frac{5}{16} \bullet \frac{3}{8}$ 9. $\frac{3}{5} \bullet \frac{8}{15}$ 10. $\frac{1}{9} \bullet \frac{2}{27}$

11. $\frac{1}{2} \bullet \frac{2}{5}$ 12. $\frac{7}{9} \bullet \frac{5}{6}$ 13. $\frac{3}{10} \bullet \frac{4}{15}$ 14. $\frac{5}{8} \bullet \frac{3}{5}$

Rewrite the fractions in each set with a common denominator. Order the fractions from least to greatest.

15. $\left\{ \frac{3}{5}, \frac{7}{10}, \frac{1}{2} \right\}$ 16. $\left\{ \frac{9}{14}, \frac{1}{2}, \frac{5}{7} \right\}$

17. $\left\{ \frac{1}{3}, \frac{3}{4}, \frac{5}{6}, \frac{1}{2}, \frac{2}{3} \right\}$ 18. $\left\{ \frac{3}{10}, \frac{4}{5}, \frac{1}{2}, \frac{1}{3}, \frac{5}{6}, \frac{7}{10}, \frac{2}{5} \right\}$

Copy and compare. Use > or <.

1. $\frac{5}{6} \bullet \frac{2}{3}$

2. $\frac{5}{7} \bullet \frac{3}{7}$

3. $\frac{7}{8} \bullet \frac{5}{6}$

4. $\frac{3}{5} \bullet \frac{5}{8}$

5. $\frac{2}{3} \bullet \frac{5}{7}$

6. $\frac{5}{24} \bullet \frac{3}{12}$

7. $\frac{11}{38} \bullet \frac{13}{38}$

8. $\frac{3}{10} \bullet \frac{25}{100}$

9. $\frac{7}{12} \bullet \frac{11}{15}$

10. $\frac{11}{14} \bullet \frac{5}{6}$

11. $\frac{7}{10} \bullet \frac{8}{12}$

12. $\frac{3}{5} \bullet \frac{8}{13}$

Order the fractions in each set, from least to greatest.

13. $\left\{\frac{2}{3}, \frac{5}{6}, \frac{9}{10}, \frac{4}{5}, \frac{3}{10}\right\}$

14. $\left\{\frac{3}{5}, \frac{3}{4}, \frac{4}{5}, \frac{7}{10}, \frac{13}{20}\right\}$

15. $\left\{\frac{9}{10}, \frac{2}{3}, \frac{8}{15}, \frac{5}{6}, \frac{4}{5}, \frac{7}{10}, \frac{13}{15}\right\}$

16. $\left\{\frac{2}{10}, \frac{3}{4}, \frac{1}{6}, \frac{3}{5}, \frac{11}{20}, \frac{8}{15}, \frac{17}{30}\right\}$

Solve.

17. Which is more, $\frac{4}{5}$ of an hour or $\frac{3}{4}$ of an hour?

18. During the bowling tournament, Jim scored $\frac{2}{5}$ of the team's points. Lisa scored $\frac{1}{3}$ of the points. Who scored more points?

19. John divided his chocolate bar into 12 pieces and gave Bert 5. Barb divided hers into 10 pieces and gave Bert 3. Who gave the largest fraction of his bar to Bert?

20. At the end of one hour at the school bowlathon, Debbie had reached $\frac{3}{8}$ of her goal. Donna had reached $\frac{5}{12}$ of her goal, and Joanna had reached $\frac{1}{3}$ of her goal. Who had reached the most of her goal. Who had the furthest to go?

Fraction Shortcut

Tom thinks he has discovered an easy way to find a fraction between two others by adding the numerators and denominators of the two given fractions.

Use Tom's discovery to find fractions between these pairs of fractions. Write your answers in simplest terms. Does Tom's shortcut work?

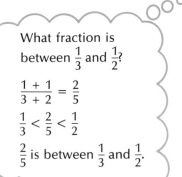

What fraction is between $\frac{1}{3}$ and $\frac{1}{2}$?

$\frac{1+1}{3+2} = \frac{2}{5}$

$\frac{1}{3} < \frac{2}{5} < \frac{1}{2}$

$\frac{2}{5}$ is between $\frac{1}{3}$ and $\frac{1}{2}$.

a. $\frac{1}{2}, \frac{1}{4}$

b. $\frac{3}{7}, \frac{5}{9}$

c. $\frac{1}{3}, \frac{5}{7}$

d. $\frac{6}{17}, \frac{15}{32}$

e. $\frac{1}{10}, \frac{98}{100}$

Mixed Numerals

A **mixed numeral** is a numeral made up of a whole number and a fraction.

This is how the *mixed numeral* $2\frac{3}{4}$ is changed to the *fraction* $\frac{11}{4}$.

$2 + \frac{3}{4} = 2\frac{3}{4}$

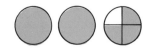

$2\frac{3}{4} = \frac{(2 \times 4) + 3}{4}$

$\frac{4}{4} + \frac{4}{4} + \frac{3}{4} = \frac{11}{4}$

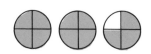

$2\frac{3}{4} = \frac{8 + 3}{4}$

$2\frac{3}{4} = \frac{11}{4}$

This is how the *fraction* $\frac{7}{3}$ is changed to the *mixed numeral* $2\frac{1}{3}$.

$\frac{7}{3} = \frac{3}{3} + \frac{3}{3} + \frac{1}{3}$

$\frac{7}{3} \rightarrow 3\overline{)7}$

$2\frac{1}{3} = 2 + \frac{1}{3}$

$\frac{7}{3} = 2\frac{1}{3}$

EXERCISES

Write each as a mixed numeral and as a fraction.

1.   **2.**   **3.**

4.
```
+--+--+--+--●--+--+--+→
0        1        2
```

5.
```
←+++++++++++++++++++●+→
  0     1     2     3
```

Write the fractions as mixed numerals.

6. $\frac{5}{3}$ **7.** $\frac{12}{5}$ **8.** $\frac{7}{4}$ **9.** $\frac{9}{2}$ **10.** $\frac{11}{6}$

Write the mixed numerals as fractions.

11. $1\frac{2}{3}$ **12.** $3\frac{1}{2}$ **13.** $2\frac{3}{5}$ **14.** $4\frac{5}{6}$ **15.** $5\frac{3}{7}$

Copy and compare. Use > or <.

16. $2\frac{3}{5} \bullet \frac{11}{5}$ **17.** $\frac{19}{3} \bullet 5\frac{2}{3}$ **18.** $3\frac{1}{4} \bullet \frac{14}{4}$ **19.** $3\frac{1}{8} \bullet \frac{10}{3}$

PRACTICE

Copy and compare. Use > or <.

1. $3\frac{2}{3}$ ● $\frac{10}{3}$

2. $5\frac{3}{4}$ ● $\frac{27}{4}$

3. $\frac{17}{5}$ ● $3\frac{4}{5}$

4. $\frac{15}{8}$ ● $1\frac{3}{8}$

Draw a number line for each. Then mark the sets of numbers on the number line.

5. $\left\{\frac{1}{2}, 3\frac{1}{2}, \frac{3}{2}\right\}$

6. $\left\{\frac{5}{3}, \frac{9}{6}, 2\frac{2}{3}\right\}$

Solve.

7. Sue and Pam estimate that it will take them $\frac{1}{4}$ hour to practise each tennis stroke that they have learned. How long should they plan to spend at the courts if they practise their forehand, backhand, serve, volley, and lob?

REVIEW

Name each lettered point on the number lines.

1.
2.
3.

Copy and complete.

4. $\frac{5}{6} = \frac{\blacksquare}{30}$

5. $\frac{9}{14} = \frac{27}{\blacksquare}$

6. $\frac{8}{15} = \frac{32}{\blacksquare}$

7. $\frac{3}{5} = \frac{\blacksquare}{35}$

Write each fraction in simplest terms.

8. $\frac{16}{24}$

9. $\frac{28}{42}$

10. $\frac{14}{32}$

11. $\frac{24}{36}$

12. $\frac{44}{110}$

Copy and compare. Use > or <.

13. $\frac{3}{8}$ ● $\frac{2}{5}$

14. $\frac{7}{9}$ ● $\frac{2}{3}$

15. $\frac{5}{12}$ ● $\frac{1}{2}$

16. $\frac{15}{18}$ ● $\frac{11}{12}$

Write each mixed numeral as a fraction.

17. $3\frac{2}{5}$

18. $4\frac{3}{7}$

19. $5\frac{1}{2}$

20. $6\frac{7}{8}$

Write each as a mixed numeral.

21. $\frac{37}{6}$

22. $\frac{31}{8}$

23. $\frac{23}{9}$

24. $\frac{13}{5}$

Fractions to Decimals

School Batting Records					
Players	Hits	Times at Bat	Fraction	Decimal	Batting Average
Sandra	2	5	$\frac{2}{5}$	0.4	0.400
Paul	3	8	$\frac{3}{8}$	0.375	0.375
Henry	4	9	$\frac{4}{9}$	0.444... or $0.\overline{4}$	0.444

There are two ways to change a *fraction* to a *decimal*.

Method 1:
Change the fraction to an equivalent fraction in tenths, hundredths, or thousandths.

$$\frac{2}{5} = \frac{2 \times 2}{5 \times 2} = \frac{4}{10}$$

Rewrite the fraction as a decimal.

$$\frac{4}{10} = 0.4$$

Method 2:
Divide the fraction's numerator by its denominator.

terminating decimal

$$\frac{3}{8} = \begin{array}{r} 0.375 \\ 8)\overline{3.000} \\ -2\ 4 \\ \hline 60 \\ -56 \\ \hline 40 \\ -40 \\ \hline 0 \end{array}$$

repeating decimal

$$\frac{4}{9} = \begin{array}{r} 0.444 \\ 9)\overline{4.000} \\ -3\ 6 \\ \hline 40 \\ -36 \\ \hline 40 \\ -36 \\ \hline 4 \end{array} \text{ or } 0.\overline{4}$$

EXERCISES

Write as a fraction with a denominator of 10, 100, or 1000.
Then rewrite as a decimal.

1. $\frac{4}{5}$
2. $\frac{27}{50}$
3. $\frac{127}{500}$
4. $\frac{9}{20}$
5. $\frac{3}{2}$

Divide to change the fraction to a *terminating* decimal.

6. $\frac{5}{8}$
7. $\frac{3}{4}$
8. $\frac{11}{25}$
9. $\frac{9}{15}$
10. $\frac{17}{4}$

Divide to change the fraction to a *repeating* decimal.
Draw a bar over the repeating pattern.

11. $\frac{1}{3}$
12. $\frac{1}{6}$
13. $\frac{2}{3}$
14. $\frac{7}{9}$
15. $\frac{5}{11}$

PRACTICE

Write as decimals.

1. $\frac{6}{10}$ 2. $\frac{21}{100}$ 3. $\frac{179}{100}$ 4. $\frac{696}{1000}$ 5. $\frac{283}{1000}$

6. $\frac{3}{4}$ 7. $\frac{7}{8}$ 8. $\frac{4}{50}$ 9. $\frac{7}{2}$ 10. $\frac{9}{12}$

11. $\frac{21}{5}$ 12. $\frac{19}{19}$ 13. $\frac{11}{16}$ 14. $\frac{5}{7}$ 15. $\frac{5}{9}$

Copy and compare. Use <, =, or >.

16. $\frac{1}{2}$ ● 0.2   17. $\frac{1}{3}$ ● 0.3   18. $\frac{5}{8}$ ● 0.8

Write as decimals rounded to the nearest thousandth.

19. $\frac{5}{6}$ 20. $\frac{5}{9}$ 21. $\frac{4}{11}$ 22. $\frac{8}{15}$ 23. $\frac{21}{6}$

Solve.

24. What is the batting average of each base-ball player in the table at the right?

25. Donovan had a batting average of 0.309. Peter had 9 hits in 28 times at bat. Who had the better batting average?

Players	Hits	At Bats	Average
Tom	25	40	
Rhonda	15	60	
Sue	33	48	
Bill	36	96	

Calculator Corner

You can use a calculator to change fractions into decimals.

$\frac{5}{8}$ [5] [÷] [8] [=]   =   0.625

$\frac{2}{9}$ [2] [÷] [9] [=]   =   0.222 222 22 ...

$3\frac{5}{16}$ [5] [÷] [1] [6] [+] [3] [=]   3.3125

Change these to decimals on a calculator.

a. $\frac{3}{4}$ b. $\frac{3}{16}$ c. $\frac{11}{5}$ d. $6\frac{7}{8}$ e. $3\frac{9}{25}$

Use a calculator to compare these fractions as decimals.

f. $\frac{3}{5}$ ● $\frac{8}{13}$ g. $\frac{2}{3}$ ● $\frac{5}{7}$ h. $\frac{3}{7}$ ● $\frac{5}{9}$ i. $\frac{5}{8}$ ● $\frac{4}{7}$ j. $2\frac{2}{5}$ ● $\frac{10}{3}$

203

Decimals to Fractions

Both *terminating decimals* and *repeating decimals* can be rewritten as *fractions*.

Terminating Decimals to Fractions

The place value of the last digit tells you the denominator.

Simplify the fraction.

tenths

$$0.8 \quad = \quad \frac{8}{10} \quad = \quad \boxed{\frac{4}{5}}$$

hundredths

$$0.42 \quad = \quad \frac{42}{100} \quad = \quad \boxed{\frac{21}{50}}$$

thousandths

$$0.625 \quad = \quad \frac{625}{1000} \quad = \quad \boxed{\frac{5}{8}}$$

Repeating Decimals to Fractions

Look for patterns.

thirds

$$0.333 \ldots \quad (0.\bar{3}) \quad = \quad \frac{1}{3}$$
$$0.666 \ldots \quad (0.\bar{6}) \quad = \quad \frac{2}{3}$$

ninths

$$0.111 \ldots \quad (0.\bar{1}) \quad = \quad \frac{1}{9}$$
$$0.222 \ldots \quad (0.\bar{2}) \quad = \quad \frac{2}{9}$$
$$0.333 \ldots \quad (0.\bar{3}) \quad = \quad \frac{3}{9}$$
$$0.444 \ldots \quad (0.\bar{4}) \quad = \quad \frac{4}{9}$$

EXERCISES

Write as a *fraction* or *mixed numeral* in simplest terms.

1. $0.3 = \frac{\blacksquare}{10}$ 2. 0.7 3. 0.1 4. 2.9

5. $0.4 = \frac{\blacksquare}{10} = \frac{\blacksquare}{\blacksquare}$ 6. 0.5 7. 0.2 8. 1.8

9. $0.21 = \frac{\blacksquare}{100}$ 10. 0.99 11. 0.57 12. 4.13

13. $0.35 = \frac{\blacksquare}{100} = \frac{\blacksquare}{\blacksquare}$ 14. 0.28 15. 0.08 16. 2.45

17. $0.427 = \frac{\blacksquare}{1000}$ 18. 0.893 19. 0.311 20. 7.209

21. $0.375 = \frac{\blacksquare}{1000} = \frac{\blacksquare}{\blacksquare}$ 22. 0.250 23. 0.025 24. 3.002

25. $0.\bar{3}$ 26. $0.\bar{6}$ 27. $0.\bar{4}$ 28. $0.\bar{2}$ 29. $0.\bar{8}$

Copy the number lines. Write the fraction and decimal equivalents for each mark on the number line.

30.

31.

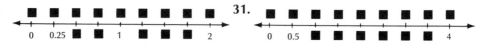

204

PRACTICE

Write as a fraction or mixed numeral in simplest terms.

1. 0.7
2. 0.6
3. 0.75
4. 3.25
5. 0.8

6. 0.65
7. 0.86
8. 4.72
9. 3.2
10. 4.5

11. 0.451
12. 7.101
13. 0.9
14. 0.200
15. 1.48

16. 0.125
17. 0.04
18. 0.006
19. 4.600
20. 10.4

21. 0.045
22. 0.875
23. 3.625
24. 4.72
25. 0.255

26. $0.\overline{7}$
27. $0.\overline{5}$
28. $0.\overline{1}$
29. $8.\overline{8}$
30. $2.\overline{8}$

31. Write $0.\overline{9}$ as a fraction in simplest terms. (Surprised?)

Copy the number line. Write the fraction and decimal equivalents for each mark on the number line.

32.

33.

Repeating Patterns

Use a calculator to divide and change these fractions to decimals.

Look for patterns.

a. $\frac{47}{99}$
b. $\frac{83}{99}$
c. $\frac{7}{99}$
d. $\frac{62}{99}$

e. $\frac{842}{999}$
f. $\frac{176}{999}$
g. $\frac{36}{999}$
h. $\frac{8}{999}$

i. $\frac{2765}{9999}$
j. $\frac{7382}{9999}$
k. $\frac{46\,531}{99\,999}$
l. $\frac{17\,418}{99\,999}$

Remember the patterns above as you change these decimals to fractions. Use a calculator to check.

m. $0.\overline{32}$
n. $0.\overline{57}$
o. $0.\overline{09}$
p. $0.\overline{70}$
q. $0.\overline{328}$

r. $0.\overline{493}$
s. $0.\overline{685}$
t. $0.\overline{007}$
u. $0.\overline{5912}$
v. $0.\overline{3877}$

Adding Fractions < 1

At a football game, Tim threw a pass that travelled $\frac{3}{10}$ of the length of the field and Scott kicked the ball $\frac{1}{4}$ of the length of the field. What fraction of the field did the kick and pass travel in all?

Different denominators.

$$\frac{3}{10}$$
$$+\frac{1}{4}$$

Find the **least common denominator (LCD)** of 10 and 4.

$$10 = 2 \qquad \times 5$$
$$4 = 2 \times 2$$
$$LCD = 2 \times 2 \times 5$$

$$LCD = 20$$

Write equivalent fractions with the LCD.

$$\frac{3}{10} = \frac{6}{20}$$
$$+\frac{1}{4} = \frac{5}{20}$$

Add.

$$\frac{6}{20}$$
$$+\frac{5}{20}$$
$$\frac{11}{20}$$

The kick and pass travelled over $\frac{11}{20}$ of the field.

> Add fractions with the same denominator.

EXERCISES

Write the LCD for these pairs of fractions.

1. $\frac{3}{8}, \frac{1}{4}$ 2. $\frac{5}{6}, \frac{2}{3}$ 3. $\frac{7}{8}, \frac{5}{12}$ 4. $\frac{2}{15}, \frac{7}{10}$

Add. Write the sum in simplest terms.

5. $\frac{3}{8} + \frac{1}{8}$ 6. $\frac{3}{10} + \frac{5}{10}$ 7. $\frac{5}{12} + \frac{4}{12}$ 8. $\frac{2}{7} + \frac{4}{7}$

9. $\frac{1}{2} = \frac{\blacksquare}{\blacksquare}$
   $+\frac{1}{4} = +\frac{\blacksquare}{\blacksquare}$

10. $\frac{3}{8}$
    $+\frac{1}{4}$

11. $\frac{1}{8}$
    $+\frac{3}{10}$

12. $\frac{1}{6}$
    $+\frac{1}{4}$

13. $\frac{3}{8}$
    $+\frac{1}{6}$

14. $\frac{7}{15}$ ✓
    $+\frac{7}{10}$ ✓

15. $\frac{5}{9}$
    $+\frac{5}{6}$

16. $\frac{3}{5}$ ✓
    $+\frac{2}{3}$ ✓

17. $\frac{1}{3} + \frac{1}{6}$ 18. $\frac{5}{18} + \frac{2}{9}$ 19. $\frac{3}{8} + \frac{5}{12}$ 20. $\frac{3}{10} + \frac{7}{15}$

PRACTICE

Add. Write the sum in simplest terms.

1. $\dfrac{2}{9}$ $+\dfrac{3}{9}$

2. $\dfrac{2}{6}$ $+\dfrac{3}{6}$

3. $\dfrac{2}{3}$ $+\dfrac{1}{5}$

4. $\dfrac{5}{9}$ $+\dfrac{1}{4}$

5. $\dfrac{3}{4}$ $+\dfrac{1}{8}$

6. $\dfrac{2}{10} + \dfrac{3}{10}$

7. $\dfrac{3}{8} + \dfrac{3}{6}$

8. $\dfrac{2}{9} + \dfrac{4}{9}$

9. $\dfrac{1}{2} + \dfrac{4}{10}$

10. $\dfrac{5}{18} + \dfrac{5}{12}$

11. $\dfrac{8}{15} + \dfrac{7}{20}$

12. $\dfrac{5}{16} + \dfrac{11}{24}$

13. $\dfrac{17}{30} + \dfrac{7}{20}$

14. $\dfrac{3}{10} + \dfrac{1}{10} + \dfrac{2}{10}$

15. $\dfrac{1}{3} + \dfrac{1}{4} + \dfrac{1}{6}$

16. $\dfrac{1}{3} + \dfrac{1}{5} + \dfrac{2}{10} + \dfrac{2}{15}$

17. $\dfrac{1}{6} + \dfrac{1}{27} + \dfrac{1}{9} + \dfrac{1}{3}$

Solve.

18. During the football game, Don played the first two quarters and the last quarter. What fraction of the game did he play?

19. The best pass receiver at the football game caught 2 passes and ran for a touchdown. After the first pass, he ran down $\dfrac{1}{2}$ of the field. After the second pass, he ran down $\dfrac{1}{10}$ of the field. What fraction of the field did he run in all?

Egyptian Fractions

The ancient Egyptians used only *unit fractions* (fractions that have numerators of 1).

$\dfrac{1}{5} = $ ⎼⎼⎼ $\dfrac{1}{12} = $ ⎼⎼⎼

They wrote other fractions as the sums of unit fractions.

$\dfrac{4}{9} = $ ⎼⎼⎼ $= \dfrac{1}{3} + \dfrac{1}{9}$

Write each as the sum of unit fractions.
Then write each using Egyptian symbols. (See page 184).

a. $\dfrac{3}{8}$

b. $\dfrac{7}{10}$

c. $\dfrac{11}{12}$

d. $\dfrac{5}{6}$

207

Subtracting Fractions < 1

Marcella practised the piano for $\frac{3}{4}$ of an hour.
Joanne practised for $\frac{5}{6}$ of an hour. What fraction
of an hour longer did Joanne practise?

Different denominators.

$$\frac{5}{6}$$
$$-\frac{3}{4}$$

Find the **LCD** of 6 and 4.

$$6 = 2 \qquad \times 3$$
$$4 = 2 \times 2$$
$$LCD = 2 \times 2 \times 3$$
$$LCD = 12$$

Write equivalent fractions with the **LCD**.

$$\frac{5}{6} = \frac{10}{12}$$
$$-\frac{3}{4} = \frac{9}{12}$$

Subtract.

$$\frac{10}{12}$$
$$-\frac{9}{12}$$
$$\frac{1}{12}$$

Joanne practised $\frac{1}{12}$ of an hour longer (or 5 min).

Subtract fractions with the same denominator.

EXERCISES

Write the LCD for these pairs of fractions.

1. $\frac{5}{8}, \frac{7}{24}$
2. $\frac{5}{6}, \frac{2}{9}$
3. $\frac{8}{11}, \frac{3}{7}$
4. $\frac{3}{16}, \frac{5}{12}$

Subtract. Write the difference in simplest terms.

5. $\frac{5}{6} - \frac{1}{6}$
6. $\frac{7}{10} - \frac{3}{10}$
7. $\frac{5}{8} - \frac{2}{8}$
8. $\frac{11}{12} - \frac{5}{12}$

9. $\frac{1}{3} = \frac{\blacksquare}{\blacksquare}$
$-\frac{1}{6} = -\frac{\blacksquare}{\blacksquare}$

10. $\frac{7}{10}$
$-\frac{2}{5}$

11. $\frac{5}{6}$
$-\frac{3}{4}$

12. $\frac{5}{8}$
$-\frac{7}{12}$

13. $\frac{8}{9}$
$-\frac{1}{6}$

14. $\frac{5}{6}$
$-\frac{3}{8}$

15. $\frac{7}{12}$
$-\frac{1}{16}$

16. $\frac{3}{4}$
$-\frac{1}{2}$

17. $\frac{8}{9} - \frac{3}{5}$
18. $\frac{5}{6} - \frac{2}{3}$
19. $\frac{5}{7} - \frac{3}{10}$
20. $\frac{7}{8} - \frac{3}{10}$

PRACTICE

Subtract. Write the difference in simplest terms.

1. $\dfrac{3}{8}$ $-\dfrac{1}{8}$

2. $\dfrac{5}{7}$ $-\dfrac{2}{7}$

3. $\dfrac{5}{6}$ $-\dfrac{1}{3}$

4. $\dfrac{7}{12}$ $-\dfrac{2}{6}$

5. $\dfrac{3}{4}$ $-\dfrac{7}{10}$

6. $\dfrac{3}{4} - \dfrac{5}{7}$

7. $\dfrac{7}{10} - \dfrac{12}{25}$ ✓

8. $\dfrac{5}{7} - \dfrac{2}{5}$

9. $\dfrac{11}{16} - \dfrac{5}{12}$

10. $\dfrac{5}{9} - \dfrac{3}{8}$

11. $\dfrac{11}{12} - \dfrac{5}{16}$

12. $\dfrac{7}{8} - \dfrac{1}{12}$

13. $\dfrac{11}{18} - \dfrac{5}{12}$ ✓

14. $\left(\dfrac{11}{12} - \dfrac{5}{12}\right) - \dfrac{1}{12}$

15. $\left(\dfrac{3}{4} - \dfrac{1}{6}\right) - \dfrac{1}{3}$ ✓

16. $\dfrac{3}{5} - \left(\dfrac{3}{4} - \dfrac{1}{2}\right)$

17. $\left(\dfrac{9}{10} - \dfrac{2}{5}\right) - \dfrac{1}{3}$

Solve.

18. Ken scored $\dfrac{1}{3}$ of the points in the game and Don scored $\dfrac{1}{2}$ of the points.
    a. What fraction of the points did they score together?
    b. What fraction more did Don score then Ken?

19. Out of one hour on the radio, there were 37 min of rock music played, 5 min of news, 3 min of weather, 13 min of commercials, and 2 min of public service announcements.
    a. What fraction of the time was news and commercials?
    b. What fraction of the time was news and weather?
    c. What fraction of the time was not music?

Decimal Detour on Fraction Freeway

Use a calculator to complete these problems as decimals.

a. $\dfrac{7}{10} - \dfrac{2}{5}$ b. $\dfrac{1}{4} + \dfrac{3}{10}$ c. $\dfrac{3}{4} - \dfrac{1}{8}$

Now change your decimal answers to fractions. Are your answers what they should be?

Adding Mixed Numerals

Gail played in the junior women's singles and the junior mixed doubles. The singles match took $1\frac{1}{2}$ hours and the doubles match took $1\frac{3}{4}$ hours. How long did she play?

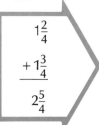

Different denominators.

$$1\frac{1}{2}$$
$$+1\frac{3}{4}$$

Write equivalent fraction with the **LCD**.

$$1\frac{1}{2} = 1\frac{2}{4}$$
$$+1\frac{3}{4} = +1\frac{3}{4}$$

Add.

$$1\frac{2}{4}$$
$$+1\frac{3}{4}$$
$$\overline{2\frac{5}{4}}$$

Regroup to simplify the sum.

$$2\frac{5}{4} = 2 + 1\frac{1}{4}$$
$$= 3\frac{1}{4}$$

Gail played for $3\frac{1}{4}$ hours.

EXERCISES

Treat each mixed numeral as a sum.
Regroup to simplify the sum.

1. $3\frac{7}{5} = 4\frac{\blacksquare}{5}$
2. $5\frac{8}{4} = 6\frac{\blacksquare}{4}$
3. $7\frac{9}{6} = 8\frac{\blacksquare}{6}$
4. $4\frac{8}{7} = 5\frac{\blacksquare}{7}$

5. $6\frac{9}{8} = 7\frac{\blacksquare}{\blacksquare}$
6. $11\frac{12}{10} = 12\frac{\blacksquare}{\blacksquare}$
7. $2\frac{7}{4} = 3\frac{\blacksquare}{\blacksquare}$
8. $1\frac{18}{9} = 2\frac{\blacksquare}{\blacksquare}$

Add. Write the sum in simplest terms.

9. $1\frac{5}{7}$
  $+2\frac{4}{7}$

10. $4\frac{3}{4}$
  $+3\frac{1}{4}$

11. $16\frac{3}{5}$
  $+\ 4\frac{1}{5}$

12. $7\frac{1}{9}$
  $+10\frac{5}{9}$

13. $8\frac{1}{6}$
  $+\ \ \frac{1}{6}$

14. $4\frac{3}{4}$
  $+3\frac{5}{12}$

15. $7\frac{9}{10}$
  $+2\frac{3}{5}$

16. $5\frac{7}{12}$
  $+7\frac{5}{8}$

17. $2\frac{2}{3}$
  $+5\frac{1}{4}$

18. $3\frac{7}{20}$
  $+12\frac{1}{30}$

19. $5\frac{7}{9} + 6\frac{5}{6}$

20. $11\frac{1}{8} + \frac{5}{6}$

21. $12\frac{11}{12} + 6\frac{5}{18}$

22. $1\frac{3}{25} + \frac{1}{2}$

PRACTICE

Add. Write the sum in simplest terms.

1. $5\frac{11}{15}$
   $+7\frac{14}{15}$

2. 7
   $+3\frac{5}{8}$

3. $13\frac{3}{4}$
   $+11\frac{11}{12}$

4. $7\frac{2}{3}$
   $+4\frac{5}{9}$

5. $7\frac{6}{9}$
   $+\ \frac{5}{6}$

6. $3\frac{3}{8} + 5\frac{5}{6}$

7. $7\frac{3}{10} + 8\frac{8}{10}$

8. $9\frac{7}{12} + 5\frac{5}{8}$

9. $2\frac{7}{10} + 5\frac{3}{4}$

10. $6\frac{3}{10} + 4\frac{7}{15}$

11. $5\frac{3}{9} + 2\frac{11}{18}$

12. $7\frac{9}{14} + 12\frac{11}{14}$

13. $8\frac{1}{2} + 3\frac{1}{11}$

14. $3\frac{7}{8} + 2\frac{1}{4} + 5\frac{1}{2}$

15. $4\frac{1}{3} + 2\frac{1}{2} + \frac{5}{6}$

16. $15 + 5\frac{3}{4} + 19\frac{5}{6} + \frac{3}{8}$

17. $7\frac{5}{9} + 12 + 1\frac{3}{4} + 2\frac{1}{6}$

Solve.

18. To train for the tennis tournament, Bob spends $\frac{1}{2}$ hour practising serves, $1\frac{1}{4}$ hours practising ground strokes, and $\frac{3}{4}$ hour running. How long in total does Bob train?

A Mixed Numeral Computer Program

Try this BASIC computer program.

```
10 PRINT "ENTER THE FIRST MIXED NUMBER"
20 INPUT "THE WHOLE NUMBER IS ";W1
30 INPUT "THE NUMBERATOR IS ";N1
40 INPUT "THE DENOMINATOR IS ";D1
50 PRINT "ENTER THE SECOND MIXED MUMBER"
60 INPUT "THE WHOLE NUMBER IS ";W2
70 INPUT "THE NUMERATOR IS ";N2
80 INPUT "THE DENOMINATOR IS ";D2
90 PRINT "THE DECIMAL SUM IS ";
100 PRINT W1+N1/D1+W2+N2/D2
110 GOTO 10
```

For $7\frac{1}{4} + 3\frac{3}{10}$, what would I type for W1? N1? D1? W2? N2? D2?

211

Subtracting Mixed Numerals

The Bovari family owns 2 cars. The older car is $4\frac{1}{2}$ years old. The newer car is $1\frac{3}{4}$ years old. What is the age difference of the 2 cars?

Different denominators.

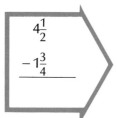

$$4\frac{1}{2}$$
$$-1\frac{3}{4}$$

Write equivalent fractions with the **LCD**.

$$4\frac{1}{2} = 4\frac{2}{4}$$
$$-1\frac{3}{4} = -1\frac{3}{4}$$

Regroup, so you can subtract.

$$4\frac{2}{4} = 3 + \frac{4}{4} + \frac{2}{4} = 3\frac{6}{4}$$
$$-1\frac{3}{4}$$

Subtract.

$$3\frac{6}{4}$$
$$-1\frac{3}{4}$$
$$2\frac{3}{4}$$

The age difference is $2\frac{3}{4}$ years.

EXERCISES

Regroup each mixed numeral.

1. $3\frac{2}{3} = 2\frac{\blacksquare}{3}$

2. $5\frac{7}{8} = 4\frac{\blacksquare}{8}$

3. $2\frac{1}{9} = 1\frac{\blacksquare}{9}$

4. $9\frac{3}{7} = 8\frac{\blacksquare}{7}$

5. $6\frac{3}{4} = 5\frac{\blacksquare}{\blacksquare}$

6. $5\frac{2}{7} = 4\frac{\blacksquare}{\blacksquare}$

7. $3\frac{7}{10} = 2\frac{\blacksquare}{\blacksquare}$

8. $10\frac{11}{15} = 9\frac{\blacksquare}{\blacksquare}$

Subtract. Write the difference in simplest terms.

9. $\quad 3\frac{5}{8}$
$\quad -1\frac{1}{8}$

10. $\quad 8\frac{7}{9}$
$\quad -2\frac{5}{9}$

11. $\quad 5\frac{1}{5}$
$\quad -2\frac{3}{4}$

12. $\quad 6\frac{2}{7}$
$\quad -3\frac{5}{7}$

13. $\quad 10\frac{7}{12}$
$\quad -6\frac{11}{12}$

14. $\quad 8$
$\quad -2\frac{3}{4}$

15. $\quad 10$
$\quad -5\frac{5}{9}$

16. $\quad 4$
$\quad -\frac{1}{3}$

17. $\quad 18$
$\quad -\frac{5}{21}$

18. $\quad 16$
$\quad -6\frac{7}{8}$

19. $5\frac{1}{3} - 2\frac{5}{6}$

20. $4\frac{3}{8} - 2\frac{1}{4}$

21. $6\frac{3}{10} - 4\frac{7}{15}$

22. $12\frac{3}{4} - 7\frac{4}{5}$

23. $12 - 5\frac{7}{8}$

24. $3\frac{1}{3} - \frac{5}{6}$

25. $42 - 35\frac{3}{5}$

26. $4 - \frac{5}{8}$

Add or subtract.

1. $4\frac{3}{7}$
   $-1\frac{5}{7}$

2. 9
   $-3\frac{2}{9}$

3. $10\frac{2}{3}$
   -6

4. 4
   $-\frac{6}{10}$

5. $3\frac{5}{9}$
   $-\frac{2}{3}$

6. $5\frac{1}{3} - 4\frac{2}{3}$

7. $12 - 6\frac{1}{2}$

8. $4\frac{3}{5} - 2\frac{3}{10}$

9. $3\frac{5}{9} - \frac{2}{3}$

10. $6\frac{7}{12} - 3\frac{5}{6}$

11. $8\frac{1}{6} - 2\frac{4}{9}$

12. $6\frac{5}{6} - 3\frac{1}{4}$

13. $11\frac{3}{8} - 3\frac{7}{12}$

14. $5\frac{1}{2} - 1\frac{1}{4} - 2$

15. $3\frac{1}{6} - \left(1\frac{1}{2} - 1\frac{1}{3}\right)$

16. $3\frac{5}{6} + 2\frac{1}{4} - 1\frac{2}{3}$

17. $3\frac{3}{10} - \left(5\frac{1}{2} - 3\frac{4}{5}\right)$

18. $\left(4\frac{1}{3} + 3\frac{5}{8}\right) - 5\frac{1}{6}$

19. $3\frac{7}{15} + \frac{2}{3} - 1\frac{3}{5}$

20. $5\frac{3}{4} + \left(4\frac{4}{5} - 3\frac{1}{10}\right)$

21. $7\frac{1}{3} - 1\frac{3}{4} + 2\frac{5}{6}$

Solve.

22. The senior women's tennis match took $3\frac{3}{4}$ hours. The junior women's match took $1\frac{1}{2}$ hours. How much longer did the senior women's match take?

23. Mr. Snyder plans to cook a ham for $4\frac{1}{2}$ hours. Then he will pour a sugar glaze over the ham and let it cook for $\frac{2}{3}$ hour more. For how many hours does the ham cook in all?

Another Way

Mixed numerals can be added and subtracted on a calculator. To add $3\frac{1}{2} + 2\frac{3}{4}$ on a calculator:

Step 1 [1] [÷] [2] [+] [3] [=] 3.5 [M+]

Step 2 [3] [÷] [4] [+] [2] [=] 2.75 [M+]

Step 3 [MR] 6.25

Step 4 $6.25 = 6\frac{25}{100} = 6\frac{1}{4}$

Try these:

a. $\frac{7}{10} + \frac{3}{5}$

b. $\frac{5}{8} - \frac{1}{4}$

c. $3\frac{1}{2} + 2\frac{4}{5}$

d. $5\frac{3}{8} - 2\frac{3}{5}$

Problem Solving

Michelle estimates that she spends $\frac{1}{6}$ of her time at a one-hour fitness class doing arm exercises and $\frac{1}{3}$ of her time doing calisthenics. The rest of her time is spent running.
What fraction of her time is spent running at the fitness class?

Decide.

Some problems require several computation steps.

Step 1:
Add to find the total time spent not running.

$$\frac{1}{6} + \frac{1}{3} = \frac{1}{6} + \frac{2}{6} = \frac{3}{6} \text{ or } \frac{1}{2} \text{ h}$$

Step 2:
Subtract to find the time spent running.

$$1 - \frac{1}{2} = \frac{1}{2} \text{ h}$$

Michelle spends $\frac{1}{2}$ of her time running in her fitness class.

EXERCISES

Solve.

1. In exhibition play, the Tigers football team scored a total of 56 points. Thirty of those points were scored on running plays and 12 of the points were scored on passing plays. The rest were scored on field goals and conversions.
   What fraction of the points were scored on running plays? On passing plays? On field goals and conversions?

2. In the gymnastics meet, Cheryl lost $\frac{4}{10}$ of a point on one fault and $\frac{3}{10}$ of a point on a second fault. How much did she lose altogether? If the maximum score is 10, what was her score?

3. Hockey games are split into 3 periods of equal length. Don scored a goal halfway through the first period. What fraction of the whole game had passed before he scored?

Solve.

1. At the start of the season, the Rockets played 14 periods of hockey without allowing a goal. How many games is this?

2. Maurice scored one goal in $\frac{1}{4}$ of the games he played and he scored 2 goals in $\frac{1}{6}$ of the games he played. What is the least number of games that he could have played?

3. In ringette, Debbie allowed 5 goals in 8 games. Stacey allowed 7 goals in 10 games. Express each of these as a decimal. Who has allowed fewer goals per game on the average?

4. At the orienteering meet, John is allowed 60 s to complete 3 events. He makes 1 point for every tenth of a second that he is under the 60 s. He spends $18\frac{1}{2}$ seconds copying a map, $26\frac{3}{5}$ seconds finding a first flag, and $13\frac{1}{10}$ seconds returning to the start. How many points does he make?

Write the fractions as decimals.

1. $\frac{8}{100}$ 2. $\frac{1}{4}$ 3. $\frac{3}{8}$ 4. $\frac{14}{25}$ 5. $\frac{1}{3}$

Write the decimals as fractions in simplest terms.

6. 0.9   7. 0.75   8. 0.65   9. 0.057   10. 0.125

Add. Write the sum in simplest terms.

11. $\frac{2}{3} + \frac{1}{4}$ 12. $\frac{1}{9} + \frac{2}{5}$ 13. $\frac{3}{7} + \frac{1}{6}$

Subtract. Write the difference in simplest terms.

14. $\frac{11}{12} - \frac{2}{10}$ 15. $\frac{5}{8} - \frac{1}{6}$ 16. $\frac{5}{6} - \frac{4}{9}$

Add. Write the sum in simplest terms.

17. $3\frac{1}{2} + 2\frac{2}{5}$ 18. $1\frac{5}{7} + \frac{9}{14}$ 19. $4\frac{3}{4} + 1\frac{2}{5}$

Subtract. Write the difference in simplest terms.

20. $15 - 4\frac{7}{8}$ 21. $2\frac{3}{10} - \frac{3}{4}$ 22. $8\frac{1}{12} - 7\frac{4}{15}$

The Stock Market

1984 High	1984 Low	Stock	Day's High	Day's Low	Day's Close	Change From Yesterday's Close
47	$31\frac{1}{2}$	Super Save Co.	$47	$46	$47\frac{3}{4}$	$+1\frac{7}{8}$
$20\frac{3}{8}$	$16\frac{5}{8}$	E-Z Computers	$19\frac{1}{4}$	$19	$19	$-\frac{1}{4}$
27	18	Canada Tours	$21\frac{5}{8}$	$21\frac{1}{4}$	$21\frac{1}{4}$	$-\frac{3}{4}$
9	$5\frac{1}{2}$	Lite Power Co.	$8\frac{7}{8}$	$8\frac{3}{4}$	$8\frac{7}{8}$	$+\frac{1}{8}$
$17\frac{1}{8}$	$12\frac{1}{4}$	BC Parts	$15	$14\frac{5}{8}$	$14\frac{5}{8}$	$-\frac{3}{8}$

Table heading: STOCK EXCHANGE QUOTATIONS

1. What was the cost of one share of stock for each company at the close of the day in dollars and cents?

2. What was the cost of one share of stock for each company on the previous day in dollars and cents?

3. In dollars and cents, how much did each stock go up or down from yesterday's closing to today's closing?

4. At this time, which stock is selling for more than its yearly high?

Foods of the World

The three graphs below show the fractions of cereals, animal products, and other kinds of foods in the diets of people from three world regions.

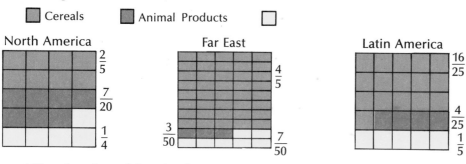

■ Cereals   ■ Animal Products   □

North America

$\frac{2}{5}$
$\frac{7}{20}$
$\frac{1}{4}$

Far East

$\frac{4}{5}$
$\frac{3}{50}$
$\frac{7}{50}$

Latin America

$\frac{16}{25}$
$\frac{4}{25}$
$\frac{1}{5}$

1. What fraction of the North American diet consists of cereals and animal products? the Far Eastern diet? the Latin American diet?

2. How much more of the North American diet consists of cereals than animal products?

Symmetrical Figures from Repeating Decimals

The decimal equivalents for the set of fractions $\left\{\frac{1}{7}, \frac{2}{7}, \frac{3}{7}, \frac{4}{7}, \frac{5}{7}, \frac{6}{7}\right\}$ form repeating, 6-digit patterns.

For example: $\frac{1}{7} = 0.142\,857\,142\,857 \ldots = 0.\overline{142\,857}$

The sevenths' repeating decimal patterns form symmetrical figures.

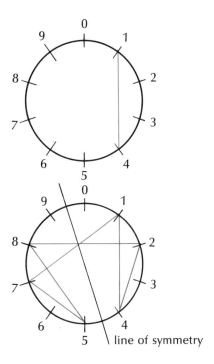

To make the symmetrical figure:

a. Draw a circle with a protractor and put a mark every 36°.

b. Number the 10 marks from 0 to 9.

c. Draw a chord connecting the first two digits of the decimal pattern.

For example: $\frac{1}{7} = 0.\overline{142\,857}$
↟↟

d. Connect the remaining decimal pattern numbers in order.

1. Find the symmetrical figure formed by all of the sevenths in the set above.

2. Find the symmetrical figure formed by $\frac{1}{13}$, $\frac{2}{13}$, and $\frac{3}{13}$.

line of symmetry

Fraction Patterns on a Computer

Computers are often used to perform repetitive calculations. Try the BASIC program below.

a. What does the program do?

b. How would you change the program to print the fraction *before* the decimal?

For example: $\frac{2}{3} = 0.666\,666\,666$

```
10 PRINT "PICK A DENOMINATOR ";
20 INPUT D
30 FOR N = 1 TO D
40 PRINT N/D
50 NEXT N
60 GOTO 10
```

Write a fraction or mixed numeral for each letter in simplest terms.

1.

2.

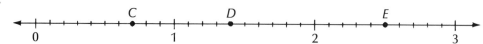

Copy and complete.

3. $\frac{3}{4} = \frac{\blacksquare}{28}$ **4.** $\frac{5}{9} = \frac{15}{\blacksquare}$ **5.** $\frac{7}{\blacksquare} = \frac{63}{81}$ **6.** $\frac{7}{20} = \frac{\blacksquare}{100}$

Write the fraction in simplest terms.

7. $\frac{30}{66}$ **8.** $\frac{36}{45}$ **9.** $\frac{48}{72}$ **10.** $\frac{40}{50}$ **11.** $\frac{52}{70}$

Copy and compare. Use > or <.

12. $\frac{7}{10} \bullet \frac{7}{8}$ **13.** $\frac{7}{8} \bullet \frac{9}{10}$ **14.** $\frac{5}{12} \bullet \frac{7}{15}$ **15.** $\frac{1}{8} \bullet \frac{2}{12}$

Change the fraction to a mixed numeral in simplest terms.

16. $\frac{11}{5}$ **17.** $\frac{7}{3}$ **18.** $\frac{28}{6}$ **19.** $\frac{42}{7}$ **20.** $\frac{33}{15}$

Change the mixed numeral to a fraction.

21. $3\frac{1}{4}$ **22.** $5\frac{2}{7}$ **23.** $3\frac{8}{10}$ **24.** $4\frac{13}{15}$ **25.** $15\frac{5}{6}$

Write the fraction as a decimal.

26. $\frac{7}{8}$ **27.** $\frac{17}{20}$ **28.** $\frac{13}{40}$ **29.** $\frac{7}{20}$ **30.** $\frac{2}{3}$

Write the decimal as a fraction in simplest terms.

31. 0.6   **32.** 0.18   **33.** 0.03   **34.** 0.075   **35.** 0.750

Add or subtract. Write the answer in simplest terms.

36. $\frac{3}{5} + \frac{1}{4}$ **37.** $\frac{5}{8} + \frac{1}{12}$ **38.** $\frac{2}{7} + \frac{2}{9}$ **39.** $\frac{5}{9} - \frac{1}{6}$

40. $\frac{7}{10} - \frac{3}{5}$ **41.** $\frac{5}{6} - \frac{4}{9}$ **42.** $2\frac{3}{5} + \frac{7}{12}$ **43.** $6\frac{11}{18} + \frac{11}{12}$

44. $3\frac{5}{7} + 5\frac{3}{4}$ **45.** $6\frac{1}{6} - 2\frac{4}{9}$ **46.** $5\frac{3}{8} - \frac{7}{10}$ **47.** $17 - 6\frac{3}{7}$

Number Theory

Is 386 415 divisible by the number?

1. 2   **2.** 3   **3.** 4   **4.** 5   **5.** 9

Which of the following numbers are factors of 135?

6. {1, 2, 3, 4, 5, 6, 7, 8, 9, 12, 15, 16, 18, 25, 27, 35}

Write the set of factors for each.

7. 18   **8.** 45   **9.** 56   **10.** 110   **11.** 200

Is the number prime or composite?

12. 13   **13.** 9   **14.** 51   **15.** 73   **16.** 95

Use a factor tree to write each as a product of prime factors.

17. 78   **18.** 118   **19.** 140   **20.** 256   **21.** 600

Find the GCF.

22. 70 and 105   **23.** 102 and 170   **24.** 225 and 375

Which of the following numbers are multiples of 12?

25. {0, 2, 4, 6, 12, 28, 36, 60, 82, 96, 108, 112, 132}

List the first five multiples of each.

26. 4   **27.** 9   **28.** 15   **29.** 25   **30.** 32

Find the LCM.

31. 15 and 12   **32.** 14 and 21   **33.** 24 and 36

Solve.

34. Fran has to have the oil changed in her new car every 12 000 km and the engine tuned every 15 000 km.

    How far will Fran have to drive before she has the oil changed and the engine tuned up at the same time?

35. Mr. Walsh is packing food for his outdoors-club hike. He packs 18 fruit drinks, 24 sandwiches, and 42 oranges. Each member of the club receives the same amount of each type of food. What is the largest number of people that could be on the hike?

UNIT 9   Fractions II

Multiplying With Fractions

Doug's family grows alfalfa on $\frac{2}{3}$ of their farm land. Their farm land consists of four fields. Each field is 1 ha. How much of their farm land is used to grow alfalfa?

$$\frac{2}{3} \text{ of } 4 = \text{farm land used to grow alfalfa}$$

$\frac{2}{3}$ of 4	means the same as	$\frac{2}{3} + \frac{2}{3} + \frac{2}{3} + \frac{2}{3}$ or $\frac{2}{3} \times 4$

$$\frac{2}{3} \times 4 = \frac{2}{3} + \frac{2}{3} + \frac{2}{3} + \frac{2}{3}$$
$$= \frac{2 \times 4}{3} = \frac{8}{3} = 2\frac{2}{3}$$

Doug's family grows alfalfa on $2\frac{2}{3}$ ha of their land.

Multiply. Write the product in simplest terms.

1.

   $\frac{1}{4}$ of 5

2.

   $\frac{4}{5}$ of 2

3.

   $\frac{1}{6}$ of 3

4.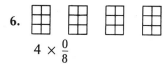

   $\frac{1}{3}$ of 5

5.

   $2 \times \frac{10}{10}$

6.

   $4 \times \frac{0}{8}$

7. $\frac{1}{4}$ of 30

8. $\frac{2}{4}$ of 30

9. $\frac{3}{4}$ of 30

10. $\frac{4}{4}$ of 30

11. $\frac{1}{3}$ of 34

12. $\frac{2}{3}$ of 34

13. $\frac{3}{3}$ of 34

14. $\frac{4}{3}$ of 34

15. $17 \times \frac{0}{2}$

16. $17 \times \frac{1}{2}$

17. $17 \times \frac{2}{2}$

18. $17 \times \frac{3}{2}$

19. $\frac{1}{3} \times 12$

20. $4 \times \frac{2}{2}$

21. $\frac{5}{6} \times 7$

22. $5 \times \frac{7}{12}$

Draw a diagram. Write the product in simplest terms.

1. $\frac{1}{4}$ of 3

2. $\frac{1}{2}$ of 5

3. $\frac{1}{3}$ of 12

4. $\frac{3}{5}$ of 20

5. $\frac{3}{4} \times 6$

6. $\frac{2}{5} \times 2$

7. $8 \times \frac{3}{4}$

8. $15 \times \frac{1}{3}$

Multiply. Write the product in simplest terms.

9. $\frac{2}{3} \times 12$

10. $\frac{3}{10} \times 4$

11. $15 \times \frac{1}{9}$

12. $13 \times \frac{4}{7}$

13. $\frac{7}{12} \times 9$

14. $\frac{7}{8} \times 17$

15. $21 \times \frac{1}{6}$

16. $\frac{2}{15} \times 11$

17. $220 \times \frac{4}{5}$

18. $185 \times \frac{1}{5}$

19. $350 \times \frac{1}{25}$

20. $216 \times \frac{3}{4}$

Solve. (Refer to page 220.)

21. How many hectares of Doug's family's farm land is not used for growing alfalfa?

22. One twelfth of Doug's family's farm land is used for grazing horses. How many hectares of their land is used for grazing horses?

Fractions of a Set

Dawn has 10 plants in her indoor garden. Three-fifths of the plants are flowering. How many of the plants are flowering?

$\frac{3}{5}$ of 10 = the number of plants flowering

There are three ways to find the *fraction of a set.*

Unit Fraction Method:

$\frac{1}{5}$ of 10 = 2

$\frac{3}{5}$ of 10 = 6

Multiplication Method:

$\frac{3}{5}$ of 10 = $\frac{3}{5} \times 10 = \frac{3 \times 10}{5} = \frac{30}{5} = 6$

Equivalent Fraction Method:

$\frac{3 \text{ flowering plants}}{5 \text{ plants in all}} = \frac{\blacksquare}{10}$

$\frac{3}{5} = \frac{3 \times 2}{5 \times 2} = \boxed{6}$ flowering plants
over 10 plants in all

There are 6 flowering plants.

EXERCISES

Find the fraction of a set using the *unit fraction method.*

1. Draw 20 dots.

   What is $\frac{2}{5}$ of 20 dots?

   $\frac{1}{5}$ of 20 = $\blacksquare$ $\frac{2}{5}$ of 20 = $\blacksquare$

2. Draw 16 △s.

   What is $\frac{3}{4}$ of 16 △s?

   $\frac{1}{4}$ of 16 = $\blacksquare$ $\frac{3}{4}$ of 16 = $\blacksquare$

Find the fraction of a set using the *equivalent fraction method.*

3. Draw 40 dots.

   What is $\frac{3}{5}$ of 40 dots?

   $\frac{3}{5} = \frac{\blacksquare}{40}$ $\frac{3}{5}$ of 40 = $\blacksquare$

4. Draw 21 △s.

   What is $\frac{2}{7}$ of 21 △s?

   $\frac{2}{7} = \frac{\blacksquare}{21}$ $\frac{2}{7}$ of 21 = $\blacksquare$

Find fraction of a set using the *multiplication method.*

5. $\frac{3}{4}$ of 20

   $\frac{3}{4} \times 20$

6. $\frac{5}{6}$ of 30

   $\frac{5}{6} \times 30$

7. $\frac{1}{9}$ of 36

   $\frac{1}{9} \times 36$

PRACTICE

Find the fraction of a set in simplest terms.

1. $\frac{3}{4}$ of 20   2. $\frac{7}{8}$ of 48   3. $\frac{5}{6}$ of 54

4. $\frac{5}{9}$ of 45   5. $\frac{3}{5}$ of 12   6. $\frac{2}{3}$ of 5

7. $\frac{3}{7}$ of 56   8. $\frac{9}{10}$ of 18   9. $\frac{2}{3}$ of 9

10. $\frac{5}{8}$ of 72   11. $\frac{4}{9}$ of 50   12. $\frac{5}{7}$ of 40

Match the multiplication in Column A to the diagram in Column B.

Column A   **Column B**

13. $\frac{2}{3}$ of 24 = 16   a.

14. $\frac{5}{6}$ of 24 = 20   b.

15. $\frac{3}{4}$ of 24 = 18   c.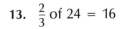

Solve.

16. The goalkeeper on Brian's hockey team allowed less than 2 goals in $\frac{3}{4}$ of the games he played. If he played 20 games, in how many games did he allow less than 2 goals?

17. There are 28 students in Charlotte's class. Sixteen of her classmates are boys.

a. If $\frac{1}{4}$ of the students in Charlotte's class wear glasses, how many wear glasses?

b. If $\frac{3}{8}$ of the boys play tennis, how many play tennis?

c. If $\frac{5}{6}$ of the girls own a bike, how many girls own a bike?

Ready, Set, Go!

Janet ran 3 km in $\frac{2}{3}$ of the time that it took Bob to run the same distance. Wally ran 3 km in $\frac{4}{5}$ of the time that Janet took.
If Bob took 15 minutes to run 3 km, what was the fastest time for the 3 km run?

Multiplying Fractions

Barry has cultivated $\frac{2}{5}$ of the garden, and Judy has planted vegetables in $\frac{1}{2}$ of the cultivated part. What fraction of the garden is planted with vegetables?

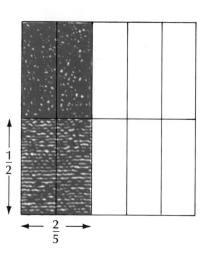

$\frac{1}{2}$ of $\frac{2}{5}$ = fraction of garden planted with vegetables

Multiply.

$$\frac{1}{2} \times \frac{2}{5} = \frac{1 \times 2}{2 \times 5} = \frac{2}{10}$$

Simplify.

$$\frac{2}{10} = \frac{1}{5}$$

Sometimes you can simplify *before* multiplying numerators and denominators.

Simplify. (Divide by the common factor 2.)

$$\frac{1}{2} \times \frac{2}{5} = \frac{1 \times \overset{1}{\cancel{2}}}{\underset{1}{\cancel{2}} \times 5} =$$

Multiply.

$$\frac{1 \times \overset{1}{\cancel{2}}}{\underset{1}{\cancel{2}} \times 5} = \frac{1}{5}$$

One fifth of the garden is planted with vegetables.

EXERCISES

Find the product in simplest terms.

1.

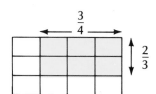

$$\frac{2}{3} \text{ of } \frac{3}{4} = \frac{2}{3} \times \frac{3}{4} = \frac{2 \times 3}{3 \times 4} = \blacksquare$$

2.

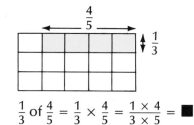

$$\frac{1}{3} \text{ of } \frac{4}{5} = \frac{1}{3} \times \frac{4}{5} = \frac{1 \times 4}{3 \times 5} = \blacksquare$$

3. $\frac{1}{3} \times \frac{6}{11}$ 4. $\frac{2}{3} \times \frac{6}{11}$ 5. $\frac{3}{3} \times \frac{6}{11}$ 6. $\frac{4}{3} \times \frac{6}{11}$

7. $\frac{1}{4} \times \frac{8}{9}$ 8. $\frac{2}{4} \times \frac{8}{9}$ 9. $\frac{3}{4} \times \frac{8}{9}$ 10. $\frac{4}{4} \times \frac{8}{9}$

11. $\frac{2}{5} \times \frac{3}{7}$ 12. $\frac{3}{8} \times \frac{7}{10}$ 13. $\frac{6}{7} \times \frac{7}{12}$ 14. $\frac{5}{8} \times \frac{12}{30}$

PRACTICE

Match the diagram to the multiplication.
Then write the product in simplest terms.

1. $\frac{3}{4}$ of $\frac{1}{6}$

2. $\frac{1}{2}$ of $\frac{2}{5}$

3. $\frac{2}{3}$ of $\frac{4}{5}$

a. 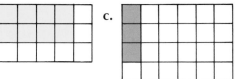 **b.** **c.**

Draw a diagram. Write the product in simplest terms.

4. $\frac{1}{2} \times \frac{2}{3}$

5. $\frac{1}{8} \times \frac{7}{10}$

6. $\frac{1}{3} \times \frac{1}{4}$

Find the product in simplest terms.

7. $\frac{9}{10} \times \frac{2}{3}$

8. $\frac{3}{5} \times \frac{7}{10}$

9. $\frac{2}{5} \times \frac{4}{4}$

10. $\frac{4}{7} \times \frac{7}{8}$

11. $\frac{2}{5} \times \frac{3}{10}$

12. $\frac{4}{11} \times \frac{3}{8}$

13. $\frac{5}{12} \times \frac{3}{4}$

14. $\frac{2}{5} \times \frac{13}{20}$

15. $\frac{12}{11} \times \frac{2}{9}$

16. $\frac{5}{8} \times \frac{4}{15}$

17. $\frac{2}{15} \times \frac{3}{10}$

18. $\frac{5}{16} \times \frac{4}{3}$

19. $\frac{1}{2} \times \frac{3}{4} \times \frac{2}{3}$

20. $3 \times \frac{5}{7} \times \frac{1}{6}$

21. $\frac{3}{4} \times 8 \times \frac{5}{6}$

Solve.

22. Alex scored $\frac{1}{5}$ of the team's goals in the playoffs. Of those goals, $\frac{1}{3}$ of them were scored during a power play.
What fraction of the team's playoff goals were scored by Alex on the power play?

23. Anna jogged for $\frac{1}{6}$ hour on Saturday and $\frac{1}{4}$ hour on Sunday.
Beatrice jogged for half of Anna's time on the two days.
What fraction of an hour did Beatrice jog?

Fraction Order of Operations

Use the order of operations rules to calculate the answer in simplest terms.

a. $\frac{3}{5} \times \left(3\frac{1}{2} + 2\frac{1}{2}\right)$

b. $7 \times \left(\frac{2}{5} + \frac{1}{2}\right)$

c. $\left(\frac{3}{8} + \frac{1}{4}\right) \times \left(\frac{3}{5} - \frac{1}{4}\right)$

d. $\left(\frac{3}{5} \times \frac{5}{8}\right) + \left(3 \times \frac{5}{6}\right)$

e. $\left(3 \times \frac{3}{4}\right) - \left(5 \times \frac{1}{3}\right)$

f. $\frac{2}{3} \times \left(14 - 6\frac{3}{5}\right)$

225

Multiplying Mixed Numerals

John's lawnmower uses $1\frac{1}{5}$ containers of gasoline each hour. If John cuts lawns for $3\frac{3}{4}$ h, how many containers of gasoline does he use?

$$1\frac{1}{5} \times 3\frac{3}{4} = \text{gasoline containers used}$$

Change to fractions.

$$1\frac{1}{5} \times 3\frac{3}{4} = \frac{6}{5} \times \frac{15}{4} =$$

Multiply.

$$\frac{6 \times 15}{5 \times 4} = \frac{90}{20}$$

Change to a mixed numeral. Simplify.

$$\frac{90}{20} = 4\frac{10}{20} = 4\frac{1}{2}$$

You can also simplify before multiplying.

Change to fractions.

$$1\frac{1}{5} \times 3\frac{3}{4} = \frac{6}{5} \times \frac{15}{4} =$$

Simplify. Then Multiply.

$$\frac{\overset{3}{\cancel{6}} \times \overset{3}{\cancel{15}}}{\underset{1}{\cancel{5}} \times \underset{2}{\cancel{4}}} = \frac{9}{2}$$

Change to a mixed numeral.

$$\frac{9}{2} = 4\frac{1}{2}$$

John uses $4\frac{1}{2}$ containers of gasoline.

EXERCISES

Find the product in simplest terms.

1.

$1\frac{1}{2}$ or $\frac{3}{2}$

$1\frac{1}{3}$ or $\frac{4}{3}$

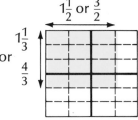

$$1\frac{1}{2} \times 1\frac{1}{3} = \frac{3}{2} \times \frac{4}{3} = \frac{3 \times 4}{2 \times 3} = \blacksquare$$

2.

$2\frac{2}{3}$ or $\frac{8}{3}$

$1\frac{1}{4}$ or $\frac{5}{4}$

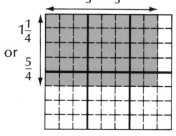

$$2\frac{2}{3} \times 1\frac{1}{4} = \frac{8}{3} \times \frac{5}{4} = \frac{8 \times 5}{3 \times 4} = \blacksquare$$

3. $3 \times 1\frac{1}{3}$

4. $2 \times 1\frac{1}{3}$

5. $\frac{2}{2} \times 1\frac{1}{3}$

6. $\frac{1}{2} \times 1\frac{1}{3}$

7. $6 \times 2\frac{5}{6}$

8. $3 \times 2\frac{5}{6}$

9. $\frac{6}{6} \times 2\frac{5}{6}$

10. $\frac{1}{6} \times 2\frac{5}{6}$

11. $\frac{1}{2} \times 2\frac{3}{4}$

12. $\frac{2}{2} \times 2\frac{3}{4}$

13. $1\frac{1}{2} \times 2\frac{3}{4}$

14. $\frac{4}{2} \times 2\frac{3}{4}$

15. $4\frac{1}{2} \times 1\frac{1}{6}$

16. $1\frac{1}{4} \times 1\frac{3}{10}$

17. $1\frac{2}{3} \times 2\frac{2}{5}$

18. $3\frac{3}{5} \times 3\frac{1}{6}$

Multiply. Write the product in simplest terms.

1. $2\frac{2}{3} \times \frac{4}{5}$ 2. $1\frac{4}{5} \times 1\frac{1}{9}$ 3. $5\frac{3}{4} \times 4$ 4. $3\frac{1}{2} \times \frac{5}{7}$

5. $2 \times 1\frac{7}{10}$ 6. $\frac{1}{4} \times 2\frac{1}{2}$ 7. $2\frac{2}{3} \times 1\frac{1}{4}$ 8. $5 \times 4\frac{3}{5}$

9. $3\frac{4}{7} \times 2\frac{4}{5}$ 10. $2\frac{3}{4} \times 2$ 11. $3\frac{1}{5} \times 1\frac{7}{8}$ 12. $2\frac{7}{8} \times 6\frac{6}{7}$

13. $2\frac{4}{7} \times 4\frac{1}{12}$ 14. $3\frac{3}{5} \times 2\frac{11}{12}$ 15. $\frac{3}{8} \times 1\frac{3}{5}$ 16. $5\frac{1}{6} \times 3\frac{3}{5}$

17. $1\frac{2}{3} \times \frac{7}{10} \times 3\frac{4}{7}$ 18. $2\frac{5}{8} \times 1\frac{5}{7} \times 1\frac{5}{9}$ 19. $2\frac{1}{3} \times \left(3\frac{3}{4} + \frac{3}{4}\right)$

20. $2\frac{2}{5} \times \left(5\frac{2}{3} - 2\frac{3}{4}\right)$ 21. $1\frac{3}{8} \times 2\frac{2}{9} + 1\frac{5}{6}$ 22. $4\frac{1}{2} \times 1\frac{2}{3} - 3\frac{5}{8}$ ✔

23. $\left(4\frac{7}{10} - 1\frac{1}{10}\right) \times \left(1\frac{1}{2} - \frac{2}{3}\right)$ 24. $\left(\frac{5}{8} + 1\frac{1}{4}\right) \times \left(2\frac{1}{2} - 1\frac{3}{5}\right)$

What part of an hour is:

25. $\frac{1}{2}$ of $\frac{1}{3}$ hour?   26. $\frac{1}{4}$ of $1\frac{1}{2}$ hours?   27. $\frac{1}{3}$ of $2\frac{1}{6}$ hours?

28. $\frac{5}{6}$ of $1\frac{1}{5}$ hours?   29. $\frac{2}{3}$ of $4\frac{1}{2}$ hours?   30. $\frac{2}{5}$ of $1\frac{1}{2}$ hours?

31. What is the answer to question 30 in minutes?

Explaining Patterns

Find the pattern.
Then try to explain why each pattern happens.

a.

$\frac{1}{2} =$	$\frac{1}{2}$
$\frac{1}{2} \times \frac{2}{3} =$	?
$\frac{1}{2} \times \frac{2}{3} \times \frac{3}{4} =$	?
$\frac{1}{2} \times \frac{2}{3} \times \frac{3}{4} \times \frac{4}{5} =$	?
$\frac{1}{2} \times \frac{2}{3} \times \frac{3}{4} \times \frac{4}{5} \times \frac{5}{6} =$	?
$\frac{1}{2} \times \frac{2}{3} \times \frac{3}{4} \times ... \times \frac{99}{100} =$	?

b.

$1\frac{1}{2} =$	$1\frac{1}{2}$
$1\frac{1}{2} \times 1\frac{1}{3} =$	?
$1\frac{1}{2} \times 1\frac{1}{3} \times 1\frac{1}{4} =$	?
$1\frac{1}{2} \times 1\frac{1}{3} \times 1\frac{1}{4} \times 1\frac{1}{5} =$	?
$1\frac{1}{2} \times 1\frac{1}{3} \times 1\frac{1}{4} \times 1\frac{1}{5} \times 1\frac{1}{6} =$	?
$1\frac{1}{2} \times 1\frac{1}{3} \times 1\frac{1}{4} \times 1\frac{1}{5} \times 1\frac{1}{6} \times ... \times 1\frac{1}{100} =$	?

Problem Solving

It takes Bradley $3\frac{1}{2}$ min to spread one bag of lawn fertilizer. How long does it take him to spread $9\frac{1}{2}$ bags?

Identify.

$3\frac{1}{2}$ min to spread 1 bag

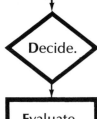
Decide.

Multiply.
$3\frac{1}{2} \times 9\frac{1}{2}$

Evaluate.

$3\frac{1}{2} \times 9\frac{1}{2} = \frac{7}{2} \times \frac{19}{2} = \frac{7 \times 19}{2 \times 2} = \frac{133}{4} = 33\frac{1}{4}$

Answer.

It takes him $33\frac{1}{4}$ min or about 33 min to spread $9\frac{1}{2}$ bags of lawn fertilizer.

Look back.

Since $3\frac{1}{2} \times 9\frac{1}{2} \approx 4 \times 9$, the answer of 33 min is reasonable.

EXERCISES

Solve. Round and estimate to see if your answer is reasonable.

1. Ron spent 2 h exercising. Of this time, $\frac{3}{4}$ hour was spent running and $\frac{2}{3}$ hour was spent walking. The rest of the time was spent doing calisthenics. How much time was spent doing calisthenics?

2. Three-quarters of the yard work that Joan does is cutting lawns. She must use a weed-eater for $\frac{2}{3}$ of that time. What fraction of her time does she spend using a weed-eater?

3. It usually takes George $3\frac{3}{4}$ hours to cultivate his garden. Two-thirds of the way through, he was called away. About how long had he spent cultivating his garden?

4. Cecelia has $2\frac{1}{2}$ pizzas left after her party. She gave $\frac{7}{8}$ of a pizza to her neighbour. How much pizza was left after that?

228

Solve. Round and estimate to see if your answer is reasonable.

1. Keith estimates that he can trim 1 m of lawn in half of a minute. How long should it take him to trim the Adam's lawn if there are 56 m of trimming to do?

2. Joan worked as a saleslady for $4\frac{1}{2}$ years at Montreal's largest department store. Then she was promoted and has been working as a department manager for $2\frac{1}{4}$ years. For how many years in all has Joan worked at the store?

3. The pump at the old well can deliver 1 L of water every half second. How many litres will it deliver after $2\frac{1}{4}$ min?

4. The Rockets won $\frac{11}{55}$ of their regular season hockey games. The Blades won $\frac{5}{6}$ of their regular season games. Who had the better record? By how much?

5. Ian did push-ups for $3\frac{1}{2}$ minutes and sit-ups for $2\frac{1}{3}$ minutes every day for 5 weeks. How much time did Ian spend doing sit-ups and push-ups in all?

6. It takes $2\frac{1}{3}$ hours to fly from Winnipeg to Calgary and $1\frac{1}{4}$ hours to fly from Calgary to Vancouver. How long will the two flights combined last?

REVIEW

Multiply. Write the product in simplest terms.

1. $3 \times \frac{1}{7}$	2. $2 \times \frac{3}{5}$	3. $\frac{2}{3} \times 6$	4. $10 \times \frac{5}{12}$
5. $\frac{2}{3}$ of 18	6. $\frac{3}{4}$ of 16	7. $\frac{5}{6}$ of 24	8. $\frac{7}{8}$ of 56
9. $\frac{2}{3} \times \frac{3}{4}$	10. $\frac{6}{7} \times \frac{28}{9}$	11. $\frac{3}{8} \times \frac{4}{9}$	12. $\frac{5}{8} \times \frac{6}{7}$
13. $3\frac{7}{8} \times 4$	14. $2\frac{2}{5} \times \frac{5}{8}$	15. $1\frac{5}{9} \times 4\frac{2}{7}$	16. $2\frac{5}{8} \times 3\frac{1}{7}$

Reciprocals

Two numbers which have a product of 1 are called **reciprocals** of each other.

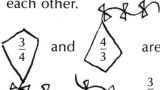 and are reciprocals of each other.

$$\frac{3}{4} \times \frac{4}{3} = \frac{3 \times 4}{4 \times 3} = \frac{12}{12} = 1$$

5 and $\frac{1}{5}$ are reciprocals of each other.

$$5 \times \frac{1}{5} = \frac{5 \times 1}{5} = \frac{5}{5} = 1$$

$2\frac{3}{8}$ and $\frac{8}{19}$ are reciprocals of each other.

$$2\frac{3}{8} \times \frac{8}{19} = \frac{19}{8} \times \frac{8}{19} = \frac{19 \times 8}{8 \times 19} = \frac{152}{152} = 1$$

EXERCISES

1. Which pairs of numbers are reciprocals of each other?

   a. $\frac{8}{7}, \frac{7}{8}$ b. $12, \frac{1}{12}$ c. $\frac{1}{6}, \frac{1}{6}$ d. $\frac{3}{7}, 2\frac{1}{3}$ e. $2\frac{3}{5}, \frac{8}{5}$

Write the reciprocal of each.

2. $\frac{3}{7}$ 3. $\frac{2}{3}$ 4. $\frac{1}{9}$ 5. $\frac{6}{7}$ 6. $\frac{7}{10}$

7. $\frac{5}{11}$ 8. $\frac{1}{4}$ 9. $\frac{5}{8}$ 10. 3   11. 7

12. $3\frac{1}{2}$ 13. $6\frac{3}{10}$ 14. $1\frac{5}{9}$ 15. 25   16. $3\frac{5}{11}$

What is n in each equation?

17. $\frac{5}{9} \times n = 1$ 18. $\frac{1}{15} \times 15 = n$ 19. $n \times \frac{3}{20} = 1$

20. $1\frac{1}{2} \times \frac{2}{3} = n$ 21. $1\frac{1}{8} \times n = 1$ 22. $4\frac{7}{8} \times \frac{8}{39} = n$

PRACTICE

Write the reciprocal for each.

1. $\frac{1}{8}$ **2.** $\frac{7}{11}$ **3.** $\frac{8}{9}$ **4.** $\frac{1}{10}$ **5.** 4

6. $2\frac{1}{3}$ **7.** $3\frac{2}{5}$ **8.** $\frac{7}{9}$ **9.** $4\frac{5}{8}$ **10.** 45

What is *n* in each equation?

11. $\frac{3}{4} \times 1\frac{1}{3} = n$ **12.** $18 \times n = 1$ **13.** $n \times \frac{11}{9} = 1$

14. $1 = 5\frac{1}{2} \times n$ **15.** $n = \frac{1}{20} \times 20$ **16.** $1 = n \times \frac{5}{12}$

17. $10 \times \left(\frac{4}{5} \times \frac{5}{4}\right) = n$ **18.** $n \times \left(\frac{3}{10} \times \frac{10}{3}\right) = 4$ **19.** $\frac{7}{8} \times \frac{8}{7} = n \times 3$

Solve.

20. What number is its own reciprocal?

21. What number does not have a reciprocal?

22. A small bucket full of water fills one sixth of a larger bucket. How many smaller buckets full of water would completely fill the larger bucket?

23. Sally can pick $\frac{1}{10}$ of a basket of strawberries in 1 min. How long will it take her to pick 1 whole basket?

Decimal Reciprocals

Find the reciprocals of these decimals. Use your calculator to check your answers.

a. 0.5 **b.** 0.4 **c.** 0.25

d. 0.025 **e.** 0.8 **f.** 0.75

g. 0.3 **h.** 0.125 **i.** 0.375

5 is the reciprocal of 0.2.
0.2 × 5 = 1 or $\frac{2}{10} \times 5 = 1$

Calculator Check:

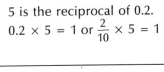

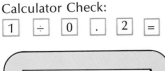

231

Dividing With Fractions

The Lawrence farm has a large field for growing fruits and vegetables. This field occupies one half of their farm land and is divided into five equal-sized regions. What fraction of the Lawrence farm land is each region?

$\frac{1}{2} \div 5 =$ fraction of farm land for each region

Multiply by the *reciprocal of the divisor.*

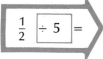

$\boxed{\frac{1}{2} \div 5} = $ $\boxed{\frac{1}{2} \times \frac{1}{5} = \frac{1}{10}}$

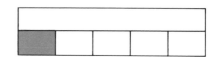

Each region is $\frac{1}{10}$ of their farm land.

The Lawrence farm also has four equal-sized pastures for grazing horses. Each horse requires about $\frac{2}{3}$ of a pasture for grazing. About how many horses can graze in the four pastures?

$4 \div \frac{2}{3} =$ the number of horses that can graze

Multiply by the *reciprocal of the divisor.*

$\boxed{4 \div \frac{2}{3}} = $ $\boxed{\frac{4}{1} \times \frac{3}{2} = \frac{12}{2} = 6}$

About six horses can graze.

EXERCISES

Find the quotient in simplest terms.

1.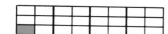

$\frac{1}{4} \div 6 = \frac{1}{4} \times \blacksquare = \blacksquare$

2.

$6 \div \frac{1}{4} = 6 \times \blacksquare = \blacksquare$

3. $5 \div \frac{1}{2} = 5 \times \blacksquare = \blacksquare$

4. $7 \div \frac{1}{3} = 7 \times \blacksquare = \blacksquare$

5. $\frac{1}{2} \div 7 = \frac{1}{2} \times \blacksquare = \blacksquare$

6. $\frac{1}{3} \div 5 = \frac{1}{3} \times \blacksquare = \blacksquare$

7. $\frac{1}{2} \div 7$

8. $\frac{2}{3} \div 5$

9. $10 \div \frac{1}{6}$

10. $14 \div \frac{3}{4}$

PRACTICE

Divide. Write the quotient in simplest terms.

1. $3 \div \frac{1}{5}$ 2. $\frac{1}{4} \div 3$ 3. $2 \div \frac{4}{5}$ 4. $\frac{4}{5} \div 2$

5. $7 \div \frac{9}{10}$ 6. $\frac{3}{7} \div 9$ 7. $3 \div \frac{3}{8}$ 8. $\frac{1}{10} \div 6$

9. $5 \div \frac{5}{6}$ 10. $\frac{1}{12} \div 5$ 11. $2 \div \frac{2}{15}$ 12. $\frac{11}{20} \div 5$

13. $10 \div \frac{3}{10}$ 14. $8 \div \frac{1}{2}$ 15. $\frac{2}{3} \div 9$ 16. $11 \div \frac{4}{7}$

17. $\frac{1}{15} \div 7$ 18. $\frac{4}{9} \div 8$ 19. $9 \div \frac{5}{6}$ 20. $\frac{8}{11} \div 2$

What is the value of x in each equation?

21. $\frac{1}{2} \div 3 = x \times \frac{1}{3}$

22. $4 \div x = 4 \times 7$

23. $x \div 12 = \frac{1}{8} \times \frac{1}{12}$

24. $11 \div \frac{3}{5} = 11 \times x$

Draw a diagram for each.

25. $\frac{1}{3} \div 2$ 26. $\frac{1}{4} \div 3$ 27. $3 \div \frac{1}{2}$ 28. $2 \div \frac{3}{4}$

Solve.

29. Brenda broke half of her candy bar into 3 equal pieces. She then gave each of 3 friends one of these pieces. How much of the candy bar did each friend get?

Reasonable Quotients

If the dividend is larger than the divisor, the quotient will be *larger than 1*.

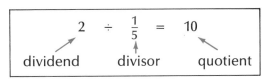

If the dividend is smaller than the divisor, the quotient will be *smaller than 1*.

Will the quotients be *larger* or *smaller* than 1?

a. $6 \div \frac{1}{9}$ b. $\frac{7}{8} \div 16$ c. $\frac{3}{4} \div 11$ d. $\frac{1}{2} \div \frac{2}{3}$ e. $\frac{5}{8} \div \frac{1}{2}$

Dividing Fractions

Each row of corn planted requires $\frac{1}{2}$ of a bag of seed. David has $\frac{7}{8}$ of a bag of seed. How many rows of corn can he plant?

How many $\frac{1}{2}$s are in $\frac{7}{8}$?

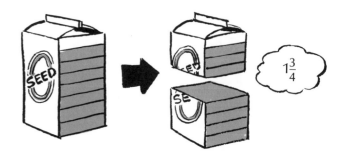

$$\frac{7}{8} \div \frac{1}{2} = \text{rows of corn he can plant}$$

Multiply by the reciprocal of the divisor.

$$\frac{7}{8} \boxed{\div \frac{1}{2}} = \frac{7}{8} \times \boxed{\frac{2}{1}} = $$

Simplify and multiply.

$$\frac{7 \times \overset{1}{\cancel{2}}}{\underset{4}{\cancel{8}} \times 1} = \frac{7}{4} = $$

Regroup.

$$\frac{7}{4} = 1\frac{3}{4}$$

David can plant $1\frac{3}{4}$ rows of corn.

EXERCISES

Find the quotient in simplest terms.

1. How many $\frac{1}{4}$s in $\frac{1}{2}$?

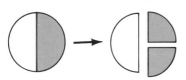

$$\frac{1}{2} \div \frac{1}{4} = \frac{1}{2} \times \frac{4}{1} = \frac{1 \times \overset{2}{\cancel{4}}}{\underset{1}{\cancel{2}} \times 1} = \blacksquare$$

2. How many $\frac{1}{4}$s in $\frac{7}{8}$?

$$\frac{7}{8} \div \frac{1}{4} = \frac{7}{8} \times \frac{4}{1} = \frac{7 \times \overset{1}{\cancel{4}}}{\underset{2}{\cancel{8}} \times 1} = \blacksquare$$

3. $\frac{2}{3} \div \frac{3}{4} = \frac{2}{3} \times \blacksquare = \blacksquare$

4. $\frac{3}{7} \div \frac{1}{6} = \frac{3}{7} \times \blacksquare = \blacksquare$

5. $\frac{4}{5} \div \frac{3}{10} = \frac{4}{5} \times \blacksquare = \blacksquare$

6. $\frac{3}{8} \div \frac{5}{6} = \frac{3}{8} \times \blacksquare = \blacksquare$

7. $\frac{1}{2} \div \frac{7}{10} = \frac{1}{2} \times \blacksquare = \blacksquare$

8. $\frac{4}{9} \div \frac{2}{3} = \frac{4}{9} \times \blacksquare = \blacksquare$

9. $\frac{7}{10} \div \frac{1}{2}$

10. $\frac{3}{4} \div \frac{3}{4}$

11. $\frac{5}{6} \div \frac{1}{3}$

12. $\frac{2}{5} \div \frac{1}{10}$

13. $\frac{1}{3} \div \frac{1}{3}$

14. $\frac{8}{9} \div \frac{5}{6}$

15. $\frac{5}{8} \div \frac{1}{2}$

16. $\frac{1}{6} \div \frac{2}{11}$

Divide. Write the quotient in simplest terms.

1. $\frac{3}{4} \div \frac{2}{3}$ 2. $\frac{1}{2} \div \frac{2}{3}$ 3. $\frac{3}{4} \div \frac{1}{2}$ 4. $\frac{5}{6} \div \frac{3}{5}$

5. $\frac{7}{10} \div \frac{2}{5}$ 6. $\frac{3}{7} \div \frac{2}{9}$ 7. $\frac{5}{9} \div \frac{3}{8}$ 8. $\frac{7}{8} \div \frac{3}{5}$

9. $\frac{2}{3} \div \frac{4}{9}$ 10. $\frac{4}{5} \div \frac{8}{15}$ 11. $\frac{9}{20} \div \frac{3}{10}$ 12. $\frac{1}{3} \div \frac{5}{9}$

13. $\frac{3}{5} \div \frac{3}{5}$ 14. $\frac{4}{7} \div \frac{1}{3}$ 15. $\frac{3}{8} \div \frac{6}{7}$ 16. $\frac{5}{6} \div \frac{5}{6}$

17. $\frac{2}{11} \div \frac{4}{9}$ 18. $\frac{5}{8} \div \frac{15}{16}$ 19. $\frac{3}{7} \div \frac{6}{14}$ 20. $\frac{3}{10} \div \frac{1}{20}$

Calculate. Write the answer in simplest terms.

21. $\frac{3}{4} \times \frac{2}{9} \div \frac{5}{6}$

22. $\frac{5}{8} \div \frac{3}{4} \times \frac{2}{9}$

23. $\left(\frac{1}{3} + \frac{1}{2}\right) \div \frac{3}{4}$

24. $\left(\frac{8}{9} - \frac{5}{6}\right) \div \frac{5}{12}$

25. $\left(\frac{3}{5} + \frac{8}{10}\right) \div \left(\frac{3}{8} - \frac{1}{6}\right)$

26. $\left(\frac{2}{3} - \frac{1}{2}\right) \div \left(\frac{2}{5} + \frac{3}{8}\right)$

27. $\left(\frac{1}{4} \div 5\right) \div \left(2 \div \frac{1}{5}\right)$

28. $\left(4 \div \frac{1}{3}\right) \div \left(\frac{1}{3} \div 2\right)$

29. $\frac{4}{9} \times n = \frac{1}{3}$ 30. $n \times \frac{2}{5} = \frac{9}{10}$ 31. $\frac{3}{4} \times n = \frac{7}{8}$

Draw a diagram. Then solve.

32. Ann takes $\frac{1}{10}$ of an hour to make a paper flower. How many flowers can she make in $\frac{4}{5}$ of an hour?

Computer Fractions

Try the BASIC program below?
a. What does the program do?
b. What do N1, N2, D1, and D2 represent?

```
10   PRINT "TYPE THE NUMERATOR, DENOMINATOR"
20   INPUT "ENTER FRACTION 1: ";N1,D1
30   INPUT "ENTER FRACTION 2: ";N2,D2
40   LET N3 = N1 * D2: LET D3 = D1 * N2
50   FOR GCF = D3 TO 1 STEP  - 1
60   LET N = N3 / GCF: LET D = D3 / GCF
70   IF N =  INT (N) AND D =  INT (D) THEN  GOTO 90
80   NEXT GCF
90   PRINT "THE ANSWER IN SIMPLEST TERMS IS: ";N;"/";D: END
```

235

Dividing Mixed Numerals

It takes Fred $1\frac{1}{2}$ hours to give a car a complete tune-up. If Fred tunes cars for $7\frac{1}{2}$ hours, how many cars will he do?

How many $1\frac{1}{2}$s are in $7\frac{1}{2}$?

$7\frac{1}{2} \div 1\frac{1}{2}$ = cars that will be tuned

$$\underbrace{}_{1}\ \underbrace{}_{2}\ \underbrace{}_{3}\ \underbrace{}_{4}\ \underbrace{}_{5}$$

Change to fractions.

$$7\frac{1}{2} \div 1\frac{1}{2} = \frac{15}{2} \div \frac{3}{2} =$$

Fred will tune 5 cars.

Multiply by the reciprocal of the divisor.

$$\frac{15}{2} \times \frac{2}{3} =$$

Simplify and multiply.

$$\frac{\overset{5}{\cancel{15}} \times \overset{1}{\cancel{2}}}{\underset{1}{\cancel{2}} \times \underset{1}{\cancel{3}}} = \frac{5}{1} = 5$$

EXERCISES

Divide. Write the quotient in simplest terms.

1. How many $1\frac{2}{3}$s in $4\frac{1}{3}$?

    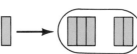

$$4\frac{1}{3} \div 1\frac{2}{3} = \frac{13}{3} \div \frac{5}{3} = \frac{13}{3} \times \frac{3}{5} = \frac{13 \times \overset{1}{\cancel{3}}}{\underset{1}{\cancel{3}} \times 5} = \blacksquare$$

2. How many $2\frac{1}{2}$s in $3\frac{1}{4}$?

$$3\frac{1}{4} \div 2\frac{1}{2} = \frac{13}{4} \div \frac{5}{2} = \frac{13}{4} \times \frac{2}{5} = \frac{13 \times 2}{4 \times 5} = \blacksquare$$

3. $3\frac{1}{2} \div \frac{2}{3} = \frac{7}{2} \times \frac{3}{2} = \blacksquare$

4. $\frac{1}{3} \div 2\frac{1}{2} = \frac{1}{3} \times \frac{\blacksquare}{\blacksquare} = \blacksquare$

5. $3\frac{1}{3} \div 1\frac{5}{8} = \frac{10}{3} \times \frac{\blacksquare}{\blacksquare} = \blacksquare$

6. $1\frac{3}{5} \div 2\frac{1}{10} = \frac{8}{5} \times \frac{\blacksquare}{\blacksquare} = \blacksquare$

7. $1\frac{1}{3} \div \frac{3}{8}$

8. $3\frac{5}{9} \div 3$

9. $\frac{3}{8} \div 1\frac{2}{3}$

10. $7 \div 2\frac{3}{4}$

11. $\frac{5}{6} \div 3\frac{1}{2}$

12. $2\frac{3}{4} \div \frac{7}{10}$

13. $1\frac{3}{7} \div 2\frac{5}{6}$

14. $1\frac{5}{13} \div 3\frac{1}{2}$

PRACTICE

Find the quotient in simplest terms.

1. $1\frac{2}{3} \div \frac{3}{4}$

2. $4 \div 1\frac{1}{2}$

3. $4\frac{2}{3} \div 3\frac{1}{2}$

4. $5\frac{7}{9} \div 2\frac{4}{5}$

5. $2 \div 3\frac{4}{7}$

6. $2\frac{2}{5} \div \frac{3}{7}$ ✓

7. $1\frac{3}{7} \div 4\frac{2}{7}$

8. $3\frac{5}{8} \div 2$

9. $2\frac{3}{10} \div 5\frac{1}{7}$

10. $3 \div 4\frac{2}{5}$

11. $4\frac{2}{3} \div 3\frac{5}{6}$

12. $2\frac{3}{4} \div \frac{2}{3}$

13. $2\frac{3}{5} \div 1\frac{3}{10}$

14. $5\frac{5}{7} \div 4$ ✓

15. $7\frac{1}{2} \div \frac{1}{5}$

16. $2\frac{4}{7} \div 5\frac{2}{5}$

17. $2 \div 3\frac{4}{7}$

18. $1\frac{9}{10} \div 3\frac{5}{11}$

19. $2\frac{3}{8} \div 5$

20. $3\frac{6}{13} \div 5\frac{3}{5}$

Calculate. Write the answer in simplest terms.

21. $\left(1\frac{2}{3} + 1\frac{3}{4}\right) \div 2$

22. $3\frac{1}{5} \div \left(2\frac{1}{3} - 1\frac{3}{4}\right)$

23. $\left(1\frac{3}{5} \times \frac{3}{4}\right) \div 2\frac{1}{4}$

24. $\left(2\frac{1}{2} \div 3\right) \times 1\frac{3}{5}$

25. $\left(\frac{3}{4} + 2\frac{2}{3}\right) \div \left(3\frac{5}{8} - 1\frac{1}{4}\right)$

26. $\left(5\frac{2}{3} - 3\frac{3}{4}\right) \div \left(1\frac{1}{5} + 1\frac{2}{3}\right)$

Solve.

27. It takes $2\frac{1}{4}$ hours to paint one side of the barn. How much of the barn should be painted after $5\frac{3}{4}$ hours? How long would it take to paint all 4 sides of the barn?

Calculator Fractions

Fractions can be multiplied and divided on a calculator.

To multiply $4\frac{3}{5} \times 2\frac{1}{4}$:

Step 1 Change fractions to decimals.

| 3 | ÷ | 5 | + | 4 | = |

4.6

| 1 | ÷ | 4 | + | 2 | = |

2.25

Step 2 Multiply.

| 4 | . | 6 | × | 2 | . | 2 | 5 | = |

10.35

Step 3 Change decimals to fractions.

$10.35 = 10\frac{35}{100} = 10\frac{7}{20}$

Try these on a calculator.
Write the answers as fractions.

a. $4\frac{1}{2} \times 2\frac{2}{5}$

b. $3\frac{4}{5} \div 2\frac{1}{2}$

c. $6\frac{7}{10} \times 1\frac{3}{4}$

d. $2\frac{1}{4} \div 1\frac{1}{4}$

e. $2\frac{1}{2} \times 2\frac{1}{4}$

f. $3\frac{1}{10} \div 2\frac{1}{2}$

237

Problem Solving

It takes Don and his father $\frac{3}{4}$ hour to cut hay on one field. How many fields should they be able to cut in $3\frac{1}{2}$ hours?

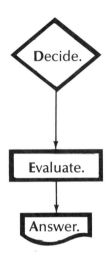

Decide.

Evaluate.

Answer.

Estimate a reasonable answer.

$\frac{3}{4}$ *rounds up* to 1. $3\frac{1}{2}$ *rounds up* to 4.

Since $3\frac{1}{2} \div \frac{3}{4} \approx 4 \div 1$, about 4 fields can be cut.

Calculate the exact answer.

$$3\frac{1}{2} \div \frac{3}{4} = \frac{7}{2} \div \frac{3}{4} = \frac{7}{2} \times \frac{4}{3} = \frac{7 \times \overset{2}{\cancel{4}}}{\underset{1}{\cancel{2}} \times 3} = \frac{14}{3} = 4\frac{2}{3}$$

They should be able to cut hay in $4\frac{2}{3}$ fields.

EXERCISES

Estimate a reasonable answer.
Then calculate the exact answer.

1. One-fourth of Mary Paulson's peas were damaged by frost. She could harvest only $8\frac{3}{4}$ rows of peas. How many rows of peas were damaged?

2. Donna has three-fifths of her garden planted with seed. She expects that $\frac{9}{10}$ of the seed will sprout and grow. What fraction of her garden will grow from seed?

3. For reading homework, Carla had to read a story that was $25\frac{1}{2}$ pages long. She read $\frac{3}{4}$ of the pages before going to bed. How many pages did she read before going to bed? How many pages did she have left to read?

4. A round trip trail ride to the lake takes $2\frac{3}{4}$ hours. Lucy rode there and back 3 times in one day. How long did she ride that day?

PRACTICE

Estimate a reasonable answer.
Then calculate the exact answer.

1. Ernie worked for 5 h on Saturday. He spent $\frac{1}{4}$ of his time trimming hedges, $2\frac{1}{2}$ hours cleaning the eaves, and the rest of his time helping to wash and wax the car. How long did Ernie help to wash and wax the car?

2. Don planted 40 cauliflower seeds. Seven-eighths of them sprouted and grew. How many cauliflowers grew from seed?

3. Sally earns $4.60/h for working $6\frac{1}{2}$ hours for her mother and $5.10/h for working $2\frac{1}{4}$ hours for her neighbour. How much money does Sally earn?

4. Dana completes her three household chores in $\frac{3}{4}$ of an hour. If she is $\frac{2}{3}$ done, how long has she worked? How many chores has she done?

5. Ian takes $3\frac{1}{2}$ minutes to read a page of his science-fiction book. How many pages can he read in an hour?

6. A recipe calls for $4\frac{1}{2}$ carrots. How many carrots would be needed to make $\frac{1}{3}$ of the recipe?

REVIEW

Write the reciprocal for each.

1. 7

2. $\frac{1}{8}$

3. $\frac{3}{5}$

4. $4\frac{3}{7}$

5. $3\frac{2}{5}$

Divide. Write the answer in simplest terms.

6. $\frac{1}{7} \div 5$

7. $3 \div \frac{1}{6}$

8. $\frac{7}{8} \div 2$

9. $6 \div \frac{3}{4}$

10. $\frac{3}{8} \div \frac{5}{6}$

11. $\frac{2}{7} \div \frac{4}{9}$

12. $\frac{3}{5} \div \frac{7}{10}$

13. $\frac{8}{15} \div \frac{4}{5}$

14. $8 \div 2\frac{5}{9}$

15. $1\frac{3}{10} \div 1\frac{2}{7}$

16. $1\frac{3}{11} \div 4$

17. $5\frac{5}{9} \div 3\frac{3}{5}$

Sale Prices

Clothing Sale

	Regular Price		Regular Price
Sweaters	$20.00	Shirts	$18.99
Jeans	$24.00	Dress Pants	$30.00
Vests	$15.60	Ties	$ 9.75

1. How much money is saved by buying a sweater on sale?

2. What is the sale price for a tie?

3. What is the amount of discount offered for a pair of jeans?

4. What is the sale price for a vest?

5. How much money is saved by buying a shirt on sale?

6. What is the sale price for a pair of dress pants?

Ski Equipment Sale

	Regular Price		Regular Price
Skis	$189	Jacket	$78
Boots	$144	Sweater	$57
Poles	$ 54	Tuque	$15
Goggles	$ 27	Gloves	$42

1. How much money is saved by buying a pair of skis on sale?

2. How much money is saved by buying both a jacket and a tuque on sale?

3. What is the sale price for each of the above ski items?

4. What is the total cost of a pair of skis, boots, and poles at the regular price? At the sale price?

5. Can goggles and a tuque be bought for under $25.00 at the sale price?

6. What is the total cost of a jacket, tuque, and gloves at the regular price? At the sale price?

Track Records

The track runners in a Sport Club kept a record for one week
of the number of laps they ran each day.

	Monday	Tuesday	Wednesday	Thursday	Friday
Marilyn	$5\frac{1}{2}$ laps	$7\frac{1}{4}$ laps	$8\frac{1}{10}$ laps	10 laps	$9\frac{1}{2}$ laps
Bill	9 laps	$9\frac{1}{3}$ laps	$10\frac{1}{2}$ laps	$11\frac{1}{3}$ laps	$11\frac{1}{2}$ laps
George	$12\frac{1}{2}$ laps	$13\frac{1}{2}$ laps	14 laps	$14\frac{1}{3}$ laps	15 laps
Debbie	3 laps	$4\frac{1}{3}$ laps	$5\frac{1}{4}$ laps	4 laps	$4\frac{1}{2}$ laps
Felicia	$6\frac{1}{2}$ laps	2 laps	$4\frac{1}{3}$ laps	$5\frac{1}{2}$ laps	$6\frac{1}{3}$ laps

1. How many laps did each runner average per day?

2. How many more laps did George run than Joe in the 5 days?

3. How many more laps did Bill run than Marilyn in the 5 days?

4. How many laps did the girls average in the 5 days?

The Stock Market

STOCK EXCHANGE QUOTATIONS						
1984			Day's	Day's	Day's	Change from
High	Low	Stock	High	Low	Close	Yesterday's Close
$29\frac{1}{2}$	$18\frac{1}{4}$	Can-Mines	$25\frac{3}{4}$	25	$25\frac{1}{2}$	$+\frac{1}{2}$
$32\frac{1}{2}$	22	Builders Ltd.	$32\frac{1}{2}$	32	$32\frac{1}{2}$	$+1\frac{1}{2}$
$30\frac{1}{8}$	$19\frac{3}{4}$	Micro-Corp.	$30\frac{1}{8}$	$29\frac{1}{4}$	30	$+\frac{3}{4}$

1. What is the cost of 100 shares of Can-Mines stock bought at the
   closing price of the day?

2. What is the cost of 75 shares of Builders Ltd. stock bought at the
   lowest price of the day?

3. What is the cost of 225 shares of Micro-Corp. stock bought at
   the closing price of the day?

TEST   UNIT 9

Write a multiplication equation for each diagram.

1.   **2.** 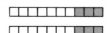 **3.**

Multiply. Write the product in simplest terms.

4. $5 \times \frac{1}{8}$ **5.** $\frac{8}{10} \times 6$ **6.** $8 \times \frac{5}{6}$ **7.** $\frac{7}{9} \times 11$

8. $\frac{3}{5}$ of 25   **9.** $\frac{5}{8}$ of 64   **10.** $\frac{9}{10}$ of 90   **11.** $\frac{2}{3}$ of 54

12. $\frac{1}{2} \times \frac{1}{6}$ **13.** $\frac{4}{7} \times \frac{5}{8}$ **14.** $\frac{2}{3} \times \frac{4}{7}$ **15.** $\frac{9}{14} \times \frac{7}{12}$

16. $\frac{2}{5} \times 2\frac{2}{9}$ **17.** $6 \times 2\frac{1}{3}$ **18.** $3\frac{3}{4} \times 2\frac{1}{10}$ **19.** $4\frac{1}{8} \times 3\frac{1}{3}$

Write the reciprocal for each.

20. 3   **21.** $\frac{4}{7}$ **22.** $\frac{1}{6}$ **23.** $2\frac{5}{6}$

Divide. Write the quotient in simplest terms.

24. $\frac{1}{5} \div 6$ **25.** $\frac{5}{7} \div 3$ **26.** $8 \div \frac{5}{6}$ **27.** $4 \div \frac{4}{5}$

28. $\frac{5}{8} \div \frac{3}{4}$ **29.** $\frac{7}{8} \div \frac{11}{16}$ **30.** $\frac{10}{13} \div \frac{5}{11}$ **31.** $\frac{7}{12} \div \frac{9}{10}$

32. $5 \div 2\frac{1}{7}$ **33.** $2\frac{3}{4} \div 1\frac{2}{5}$ **34.** $2\frac{7}{8} \div 3$ **35.** $1\frac{3}{7} \div 4\frac{2}{3}$

Solve.

36. How many $\frac{1}{2}$s are in $3\frac{1}{4}$?   **37.** How many $\frac{4}{5}$s are in $5\frac{1}{2}$?

38. How many $1\frac{1}{3}$s are in 6?

39. Sharon can run a kilometre in $5\frac{1}{2}$ minutes. How long will it take her to run 3.5 km?

40. Tom read $5\frac{1}{2}$ books in one month. How many books is that per week?

Write a fraction or mixed numeral for each letter in simplest terms?

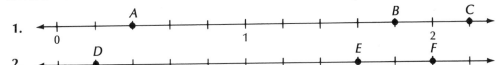

1.

2.

Copy and complete.

3. $\frac{7}{9} = \frac{\blacksquare}{27}$ ✓

4. $\frac{2}{5} = \frac{16}{\blacksquare}$

5. $\frac{3}{11} = \frac{\blacksquare}{44}$

6. $\frac{6}{7} = \frac{42}{\blacksquare}$

Write the fraction in simplest terms.

7. $\frac{15}{27}$

8. $\frac{16}{20}$

9. $\frac{36}{54}$

10. $\frac{60}{72}$

11. $\frac{72}{96}$

Copy and compare. Use < or >.

12. $\frac{3}{4} \bullet \frac{2}{3}$ ✓

13. $\frac{5}{8} \bullet \frac{7}{11}$

14. $\frac{2}{9} \bullet \frac{1}{5}$

15. $\frac{5}{16} \bullet \frac{4}{12}$ ✓

Change the fraction to a mixed numeral in simplest terms.

16. $\frac{16}{3}$

17. $\frac{32}{5}$

18. $\frac{24}{14}$

19. $\frac{50}{9}$

20. $\frac{66}{16}$

Change the mixed numeral to a fraction.

21. $7\frac{1}{2}$

22. $2\frac{5}{8}$

23. $6\frac{9}{10}$

24. $1\frac{11}{12}$

25. $16\frac{3}{4}$

Write the fraction as a decimal.

26. $\frac{1}{4}$

27. $\frac{5}{8}$

28. $\frac{7}{50}$

29. $\frac{11}{20}$

30. $\frac{1}{3}$

Write the decimal as a fraction in simplest terms.

31. 0.4

32. 0.32

33. 0.07

34. 0.025

35. 0.350

Add or subtract. Write the answer in simplest terms.

36. $\frac{5}{12} + \frac{1}{3}$

37. $\frac{1}{8} + \frac{3}{20}$

38. $\frac{1}{5} + \frac{2}{3}$

39. $\frac{4}{5} - \frac{2}{10}$

40. $\frac{13}{16} - \frac{1}{12}$

41. $\frac{21}{25} - \frac{3}{5}$

42. $4\frac{2}{3} + \frac{7}{9}$

43. $5\frac{2}{7} + 6\frac{7}{8}$

44. $11\frac{3}{5} + 4\frac{5}{6}$

45. $14 - 2\frac{3}{8}$

46. $9\frac{1}{4} - \frac{2}{3}$

47. $4\frac{1}{2} - 2\frac{4}{7}$

UNIT 10

Problem Solving II

Making a Simpler Problem

Each of the 20 persons at a party had a
conversation with every other person. How
many conversations took place?

Identify the facts.

20 persons, each conversing with every other person.

Decide.

Make a simpler problem:
3 persons, each conversing with every other person.

Each of the 3 persons would converse with 2 other persons.
$3 \times 2 = 6$
Conversations cannot be counted twice. $6 \div 2 = 3$

Evaluate.

$3 \times 2 \div 2 = 3$
3 conversations for 3 people

Answer.

Look back.

Each of the 20 persons would converse with 19 other persons.
$20 \times 19 = 380$
Conversations cannot be counted twice. $380 \div 2 = 190$

$20 \times 19 \div 2 = 190$
190 conversations for 20 people.

Solve by using the simpler problem.

1. Each of 30 persons at a party shook hands with every other person. How many handshakes took place?

Each person shakes hands with 2 others.
3 × 2 ÷ 2 handshakes

2. On a map showing 15 towns, there is one straight road connecting every pair of towns. How many straight roads connect the towns?

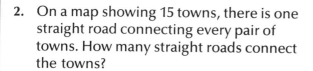
Each town connects with 3 others.
4 × 3 ÷ 2 roads

3. A man fenced his field so that the fence had the form of a square. When he finished, there were 160 fence posts on each side. How many posts did he use?

4 sides
3 posts per side

4 × 3 − 4 posts

4. How many squares are in a 6 by 6 square grid?

3 by 3   3 kinds of squares

Solve.

1. If there are 24 points on a circle and every point is joined to every other point with a chord, how many chords are there?
(A *chord* is a segment from one point on a circle to any other point on the circle.)

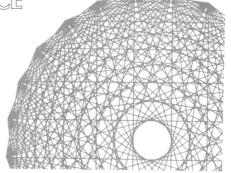

2. How many angles are formed by the 10 segments sharing a common vertex?

3. How many triangles in all?

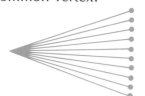

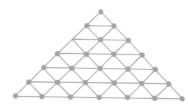

4. How many segments are formed by 16 points on a line?

245

Using Patterns

Some problems involve a pattern. Finding patterns can help you solve problems.

The Fisherman's Cove restaurant has square tables which seat 4 people. When 2 tables are placed together, 6 people can be seated. How many people can be seated if 6 tables are placed together?

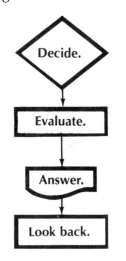

Put the facts in a table. Look for a pattern.

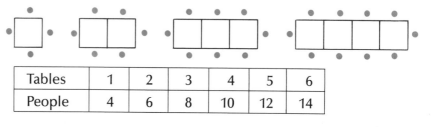

Tables	1	2	3	4	5	6
People	4	6	8	10	12	14

If 6 tables are placed together, 14 people could be seated.

After studying the pattern, the answer is reasonable.

EXERCISES

Solve by using a pattern.

1. How many people could be seated at the Fisherman's Cove restaurant (mentioned above) if 12 tables were placed together?

2. Continue the triangular array for 20 rows.
   a. What is the middle number in the 20th row?
   b. What is the sum of the numbers in the 20th row?

   ```
            1
          1 2 1
        1 2 3 2 1
      1 2 3 4 3 2 1
   ```

3. A floor is tiled with octagons and squares. For a 2 by 2 section of octagons, there is one square. For a 3 by 3 section of octagons, there are 4 squares. How many squares are there for a:
   a. 10 by 10 section of octagons?
   b. 20 by 20 section of octagons?

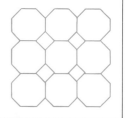

PRACTICE

Solve.

1. If the triangular array were continued, what numbers would appear in the 5th row? in the 30th row?

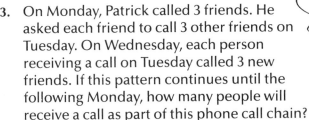

```
                1
            3       5
        7       9       11
    13      15      17      19
```

2. A slow spider tries to climb a 10 m pole. Each day he climbs up 2 m. Each night while he rests, he slips down 1 m. When will he reach the top of the pole?

3. On Monday, Patrick called 3 friends. He asked each friend to call 3 other friends on Tuesday. On Wednesday, each person receiving a call on Tuesday called 3 new friends. If this pattern continues until the following Monday, how many people will receive a call as part of this phone call chain?

4. A grocery clerk wants to stack boxes of biscuits in a window display 14 layers high. One box will be in the top layer, three boxes will be in the next layer, five boxes will be in the third layer, and so on. How many boxes will be in the window display?

Computer Pattern

Try the computer program which *outputs* the Fibonacci sequence.

$$1, 1, 2, 3, 5, 8, \ldots$$

This sequence has many interesting patterns.

a. Study any 4 consecutive numbers in the sequence.

```
    1 × 2 = 2                   3 × 5 = 15
    1  1  2  3                  2  3  5  8
    1 × 3 = 3                   2 × 8 = 16
```

What pattern do you see?

b. What pattern do you see for any 3 consecutive numbers? How does the computer program produce this pattern?

```
10  LET A = 1
20  LET B = 1
30  PRINT A
40  PRINT B
50  LET C = A + B
60  PRINT C
70  IF C > 10000
        THEN GOTO 110
80  LET A = B
90  LET B = C
100 GOTO 50
110 END
```

Working Backwards

Sometimes you can solve a problem by working backwards, using *inverse* operations.

Jill began reading a book on Sunday. Each day she read 20 more pages than the previous day. She finished the book on Saturday when she read 126 pages. How many pages were in the book?

Start with 126 pages and *work backwards* by **subtracting 20** from each day's total.

Day	Pages Read
Saturday	126
Friday	126 − 20 = 106
Thursday	106 − 20 = 86
Wednesday	86 − 20 = 66
Tuesday	66 − 20 = 46
Monday	46 − 20 = 26
Sunday	26 − 20 = 6
Total pages in book	462

EXERCISES

Solve by working backwards.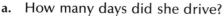

1. Mrs. Pirelli made a trip totalling 2810 km. Each day she drove 100 km more than on the previous day. On the last day she drove 762 km.
   a. How many days did she drive?
   b. How many kilometres did she drive on the first day?

2. Jason doubled his savings every day for 6 days. On the sixth day, his savings totalled $7.04. How much money had he saved on the first day?

3. If you add 7 to my age and double the result, you get 62. How old am I?

4. If you double the number of pennies in a tiny piggy bank for 20 days, on which day will the piggy bank be half full? (Assume the piggy bank is full on the 20th day.)

PRACTICE

Solve.

1. Rico chose a number, then added 5. He doubled the result, and finally tripled that result to get 72. What was the original number he chose?

2. Mary Beauchamp bought a computer. She made a down payment and then paid $150/month for one year. Her total payments amounted to $3400. What was her down payment?

3. Sheila chose a number and then took half of it. She took half of the result again and half of the new result once more. She obtained the result 7. What original number did she select?

4. The DeGroot family is flying to Europe. The plane is scheduled to leave at 10:35 in the morning. It takes 40 min to drive to the airport. At what time should the family leave home to arrive at the airport 45 min before the flight departure?

5. Rhonda had some money and earned $5.50 more. She spent $6.25 at a movie and had $11.75 left. How much did she have at the beginning?

6. Fishhooks are packed in small boxes. Twenty-four small boxes are packed into 4 bigger boxes. Altogether 2880 fishhooks are packed. How many fishhooks are packed into each small box?

Tennis Tournament

At a single elimination tennis tournament, Beth and Gina reached the final round. Altogether there had been 5 rounds. Beth and Gina had won their 4th round matches when all but 4 tennis players had been eliminated.

a. How many players were in the 4th round?

b. How many players were in the 2nd round?

c. How many players entered the tournament?

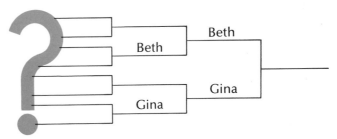

Using Calculator Patterns

A calculator can help you discover a pattern that will lead you to predicting the solution to a problem.

Multiply 1089 by 1, 2, 3, and 4 on a calculator.
List and study the products.
Can you predict the product of 1089 and 5?

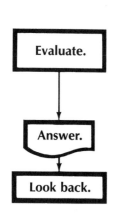

| 1 | 0 | 8 | 9 | × | 1 | = | | 1089 |

| 1 | 0 | 8 | 9 | × | 2 | = | | 2178 |

| 1 | 0 | 8 | 9 | × | 3 | = | | 3267 |

| 1 | 0 | 8 | 9 | × | 4 | = | | 4356 |

The product of 1089 and 5 is 5445.

Although the product was obtained by discovering and using the pattern, it checks as true on a calculator.

EXERCISES

Solve by using a calculator and discovering a pattern.

1. Predict the product of 1089 and 8. Recall the sample problem above.

2. List and study the products at the right.
    Then predict the product 25 and 3 333 333.

    | 2 | 5 | × | 3 | 3 | = |

    | 2 | 5 | × | 3 | 3 | 3 | = |

    | 2 | 5 | × | 3 | 3 | 3 | 3 | = |

3. List and study the quotients of $\frac{1}{9}$ and $\frac{1}{99}$. Predict the quotient of $\frac{1}{999}$ and $\frac{1}{9999}$.

4. List and study the repeated factor products at the right.
    a. Predict 2^7.
    b. Predict 2^{10}.

    2^4 | 2 | × | = | = | = |

    2^5 | 2 | × | = | = | = | = |

    2^6 | 2 | × | = | = | = | = | = |

Solve using a calculator.

1. Calculate the results below. Then predict 49×51.
   a. 19×21
      $20^2 - 1$
   b. 29×31
      $30^2 - 1$
   c. 39×41
      $40^2 - 1$

2. Find a pattern to help you predict:
   a. 18×22
   b. 28×32
   c. 38×42

3. Calculate the product below. Then predict 37×21.

   $\boxed{3}\,\boxed{7}\,\boxed{\times}\,\boxed{3}\,\boxed{=}$ $\boxed{3}\,\boxed{7}\,\boxed{\times}\,\boxed{6}\,\boxed{=}$ $\boxed{3}\,\boxed{7}\,\boxed{\times}\,\boxed{9}\,\boxed{=}$

4. The product $3 \times 2 \times 1$ can be written as 3! It is read as, "Three factorial." If $4! = 4 \times 3 \times 2 \times 1$, what is 5! and 7!?

5. Calculate the first three results. Then predict the next three. Check your predictions on a calculator.
   a. $\boxed{1}\,\boxed{\times}\,\boxed{8}\,\boxed{+}\,\boxed{1}\,\boxed{=}$ $\boxed{1}\,\boxed{2}\,\boxed{\times}\,\boxed{8}\,\boxed{+}\,\boxed{2}\,\boxed{=}$ $\boxed{1}\,\boxed{2}\,\boxed{3}\,\boxed{\times}\,\boxed{8}\,\boxed{+}\,\boxed{3}\,\boxed{=}$
   b. $1234 \times 8 + 4$ $12\,345 \times 8 + 5$ $123\,456 \times 8 + 6$

6. Discover the patterns formed by the last digits in the products. Use the patterns to complete each.
   a. $\blacksquare^7 = 78\,125$ $2^1 = \blacksquare, 2^2 = \blacksquare, 2^3 = \blacksquare, 2^4 = \blacksquare, 2^5 = \blacksquare$, and so on
   b. $\blacksquare^9 = 512$ $3^1 = \blacksquare, 3^2 = \blacksquare, 3^3 = \blacksquare, 3^4 = \blacksquare, 3^5 = \blacksquare$, and so on
   c. $\blacksquare^7 = 2187$ $5^1 = \blacksquare, 5^2 = \blacksquare, 5^3 = \blacksquare, 5^4 = \blacksquare, 5^5 = \blacksquare$, and so on

Solve.

1. A farmer fenced a field in the shape of a square so that there were 128 fence posts on each side. How many posts did he use?

2. A disc jockey plays three records for every ten minutes of his radio program. How many records would he play after an hour and a half?

3. Libby thought of a number, then subtracted 27. She multiplied the result by 5, and finally added 100 to get 215. What was Libby's original number?

4. Find the products below on a calculator. Then predict the product of 9999×9999.

   $\boxed{9}\,\boxed{\times}\,\boxed{9}\,\boxed{=}$ $\boxed{9}\,\boxed{9}\,\boxed{\times}\,\boxed{9}\,\boxed{9}\,\boxed{=}$ $\boxed{9}\,\boxed{9}\,\boxed{9}\,\boxed{\times}\,\boxed{9}\,\boxed{9}\,\boxed{9}\,\boxed{=}$

Solve.

1. How many different-sized trapezoids can you find in the figure at the right?

2. The table shows how far a dropped ball has rolled after the first few seconds.

    a. How far has the ball rolled after 5 s?
    b. How many seconds will it take for the ball to roll 245 m?

Seconds	1	2	3	4	5	6	7	8	9
Distance (m)	5	20	45	80	125				

3. Kim found a honeycomb shaped like the figure at the right, only larger. There were 12 hexagons in the largest row. Each row above and below the middle row has one less hexagon than the previous row. How many hexagons were in the honeycomb Kim found?

4. On Monday, Tim's mother made a short drive for business reasons. On Tuesday, she drove twice as far as on Monday. On Wednesday, she drove twice as far as on Tuesday. She travelled a distance of 108 km on Wednesday. How far did she drive on Monday?

5. If the *output* number is 55, what is the *input* number?

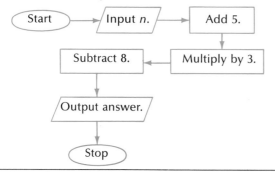

6. Calculate the results.

    a. $\boxed{9} \times \boxed{9} + \boxed{7} =$

    b. $\boxed{9} \times \boxed{9}\,\boxed{8} + \boxed{6} =$

    c. $\boxed{9} \times \boxed{9}\,\boxed{8}\,\boxed{7} + \boxed{5} =$

Predict the results.

    d. $9 \times 9876 + 4 = \blacksquare$
    e. $\blacksquare \times \blacksquare + \blacksquare = 888\ 888$
    f. $\blacksquare \times \blacksquare + \blacksquare = 8\ 888\ 888$

ELIZABETH B. PHIN
PUBLIC SCHOOL

Fractions

Write a multiplication equation for each diagram.

1.

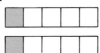

2.

3.

Multiply. Write the product in simplest terms.

4. $4 \times \frac{3}{5}$ **5.** $2 \times \frac{1}{3}$ **6.** $\frac{1}{7} \times 5$ **7.** $\frac{3}{8} \times 6$

8. $\frac{3}{4}$ of 16 **9.** $\frac{5}{6}$ of 36 **10.** $\frac{7}{8}$ of 72 **11.** $\frac{9}{10}$ of 200

12. $\frac{1}{4} \times \frac{1}{5}$ **13.** $\frac{5}{8} \times \frac{1}{2}$ **14.** $\frac{4}{5} \times \frac{7}{12}$ **15.** $\frac{1}{9} \times \frac{2}{3}$

16. $\frac{4}{5} \times 3\frac{1}{8}$ **17.** $11 \times 2\frac{1}{2}$ **18.** $2\frac{2}{3} \times 1\frac{3}{4}$ **19.** $2\frac{5}{9} \times 1\frac{1}{5}$

Write the reciprocal for each.

20. 7 **21.** $\frac{3}{11}$ **22.** $\frac{1}{16}$ **23.** $3\frac{7}{8}$

Divide. Write the quotient in simplest terms.

24. $3 \div \frac{1}{2}$ **25.** $\frac{4}{5} \div 8$ **26.** $12 \div \frac{3}{4}$ **27.** $9 \div \frac{6}{7}$

28. $\frac{2}{3} \div \frac{5}{6}$ **29.** $\frac{3}{10} \div \frac{1}{5}$ **30.** $\frac{7}{8} \div \frac{11}{12}$ **31.** $\frac{3}{4} \div \frac{1}{20}$

32. $15 \div 3\frac{1}{3}$ **33.** $1\frac{1}{8} \div 1\frac{1}{4}$ **34.** $6 \div 2\frac{4}{7}$ **35.** $1\frac{7}{8} \div 1\frac{2}{3}$

Solve.

36. How many $\frac{3}{4}$s are in 5? **37.** How many $\frac{2}{3}$s are in $1\frac{3}{5}$?

38. How many $1\frac{1}{4}$s are in $2\frac{2}{9}$? **39.** How many $5\frac{1}{2}$s are in 100?

40. Dave completes his three household chores in $\frac{3}{4}$ of an hour. If he is $\frac{2}{3}$ finished with his chores, how long has he worked? How many chores has he done?

UNIT 11
Ratio, Proportion, and Percent

Ratio

Ratio is a comparison of numbers.

The ratio of customers waiting in line to customers at teller windows is **9 to 3**.

This is often written **9:3** or $\frac{9}{3}$.

The **terms** of the ratio are **9** and **3**.

Write each as a ratio in three ways.

Football

CFL

EASTERN DIVISION

	GP	W	L	T	F	A	P
Toronto	14	7	6	1	357	376	15
Hamilton	13	6	6	1	326	344	13
Ottawa	13	3	10	0	286	383	6
Montreal	13	2	11	0	199	411	4

WESTERN DIVISION

	GP	W	L	T	F	A	P
Winnipeg	14	11	3	0	406	295	22
Calgary	14	8	5	1	359	379	17
Edmonton	13	8	5	0	451	273	16
B.C.	13	8	5	0	376	314	16
Saskatch'n	13	5	7	1	344	329	11

Sunday's results
Winnipeg 29, Toronto 16
Calgary 55, Hamilton 48

1. The points scored on Sunday by Winnipeg to the points scored by Toronto.

   ■ to ■   or   ■:■   or $\frac{■}{■}$

2. The games won by Edmonton to the games played by Edmonton.

3. The games tied by Calgary to the games played by Calgary.

Write a ratio.

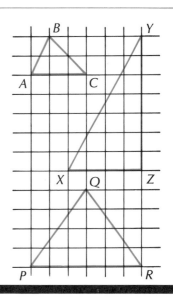

1. The base of △ABC to the height of △ABC.

2. The height of △XYZ to the height of △PQR.

3. The base of △PQR to the height of △PQR.

4. The area of △ABC to the area of △XYZ.

5. The base of △XYZ to the base of △PQR.

6. The base of △XYZ to the height of △XYZ.

7. The area of △PQR to the area of △PQR.

8. The base of △ABC to the base of △XYZ, to the base of △PQR.

Pan-Am Games

Write a ratio.

Medal standing

254 events completed

	G	S	B
United States	122	80	49
Cuba	68	44	40
Canada	16	39	43
Brazil	13	21	14
Venezuela	11	25	26
Mexico	5	11	21
Argentina	2	11	19
Colombia	1	6	11
Chile	1	3	8
Peru	1	1	4
Uruguay	1	0	2
Ecuador	1	0	0
Puerto Rico	0	4	4
Dom. Republic	0	3	5
Bahamas	0	1	0
Nicaragua	0	1	0
Jamaica	0	0	5
Panama	0	0	3
Belize	0	0	1
Guatemala	0	0	1
Trinidad	0	0	1

1. The number of gold medals for Canada to the number of events.

2. The number of gold medals for the United States to the number of gold medals for Cuba.

3. The number of gold medals for Argentina to the number of events.

4. The number of gold medals to silver medals to bronze medals for Canada.

Proportion

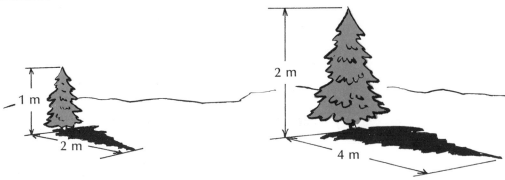

The *ratios* of tree height to shadow length are:

1:2 or $\dfrac{1}{2}$ **2:4** or $\dfrac{2}{4}$

An equation that shows two ratios are equivalent is called a **proportion**.

$$\frac{1}{2} = \frac{2}{4} \qquad\qquad \text{or} \qquad\qquad 1:2 = 2:4$$

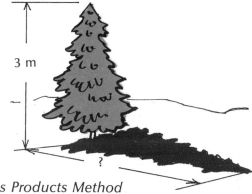

With the sun in the same place, how long would the shadow of a 3 m tree be?

Step 1   Write a proportion.

> $\dfrac{\text{tree height}}{\text{shadow length}}$ $\dfrac{1}{2} = \dfrac{3}{n}$

Step 2   Solve for *n*.

Equivalent Fractions Method	*Cross Products Method*
$\boxed{\times 3}$ $\dfrac{1}{2} = \dfrac{3}{n}$ $\boxed{\times 3}$ $n = 6$	$\dfrac{1}{2} = \dfrac{3}{n}$ $1n = 2 \times 3$ $1n = 6$ $n = \dfrac{6}{1}$ $n = 6$

The shadow of a 3 m tree would be 6 m long.

The two ratios in a proportion are identical when written in *simplest terms*.
$\dfrac{2}{4} = \dfrac{3}{6}$ **simplest terms** $\dfrac{1}{2} = \dfrac{1}{2}$ $\dfrac{9}{12} = \dfrac{15}{20}$ **simplest terms** $\dfrac{3}{4} = \dfrac{3}{4}$

EXERCISES

Write a pair of equivalent ratios for each picture.

1. △s to □s

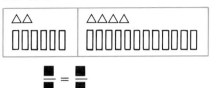

$$\frac{\blacksquare}{\blacksquare} = \frac{\blacksquare}{\blacksquare}$$

2. Xs to letters

X	XXX
ZZZ	ZZZZZZZZZ

$$\frac{\blacksquare}{\blacksquare} = \frac{\blacksquare}{\blacksquare}$$

3. hammers to nails

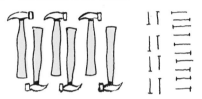

4. base to height

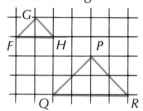

Write a proportion that expresses the ratio in simplest terms.

5. $\dfrac{5}{10} = \dfrac{\blacksquare}{\blacksquare}$
 6. $\dfrac{24}{36} = \dfrac{\blacksquare}{\blacksquare}$
 7. $4{:}6 = \blacksquare{:}\blacksquare$
 8. $14{:}16 = \blacksquare{:}\blacksquare$

9. $\dfrac{8}{40}$
 10. $\dfrac{9}{45}$
 11. $3{:}9$
 12. $25{:}75$

Find the missing term using the *equivalent-fractions method.*

13. $\dfrac{3}{4} = \dfrac{n}{16} \rightarrow \dfrac{3}{4} \overset{\boxed{\times 4}}{\underset{\boxed{\times 4}}{=}} \dfrac{\blacksquare}{16}$

14. $\dfrac{4}{7} = \dfrac{12}{n} \rightarrow \dfrac{4}{12} \overset{\boxed{\times 3}}{\underset{\boxed{\times 3}}{=}} \dfrac{12}{\blacksquare}$

15. $\dfrac{5}{6} = \dfrac{n}{36}$
 16. $\dfrac{6}{7} = \dfrac{n}{49}$
 17. $\dfrac{3}{5} = \dfrac{18}{n}$
 18. $\dfrac{n}{6} = \dfrac{35}{42}$

Find the missing term using the *cross-products method.*

19. $\dfrac{8}{12} = \dfrac{10}{n} \rightarrow \dfrac{8}{12} \diagdown\!\!\!\diagup \dfrac{10}{n}$

$8n = 10 \times 12$
$8n = \blacksquare$
$n = \blacksquare$

20. $\dfrac{9}{15} = \dfrac{n}{10} \rightarrow \dfrac{9}{15} \diagdown\!\!\!\diagup \dfrac{n}{10}$

$15n = 9 \times 10$
$15n = \blacksquare$
$n = \blacksquare$

21. $\dfrac{3}{12} = \dfrac{n}{28}$
 22. $\dfrac{4}{10} = \dfrac{6}{n}$
 23. $\dfrac{n}{8} = \dfrac{9}{12}$
 24. $\dfrac{8}{n} = \dfrac{9}{18}$

PRACTICE

Write a proportion that expresses the ratio in *simplest terms*.

1. $\dfrac{14}{35}$ 2. $\dfrac{50}{200}$ 3. $17:34$ 4. $9:6$ 5. $\dfrac{15}{9}$

6. $16:24$ 7. $\dfrac{8}{20}$ 8. $48:60$ 9. $25:175$ 10. $\dfrac{14}{42}$

Find the missing term.

11. $\dfrac{12}{21} = \dfrac{4}{n}$ 12. $\dfrac{3}{18} = \dfrac{n}{12}$ 13. $\dfrac{n}{20} = \dfrac{5}{25}$ 14. $\dfrac{18}{24} = \dfrac{n}{4}$

15. $\dfrac{7}{8} = \dfrac{n}{48}$ 16. $\dfrac{n}{22} = \dfrac{5}{55}$ 17. $\dfrac{18}{n} = \dfrac{36}{42}$ 18. $\dfrac{4}{12} = \dfrac{9}{n}$

19. $\dfrac{10}{n} = \dfrac{30}{42}$ 20. $\dfrac{n}{25} = \dfrac{7}{35}$ 21. $\dfrac{4}{n} = \dfrac{6}{30}$ 22. $\dfrac{4}{7} = \dfrac{n}{42}$

23. $16:25 = 32:n$ 24. $2:14 = n:21$ 25. $4:n = 6:75$

26. Write the ratio of length to width for each rectangle.
Find all pairs of equivalent ratios.

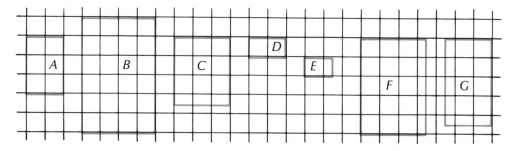

Copy and complete using $=$ or $\neq$.

27. $6:36 \bullet 4:20$ 28. $4:100 \bullet 6:150$ 29. $5:20 \bullet 9:35$

Write a proportion and find the value of n.

30. 2 large pizzas serve 5 people.
n large pizzas serve 20 people.

31. 8 people seated at 1 table.
64 people seated at n tables.

32. 12 donuts for 6 people.
n donuts for 30 people.

33. 18 test questions answered in 15 min.
n questions answered in 1 h.

Bicycle Gears

A ten-speed bike goes fastest when it is shifted to *tenth* or *high* gear.

The picture at the right shows the gear and chain position when a bike is in *tenth* gear.

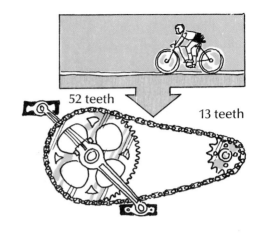

52 teeth

13 teeth

The *gear ratio* is 52:13 or 4:1.
The *turning ratio* is 1:4.

When a ten-speed bike is shifted to *first* or *low* gear, it is easier to ride uphill.

The picture at the right shows the gear and chain position when a bike is in *first* gear.

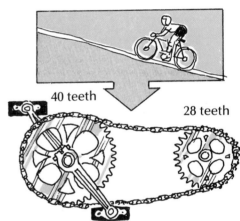

40 teeth

28 teeth

The gear ratio is 40:28 or 1.43:1.
The turning ratio is 1:1.43.

If a ten-speed bike has a wheel circumference of 216 cm, how far would it go with one turn of the pedal when it is in first gear? in tenth gear?

How High is the Flagpole?

Write two *equivalent ratios* to find the height of your school's flagpole.

Step 1   Find the *ratio* of your height to your shadow length.

Step 2   Write a *ratio* for the flagpole's height to its shadow length.

Step 3   Write a *proportion* to solve the problem.

259

Price Rates

Three kilograms of apples cost $3.99.
What is the cost of 2 kg?

Step 1   Write a proportion.

$$\frac{\text{kilograms}}{\text{cost}} \quad \frac{3}{3.99} = \frac{2}{n}$$

Step 2   Solve for n.

Equivalent Fractions Method

$$\frac{3}{3.99} \begin{array}{c} \boxed{\div 3} \boxed{\times 2} \\ = \\ \boxed{\div 3} \boxed{\times 2} \end{array} \frac{2}{n}$$

$$n = 2.66$$

or

Cross Products Method

$$\frac{3}{3.99} = \frac{2}{n}$$

$3n = 3.99 \times 2$
$3n = 7.98$
$n = \frac{7.98}{3}$
$n = 2.66$

The cost of 2 kg of apples is $2.66.

EXERCISES

Use a proportion to find the cost.

1. 5 kg of meat cost $9.95.
    What would 2 kg cost?

    $$\frac{5}{9.95} = \frac{2}{n}$$

2. 4 cauliflowers cost $2.75.
    What would 3 cost?

    $$\frac{4}{2.75} = \frac{\blacksquare}{\blacksquare}$$

3. 6 movie tickets cost $31.50.
    What would 1 cost?

    $$\frac{6}{31.50} = \frac{\blacksquare}{\blacksquare}$$

4. 2 theatre tickets cost $17.
    7 theatre tickets cost $n.

    $$\frac{2}{17} = \frac{\blacksquare}{\blacksquare}$$

5. 3 tubes of toothpaste cost $5.67.
    5 tubes of toothpaste cost $n.

6. 6 bus rides cost $3.50.
    n bus rides cost $14.00.

7. 5 coloured pencils cost $1.29.
    25 coloured pencils cost $n.

8. 10 diskettes cost $39.95.
    4 diskettes cost $n.

Copy and complete the table.

9.

Number of tickets	1	2	3	4	5	6	7	8	9
Cost in dollars	?	$9.50	?	?	?	?	?	?	?

PRACTICE

Copy and complete the table.

1.

Grams of ham slices	100	200	300	400	500
Cost in dollars			$3.81		

2.

Kilograms of potatoes	0.5	1	1.5	2	2.5
Cost in dollars			$2.96		

3.

Kilograms of pears	0.5	1	1.5	2	2.5
Cost in dollars	$2.54				

Use a proportion to help you solve the problem.

4. If 4 bars of soap cost $2.69, what do 3 bars cost?

5. If 3 cabbages cost $1.99, what do 5 cabbages cost?

6. If 2 handkerchiefs cost $7.75, what do 5 handkerchiefs cost?

7. If 6 ice-cream sandwiches cost $3.30, what do 10 ice-cream sandwiches cost?

8. If Mary earns $3.75 after 3 h of baby-sitting, how much would she earn after 4 h?

9. If it costs $29.12 for 56 L of gas, what do 3 L cost?

10. If 6 pairs of socks sell for $8.99, what do 10 pairs cost?

Consumer Affairs

Choose the better buy for each.

Cooking Onions	Swiss Cheese	Sport Socks

4.4 kg bag $2.69

0.4 kg $1.89

3 pairs/$6.95

1.5 kg bag $0.88

0.1 kg $0.89

5 pairs/$9.95

261

Speed

An airplane flew 4596 km from Montreal to Shannon, Ireland in six hours. What was the speed of the airplane?

Step 1 Write a proportion.

$$\frac{\text{kilometres}}{\text{hours}} \quad \frac{n}{1} = \frac{4596}{6}$$

Step 2 Solve for *n*.

Equivalent Fractions Method

$$\frac{n}{1} \stackrel{\times 2}{=} \frac{4596}{6}$$
$$\quad \stackrel{\times 6}{}$$
$$n = 766$$

or

Cross Products Method

$$\frac{n}{1} = \frac{4596}{6}$$
$$6n = 1 \times 4596$$
$$n = \frac{596}{6}$$
$$n = 766$$

The airplane flew 766 km for every hour of flight.

The *speed* of the airplane was 766 km/h.

$$\text{Speed} \quad \frac{766}{1} = \frac{4596}{6} \quad \begin{array}{l}\textbf{Distance} \\ \textbf{Time}\end{array}$$

EXERCISES

Find the *speed*.

1. 98 km in 7 h (kilometres per hour)
2. 4533 km in 6 h
3. 700 m in 20 s (metres per second)
4. 144 m in 9 s
5. 885 m in 15 min (metres per minute)
6. 2500 m in 5 min

Find the *distance* travelled.

7. At 88 km/h, how far does a car go in 4 h?
8. At 836 km/h, how far does a plane go in 2.5 h?
9. At 25 m/s, how far does a swimmer swim in 480 s?

Find the *time*.

10. At 90 km/h, how long does it take to travel 360 km?
11. At 45 words/min, how long does it take to type 1395 words?
12. At 760 km/h, how long does it take to travel 2765 km?

Copy and complete.

1.

Time (h)	1	2	3	4	5	6
Distance (km)		168.8				

Find the distance travelled.

2. At 95 km/h, how far can a car travel in 7.5 h?

3. At 650 km/h, how far can a plane travel in 3.5 h?

4. At 33 000 cm/s, how far does sound travel in a minute?

Find the speed.

5. Sound travels 19.8 km in 60 s (metres per second).

6. Light travels 18 000 000 km in 60 s (metres per second).

7. Mr. Lewis' secretary can type 825 words in 15 min (words per minute).

Find the time.

8. At 110 km/h, how long does it take to travel 462 km?

9. At 12.5 km/h, how long does it take to travel 37.5 km?

10. At 60 words/min, how long does it take to type 2550 words?

Solve.

11. Ted can run 8 m/s. The world's fastest humans can run 10 m/s. If Ted has a head start of 20 m, would he win a 60 m race?

Mining Sea Water

Many people believe that mining the sea will become practical in the future. The table below shows the number of parts per million of the most common elements in sea water.

Element	Milligrams per litre (mg/L)
Chlorine	18 980
Sodium	10 561
Magnesium	1 272
Sulfur	884
Calcium	400

How much sea water would have to be "mined" to obtain:

a. one tonne of chlorine?

b. two tonnes of sodium?

c. ten tonnes of calcium?

Scale Drawings

A **scale drawing** is a representation of a real object. The scale drawing shows the object as it looks, but is usually smaller than the real object.

For this scale drawing of the bicycle, 1 cm on the drawing represents 20 cm on the real bicycle.

> **Scale:**
> **1 cm = 20 cm**

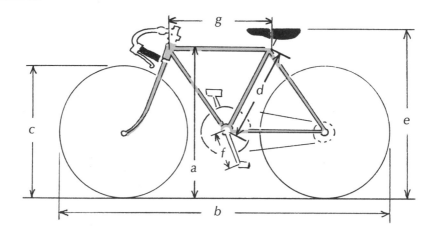

a measures 4 cm on the drawing.
What actual size does *a* represent?

Step 1 Write a proportion.

$$\frac{\text{scale drawing}}{\text{actual size}} \quad \frac{1}{20} = \frac{4}{a}$$

Step 2 Solve for *a*.

    Equivalent Fractions Method   *Cross Products Method*

    $$\frac{1}{20} \overset{\times 4}{\underset{\times 4}{=}} \frac{4}{a}$$ or $$\frac{1}{20} = \frac{4}{a}$$

                 $a = 80$ $1a = 4 \times 20$
                                           $1a = 80$
                                           $a = \frac{80}{1}$
                                           $a = 80$

a represents 80 cm.

Use the bicycle drawing at the left to find the length.

1. *b*

$$\frac{1}{20} = \frac{9}{b}$$

2. *c*

$$\frac{1}{20} = \frac{\blacksquare}{\blacksquare}$$

3. *d*

$$\frac{1}{20} = \frac{\blacksquare}{\blacksquare}$$

4. *e*

5. *f*

6. *g*

Write a proportion to find the real bird feeder measurements.

7. The height of the bird feeder.

8. The diameter of the bird feeder.

9. The distance from the first roost to the top.

10. The distance from the top roost to the bottom.

Scale:
3 mm = 2.5 cm

6 mm →

54 mm

Write a proportion to find the real distances.

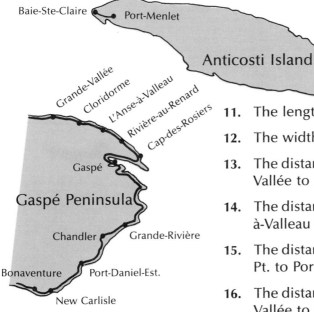

Scale:
3.7 cm = 100 km

Baie-Ste-Claire · Port-Menlet

Anticosti Island

Heath Pt.

Grande-Vallée
Cloridorme
L'Anse-à-Valleau
Rivière-au-Renard
Cap-des-Rosiers

Gaspé

Gaspé Peninsula

Chandler · Grande-Rivière

Bonaventure · Port-Daniel-Est.

New Carlisle

11. The length of Anticosti Island.

12. The width of Anticosti Island.

13. The distance to travel by boat from Grande-Vallée to Baie-Ste-Claire.

14. The distance to travel by car from L'Anse-à-Valleau to Cap-des-Rosiers.

15. The distance to travel by boat from Heath Pt. to Port-Daniel-Est.

16. The distance to travel by car from Grande-Vallée to Bonaventure.

PRACTICE

Use the scale to find the actual table measurements.

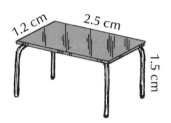

1. Length of the table.

2. Width of the table.

3. Height of the table.

Scale:
1 cm = 38 cm

Find the actual length and width for each room.

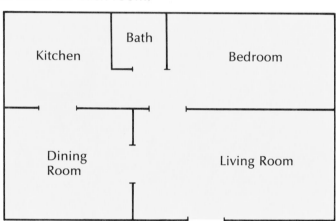

4. The kitchen.

5. The living room.

6. The bedroom.

7. The bath.

8. The dining room.

9. The whole house.

Scale: 2 cm = 5 m

Kitchen

Bath

Bedroom

Dining Room

Living Room

Find the distances between the cities if you could travel in a straight line.

10. Between London, England and Paris, France.

11. Between Dublin, Ireland and Köln, West Germany.

12. Between Glasgow, Scotland and Cardiff, Wales.

13. Between Brussels, Belgium and Dublin, Ireland.

14. Between Paris, France and Glasgow, Scotland.

Scale: 1 cm = 160 km

SCOTLAND

Glasgow

IRELAND

Dublin

North Sea

ENGLAND

WALES

Cardiff

London

NETHERLANDS

BELGIUM

Brussels

Köln

FRANCE

Paris

WEST GERMANY

The Nautical Mile

Navigation on the sea and in the air uses the **nautical mile** as the standard unit of length. Unlike land measures, the nautical mile has always been based on the size of the earth. The accepted value for the size of a nautical mile has varied over the centuries as estimates on the size of the earth varied. Columbus and Magellan, for example, considered *one degree of latitude at the equator* to be equal to 45.3 nautical miles.

Today, the standard international value for the nautical mile is set at 1852 m or 1.852 km, which is the length of *one minute of latitude at the equator.*

> Each degree of latitude is divided into 60 minutes.
> $1° = 60'$

1. What is the accepted length of one degree of latitude at the equator today in nautical miles? in kilometres?

2. What is the accepted earth's circumference at the equator today in nautical miles? in kilometres?

3. What did Magellan think the circumference of the earth was in nautical miles?

4. What would Columbus give as the length of one minute of latitude in nautical miles?

267

Meaning of Percent

Fifty-two of the hundred people at the right are male. This can be expressed in three ways.

fraction   *decimal*   *percent*

$\frac{52}{100}$ 0.52   52%

Forty-eight of the hundred people are female.

fraction   *decimal*   *percent*

$\frac{48}{100}$ 0.48   48%

The total number of people can be expressed in three ways.

fraction   *decimal*   *percent*

$\frac{100}{100}$ 1.00   100%

Percent means **per hundred**.

EXERCISES

Write the fraction in decimal and percent form.

1. $\frac{24}{100}$ 2. $\frac{8}{100}$ 3. $\frac{95}{100}$ 4. $\frac{132}{100}$ 5. $\frac{247}{100}$

Write in percent form.

6. 0.04   7. 0.27   8. 0.09   9. 1.00   10. 2.25

Write the percent in decimal and fraction form.

11. 78%   12. 5%   13. 20%   14. 186%   15. 1%

Write the fraction, decimal, and the percent for the shaded part.

16. 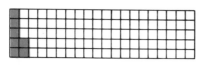   17.

18.    19. 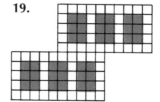   20.

Copy and complete the table.

	Amount per hundred	Ratio or fraction	Decimal	Percent
1.	35 per 100			
2.			0.02	
3.		$\frac{30}{100}$		
4.				88%
5.	9 per 100			
6.		$\frac{114}{100}$		

REVIEW

Write a ratio. AAXXXXXXCCCCAAAA

1. Cs to Xs   2. Xs to As   3. vowels to consonants

Find the missing term.

4. $\frac{n}{15} = \frac{6}{9}$ 5. $\frac{2}{3} = \frac{10}{n}$ 6. $\frac{15}{24} = \frac{n}{8}$ 7. $\frac{8}{16} = \frac{n}{18}$

Copy and complete.

8.	Number of tickets	1	2	3	4	5	6
	Cost in dollars				$35.00		

Copy and complete.

9.	Time (h)	1	2	3	4	5	6
	Distance (km)			2655			

Find the actual distance.   Bay   Scale: 1 cm = 1.5 km

10. Bay to Fay   11. Fay to Ray   Fay   Ray

Write the equivalent fraction, decimal, and percent.

12. 46 per 100   13. 225 per 100   14. 4 per 100   15. 72 per 100

Finding the Percent

In a TV commercial, this claim was made.

Four out of five people surveyed chose Suds toothpaste.

What percent of the people surveyed chose Suds toothpaste?

Method 1
Write a proportion.

Express the ratio $\frac{4}{5}$ in *hundredths*.

$$\text{percent} \quad \frac{n}{100} = \frac{4}{5} \begin{array}{l}\text{part}\\\text{whole}\end{array}$$

$$\frac{n}{100}\overset{\div\,20}{=}\frac{4}{5}_{\div\,20}$$

$$n = 80$$

Check: $\dfrac{80}{100} = \dfrac{4}{5}$

$$80\% = \frac{4}{5}$$

Method 2

The *part* is 4.
The *whole* is 5.
What *percent* is 4 out of 5?

Divide to find the *percent*.

$$\begin{array}{l}\text{part} \\ \text{whole}\end{array}\frac{4}{5} \qquad 5\overline{)4.0}^{\,0.8} \qquad 0.8 = 80\%$$

Memory Aid:
Cover the "percent" region.

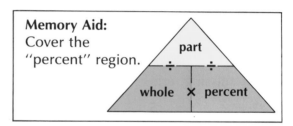

whole   ✕   percent

Eighty percent of the people chose Suds toothpaste.

EXERCISES

Find the percent by writing a proportion.

1. 19 out of 25 $\dfrac{19}{25} = \dfrac{n}{100}$ 2. 5 out of 16 $\dfrac{5}{16} = \dfrac{n}{100}$

3. 21 out of 40   4. 27 out of 80   5. 128 out of 200   6. 7 out of 8

7. a. What percent of the circles are shaded?
   b. What percent of the circles are not shaded?

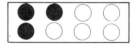

Find the percent by dividing the part by the whole.

8. 9 out of 20 $20\overline{)9.00}$ 9. 7 out of 25 $25\overline{)7.00}$

10. 1 out of 8 $8\overline{)1.000}$ 11. 33 out of 40 $40\overline{)33.000}$

12. 6 out of 10   13. 45 out of 150   14. 84 out of 140   15. 204 out of 272

16. a. What percent of the circles are shaded?
    b. What percent of the circles are not shaded?

Find the percent.

1. 13 out of 52
2. 7 out of 8
3. 24 out of 25
4. 6 out of 50
5. 35 out of 200
6. 180 out of 300
7. 13 out of 20
8. 15 out of 16
9. 12 is what percent of 24?
10. 4 is what percent of 80?
11. What percent of 25 is 16?
12. What percent of 40 is 28?
13. 500 is what percent of 800?
14. 600 is what percent of 600?

15. a. What percent of the letters in the rectangle ABCD are Xs?
    b. What percent of the letters in △ACD are Gs?
    c. What percent of the letters in △ABD are Xs?
    d. What percent of the letters in rectangle ABCD are Vs?

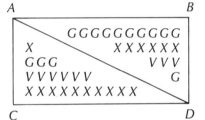

Solve.

16. Seventy-five dollars of the $120 that Marilyn earned was from baby-sitting. What percent of the money Marilyn earned was from baby-sitting?

17. Three hundred seventy-five of the 600 students at Cedarbrook School are bused there each day. What percent of the students at Cedarbrook School are *not* bused.

18. A class of 30 sailing students has 20 boys and 10 girls. What percent of the class are girls?

19. What percent of the numbers from 1 to 25 are even?

Take a Survey

Poll the students in your class to find out what percent of them:

a. play a musical instrument;
b. speak more than one language;
c. are left handed;
d. like mathematics.

Finding the Part

On a spelling test of 25 words, Sally had a score of 76%. How many words did Sally spell correctly?

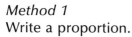

Method 1
Write a proportion.

$$\text{percent } \frac{76}{100} = \frac{n}{25} \text{ part} \atop \text{whole}$$

$$\frac{76}{100} \overset{\boxed{\div 4}}{=} \frac{n}{25}$$
$$\boxed{\div 4}$$
$$n = 19$$

Check: $\frac{76}{100} = \frac{19}{25}$

$$76\% = \frac{19}{25}$$

Method 2

The *percent* is 76%.
The *whole* is 25.
What *part* of 25 is 76%?

Multiply to find the *part*.
$$\text{whole} \times \text{percent} = \text{part}$$
$$25 \times 76\% = \text{part}$$
$$25 \times 0.76 = 19$$

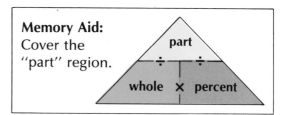

Memory Aid:
Cover the "part" region.

Sally spelled 19 words correctly.

EXERCISES

Find the part by writing a proportion.

1. 20% of 90
   $$\frac{20}{100} = \frac{n}{90}$$

2. 40% of 90
   $$\frac{40}{100} = \frac{n}{90}$$

3. 60% of 90
   $$\frac{60}{100} = \frac{n}{90}$$

4. 48% of 30

5. 16% of 32

6. 8% of 600

Find the part by multiplying the whole by the percent.

7. 25% of 140
   $0.25 \times 140 = \blacksquare$

8. 50% of 140
   $0.50 \times 140 = \blacksquare$

9. 75% of 140
   $\blacksquare \times 140 = \blacksquare$

10. 2.5% of 400
    $0.025 \times 400 = \blacksquare$

11. 10.5% of 1000
    $0.105 \times 1000 = \blacksquare$

12. $12\frac{1}{2}\%$ of 800
    $0.125 \times 800 = \blacksquare$

13. 45% of 60

14. 80% of 350

15. 20% of $19.95

16. 6.5% of 500

17. $9\frac{1}{2}\%$ of 800

18. 4.2% of 300

PRACTICE

Find the part.

1. 80% of 70
2. 45% of 36
3. 70% of 60
4. 75% of 84
5. 38% of 72
6. 6% of 14
7. 19% of 65
8. 2% of 32
9. 7.5% of 36
10. 2.3% of $60
11. $15\frac{1}{2}$% of $20
12. $6\frac{1}{4}$% of $100

13. $240.00 was earned. 90% of the money was put in the bank.
    a. How much money was put in the bank?
    b. How much money was spent?

14. $1250 is for school expenses. 80% of the money is for tuition.
    a. How much money is for tuition?
    b. How much money is for other school expenses?

Solve.

15. How much money did Sue spend on amusements?

16. How much money did Sue save?

17. How much more money did Sue spend on clothing than amusements?

Money Sue Earned One Summer—$640.

15% Clothing

10% Amusements

75% Saved

Calculator Percent

A calculator may be used for percent problems.

To find 36% of 40 use the keystrokes: $\boxed{3}\boxed{6}\boxed{\div}\boxed{1}\boxed{0}\boxed{0}\boxed{\times}\boxed{4}\boxed{0}\boxed{=}$.

To find what percent 25 is of 125 use: $\boxed{2}\boxed{5}\boxed{\div}\boxed{1}\boxed{2}\boxed{5}\boxed{\times}\boxed{1}\boxed{0}\boxed{0}\boxed{=}$.

Find the percent.

a.	2 out of 5	b.	3 out of 6
c.	5 out of 20	d.	15 out of 100
e.	4 out of 25	f.	3 out of 8
g.	1 out of 3	h.	1 out of 7

Find the part.

i.	15% of 20	j.	24% of 50
k.	40% of 15	l.	75% of 28
m.	12% of 150	n.	4% of 35
o.	82.5% of 30	p.	37.5% of 600

You may have a calculator with a $\boxed{\%}$ key.

If so, check your answers using the $\boxed{\%}$ key.

Finding the Whole

Frank went to a used sporting goods sale. He spent 60% of his money at the sale, or $18.00. How much money did Frank have at first?

Method 1
Write a proportion.

$$\text{percent } \frac{60}{100} = \frac{18}{n} \begin{array}{l} \text{part} \\ \text{whole} \end{array}$$

$$60n = 100 \times 18$$
$$60n = 1800$$
$$n = \frac{1800}{60}$$
$$n = 30$$

$$\text{Check: } \frac{60}{100} = \frac{18}{30}$$
$$60\% = \frac{18}{30}$$

Method 2

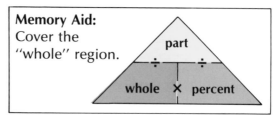

The *part* is $18.
The *percent* is 60%.
60% of what is $18?

Divide to find the *whole*.

$$\begin{array}{l}\text{part} \\ \text{percent}\end{array} \frac{18}{60\%} \qquad 0\,60.\overline{)18\,00.}^{\;\;\;30.}$$

Memory Aid:
Cover the "whole" region.

Frank had $30 at first.

EXERCISES

Find the whole by writing a proportion.

1. 48 out of what number is 80%?
$$\frac{80}{100} = \frac{48}{n}$$

2. 108 out of what number is 30%?
$$\frac{30}{100} = \frac{108}{n}$$

3. 70% of what number is 175?

4. 24% of what number is 120?

Find the whole by dividing the part by the percent.

5. 6 out of what number is 50%?
$$\frac{6}{50\%} \qquad 0.5\overline{)6}$$

6. 18 out of what number is 25%?
$$\frac{18}{25\%} \qquad 0.25\overline{)18}$$

7. 30 out of what number is 75%?

8. 115 out of what number is 20%?

9. $51.20 out of what is 32%?

10. $15.30 out of what is 45%?

11. 11 out of what is $5\frac{1}{2}$%?

12. $128 out of what is $12\frac{1}{2}$%?

PRACTICE

Find the whole.

1. 3 out of what is 75%?

2. 4 out of what is 80%?

3. 8 out of what is 40%?

4. 300 out of what is 60%?

5. 35% of what is 225?

6. 82% of what is 328?

7. 20 is 40% of what?

8. 7 is 35% of what?

9. 120 is 20% of what?

10. 340 is 5% of what?

11. $324 out of what is 8%?

12. $28.80 out of what is 15%?

13. 65% of what is $1.95?

14. 45% of what is $2.70?

15. 23 answers are correct on a test. The test score is 92%. How many questions on the test?

16. 54 band members are girls. 45% of the band are girls. How many band members are there?

Solve the following problems about the earth's surface.

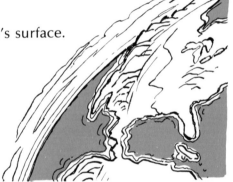

17. Land covers 29.2% of the earth's surface, or 43 508 000 km². How many square kilometres is the earth's surface?

18. Water covers 70.8% of the earth's surface. How many square kilometres of water are on the earth's surface?

Computerized Math Marks

Cathy has started to write a computer program that calculates marks for assignments.

Study the program she started at the right.

a. What is the lowest percent that results in a *B*?
b. Describe the effect of line 30.
c. Complete the program. Change the mark values to the ones used in your math class.

```
10 INPUT "NUMBER OF QUESTIONS ";N
20 INPUT "CORRECT ANSWERS ";C
30 LET P = (C/N)*100
40 PRINT "THIS ASSIGNMENT MARK IS ";
50 IF P >= 85 THEN PRINT "A"
60 IF (P)=70 AND P<85) THEN PRINT "B"
100 GOTO 10
```

Discount and Sales Tax

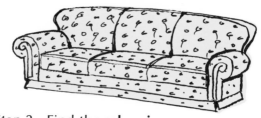

A sofa is on sale for 25% off the regular price of $625.00. What is the sale price? What is the total cost if 6% sales tax is charged?

Step 1   Find the amount of **discount**.

percent	×	whole	=	discount
25%	×	$625	=	discount
0.25	×	$625	=	$156.25

The amount of discount is $156.25.

Step 2   Find the **sale price**.

$625.00 regular price
− 156.25 amount of discount
$468.75 sale price

The sale price is $468.75.

Step 3   Find the **sales tax**.

percent	×	whole	=	sales tax
6%	×	$468.75	=	sales tax
0.06	×	$468.75	=	$28.125
			=	$28.13

The sales tax is $28.13.

Step 4   Find the **total cost**.

$468.75 sale price
+ 28.13 sales tax
$496.88 total cost

The total cost of the sofa is $496.88.

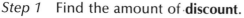

Find the amount of discount. Use Step 1 above.

1. regular price: $10
   discount rate: 25%

2. regular price: $24
   discount rate: 20%

3. regular price: $95
   discount rate: 30%

4. regular price: $200
   discount rate: 15%

Find the sale price. Use Steps 1 and 2 above.

5. regular price: $45
   discount rate: 20%

6. regular price: $16
   discount rate: 10%

7. regular price: $425
   discount rate: 30%

8. regular price: $6.95
   discount rate: 20%

Find the amount of sales tax. Use Step 3 above.

9. selling price: $100
   tax rate: 6%

10. selling price: $80
    tax rate: 7%

11. selling price: $15.95
    tax rate: 8%

12. selling price: $199.99
    tax rate: 12%

Find the amount of discount.

1. regular price: $150
   discount rate: 10%

2. regular price: $3.50
   discount rate: 30%

Find the amount of sales tax.

3. selling price: $30
   tax rate: 8%

4. selling price: $3500
   tax rate: 6%

Copy and complete.

	Regular Price	Discount Rate	Sale Price	Tax Rate	Total Cost
5.	$ 28.00	20%	?	6% (B.C.)	?
6.	$ 14.95	10%	?	5% (Sask.)	?
7.	$ 340.00	25%	?	12% (Nfld.)	?
8.	$ 985.00	30%	?	0% (Alta.)	?
9.	$2495.00	40%	?	7% (Ont.)	?

Solve.

10. What is the sale price of 0.5 kg of each kind of cheese?

25%off regular price

Cheddar	$ 9.50/kg
Roquefort	$24.00/kg
Gruyère	$15.20/kg

False Advertising?

Is the reported sale price in each ad correct?

Italian Sausage
25%off
reg. 8.58/kg
now 6.44/kg

Salmon
20%off
reg. 15.59/kg
now 12.79/kg

30%off Television Sets
reg. $495
now $360

25%off Sweaters
reg. $39.95
now $29.96

Simple Interest

John Murray deposited $850 in the bank at an interest rate of $7\frac{1}{2}\%$. How much interest will his money earn at the end of 1 year?

— The money deposited is called the **principal**, *p*.
— The money it earns is called the **interest**, *i*.
— The number of years the money is left in the account is called the **time**, *t*.
— The money earned is determined by the **interest rate**, *r*.

interest = principal × rate × time
$i = prt$

$$i = \$850 \times 7\frac{1}{2}\% \times 1$$
$$i = 850 \times 0.075 \times 1$$
$$i = \$63.75$$

After 1 year, $63.75 interest was earned.

COMMUNITY BANK		
DEPOSIT		
ACCOUNT NO. 673 - 24		DATE *Feb. 17*
NAME *John Murray*		

CHEQUES	CASH	
500 00	× 1	
	× 2	
	× 5	
	× 10	
	5 × 20	100 00
	5 × 50	250 00
500 00	CHEQUES BROUGHT FORWARD ▷	500 00
SUB TOTAL ▷		850 00
SIGNATURE		
DEPOSITOR S INITIAL *J. M.*	TOTAL ▷	850 00

EXERCISES

Find the amount of *interest* earned.

1. principal: $1000
   rate: 8%
   time: 1 year

   $i = prt$
   $i = \$1000 \times 8\% \times 1$
   $i = 1000 \times 0.08 \times 1$

2. principal: $1000
   rate: 8%
   time: $1\frac{1}{2}$ years

   $i = prt$
   $i = \$1000 \times 8\% \times 1\frac{1}{2}$
   $i = 1000 \times 0.08 \times 1.5$

3. principal: $1000
   rate: 8%
   time: 2 years

   $i = prt$
   $i = \$1000 \times 8\% \times 2$
   $i = 1000 \times 0.08 \times 2$

4. principal: $200
   rate: 12%
   time: 1 year

5. principal: $200
   rate: 12%
   time: 3 years

6. principal: $200
   rate: 12%
   time: 5 years

7. principal: $4500
   rate: $9\frac{1}{2}\%$
   time: 6 months

8. principal: $4500
   rate: $9\frac{1}{2}\%$
   time: 18 months

9. principal: $4500
   rate: $9\frac{1}{2}\%$
   time: 30 months

PRACTICE

How much interest is earned after 2 years?

1. money deposited: $400
   interest rate: 9%

2. money deposited: $1200
   interest rate: $10\frac{1}{2}$%

How much interest is earned after 6 months?

3. money deposited: $1950
   interest rate: $9\frac{3}{4}$%

4. money deposited: $450
   interest rate: $6\frac{1}{2}$%

Copy and complete.

5.

Principal	$1200	$1200	$1200	$1200	$1200	$1200
Rate	8%	$10\frac{1}{2}$%	12%	$7\frac{1}{4}$%	$8\frac{1}{2}$%	$9\frac{3}{4}$%
Time	$\frac{1}{2}$ year	1 year	$\frac{1}{4}$ year	3 years	$1\frac{1}{2}$ years	5 years
Interest	?	?	?	?	?	?

Solve.

6. Evelyn deposited $450 into her savings account at an interest rate of 10% guaranteed for 18 months. How much interest will her money earn after 18 months? How much money will she have altogether?

Compound Interest

Compound interest is interest that is calculated annually, semi-annually, quarterly, monthly, or even daily. At the end of the specified time period, the interest is *added on* to the principal. Thus, the principal and the amount of interest earned are always growing.

a. Suppose you deposit $200 at $13\frac{1}{4}$% for 3 years into a savings account. How much *simple interest* would be earned?

b. Suppose you invested $200 for 3 years under a plan which calculates the interest annually. How much *compounded interest* would be earned?

Reliable Trust Co.

13 $\frac{1}{4}$%

3 YEARS
paid annually

GUARANTEED TERM INVESTMENTS

279

Increase and Decrease

Briar School had 400 students in its first year. The number of students increased 10% the second year, but then decreased 10% the third year. How many students attended Briar School after the second year? after the third year?

Step 1
There was a 10% increase
from 400 students
after the second year.

| 10% × 400 = amount of increase |

0.10 × 400 = 40

There were 40 *more* students.

After the second year, there
were 400 + 40 or 440 students.

Step 2
There was a 10% decrease
from 440 students
after the third year.

| 10% × 440 = amount of decrease |

0.10 × 440 = 44

There were 44 *fewer* students.

After the third year, there
were 440 − 44 or 396 students.

EXERCISES

Find the amount of cost increase and the new cost.

1. cost before mark-up: $15
    percent mark-up: 20%

> 20% × $15 = amount of
> increase
> $15 + increase = new cost

2. cost before mark-up: $295
    percent mark-up: 30%

> 30% × $295 = amount of
> increase
> $295 + increase = new cost

3. cost before mark-up: $89.95
    percent mark-up: 40%

4. cost before mark-up: $15.95
    percent mark-up: 25%

Find the amount of mass loss and the new mass.

5. mass before diet: 55 kg
    mass loss: 10%

6. mass before diet: 68 kg
    mass loss: 8%

7. mass before diet: 82 kg
    mass loss: 5%

8. mass before diet: 105 kg
    mass loss: 15%

9. mass before diet: 124 kg
    mass loss: 4%

10. mass before diet: 98 kg
    mass loss: 0.9%

Solve.

1. The price of one share of an oil stock was $18.75. The next day, the price was down 20%. By how much did the cost of one share drop?

2. Melanie's math class had 30 students on the first day. Next, the number of students increased by 20%. How many students are now in Melanie's math class if about 11% are absent?

3. The cost of a phone call from Toronto to Thunder Bay at midnight is $1.50. If the phone company increases prices as shown at the right, what would be the new cost of the phone call?

Phone Company seeks 6% increase.

Find the *percent*.

1. 48 out of 50

2. 9 out of 20

3. 7 out of 8

Find the *part*.

4. 45% of 60

5. 20% of 340

6. $6\frac{1}{2}$% of 1000

Find the *whole*.

7. 16 is 25% of what?

8. 5 is 2% of what?

9. 30% of what is 60?

Find the amount of discount or of sales tax.

10. regular price: $65
    discount rate: 20%

11. selling price: $220
    tax rate: 7%

Find the amount of interest earned.

12. principal: $50
    rate: $7\frac{1}{4}$%
    time: 2 years

13. principal: $690
    rate: 8%
    time: 6 months

14. principal: $4400
    rate: $9\frac{1}{2}$%
    time: $3\frac{1}{2}$ years

Find the new mass after dieting.

15. mass before diet: 50 kg
    mass loss: 6%

16. mass before diet: 65 kg
    mass loss: 8%

TEST

UNIT 11

Write a ratio.   44FFFFF444444GGG8888

1. Gs to 4s
2. Fs to 8s
3. letters to numbers

Find the missing term.

4. $\frac{4}{3} = \frac{n}{18}$
5. $\frac{n}{25} = \frac{6}{30}$
6. $\frac{12}{18} = \frac{8}{n}$
7. $\frac{5}{n} = \frac{9}{27}$

Copy and complete.

8.

Kilograms of apples	0.5	1	1.5	2	2.5	3
Cost in dollars	?	?	?	?	$2.75	?

9.

Time (h)	0.5	1	1.5	2	2.5	3
Distance (km)	?	?	132	?	?	?

Find the actual distance.

Scale: 0.5 cm = 75 km

10. Ori to Ari

11. Ari to Uri

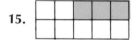

Write the equivalent decimal and percent.

12. $\frac{19}{25}$
13. $\frac{4}{5}$
14. ☐
15. ☐

Find the *percent*.

16. 11 out of 20
17. 3 out of 50
18. 7 out of 40

Find the *part*.

19. 36% of 400
20. 95% of 720
21. $6\frac{1}{2}$% of $2000

Find the *whole*.

22. 900 is 75% of what?
23. 252 is 36% of what?
24. $160 is 8% of what?

Find the amount of discount.

25. regular price: $36.95
     discount rate: 40%

Find the amount of sales tax.

26. selling price: $350
     tax rate: 5%

Find the amount of interest earned.

27. principal: $90
     rate: 9%
     time: 2 years

Find the new population.

28. old population: 840
     increase: 25%

Problem Solving

Solve.

1. Kerry arranged her collection of dimes in a shape like that at the right, only bigger.

   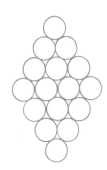

   There were 16 dimes in her largest row. Fourteen rows were above the largest row and fourteen below. The row above the largest row and the row below had 15 dimes each. How much was Kerry's dime collection worth?

2. A carpenter drives and sets a nail in 10 s. How many nails could he drive and set in 10 min?

3. Juan went to the seashore and collected a total of 13 starfish and shrimps. He counted 95 legs in his collection. Each starfish has 5 legs and each shrimp has 10 legs. How many sea creatures were starfish?

4. On a flag there were five stripes. The green stripe was next to the red and the yellow. The blue was above the white stripe. The red stripe was at the bottom. How were the stripes arranged on the flag?

5. Work backwards in the flow chart to find the Input number for each Output number in the table.

   What pattern do you find?

Input					
Output	3	7	11	24	35

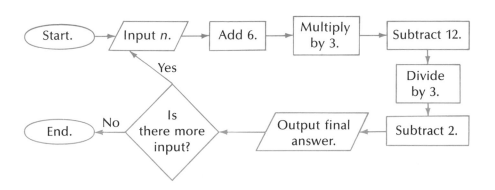

UNIT 12
Transformation Geometry

Slides and Translations

The doors of the cabinet *slide* horizontally to open and close the cabinet.

In the diagram at the right, $\triangle DEF$ is the **translation image** of $\triangle ABC$.

$$\triangle ABC \rightarrow \triangle DEF$$

> → means *maps onto*.
> A translation is a kind of mapping.

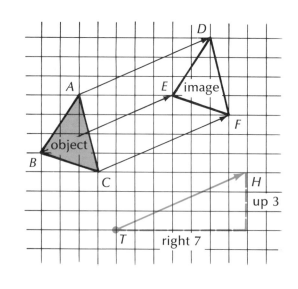

Arrow *TH* defines the translation as [R7, U3] or right 7, up 3.

In a translation, corresponding segments, like *BC* and *EF*, are congruent and parallel.

284

Refer to the diagram on the opposite page.

1. Copy and complete.

   a. $A \rightarrow$ ■   b. $B \rightarrow$ ■   c. ■ $\rightarrow F$ d. $\overline{AB} \rightarrow$ ■

   e. ■ $\rightarrow \overline{DF}$ f. $\angle A \rightarrow$ ■   g. ■ $\rightarrow \angle E$ h. $\triangle ABC \rightarrow$ ■

2. Define each translation.

   a. A to D [R■, ■ ■]   b. B to E c. C to F d. T to H

3. a. Compare the lengths of segments AD, BE, CF, and TH.
   b. Are these segments parallel?

4. a. Compare the lengths of AB and DE; AC and DF; BC and EF.
   b. Are these pairs of segments parallel?

5. Draw $\triangle EFG$ and arrow TH on plain paper.
   a. Trace $\triangle EFG$ and arrow TH. Name the traced points E', F', G', T', and H'.
   b. Slide the tracing along arrow TH until T' meets H.
   c. Press E', F', and G' onto the plain paper.
   d. Draw $\triangle E'F'G'$.

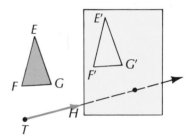

1. On grid paper, draw the translation arrows.
   a. [R5, U3]   b. [R4, D2]   c. [L3, U1]   d. [L2, D5]   e. [R0, D7]

2. Define each translation.

   a.
   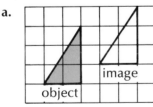

   b.
   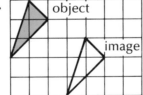

   c.
   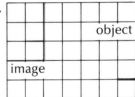

3. Draw the object and image on grid paper.
   a. [R5, U0]   b. [R0, D3]   c. [L3, D4]

   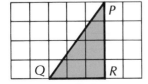
   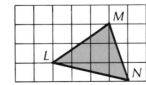
   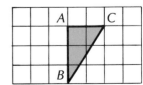

Turns and Rotations

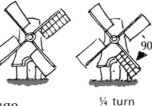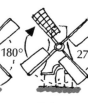

The windmill *turns* about a
fixed point in a clockwise direction.

¼ turn   ½ turn   ¾ turn

In the diagram, $\triangle DEF$ is the *rotation image*
of $\triangle ABC$ about point O.

Point O is the **centre** of the rotation.

Arc TH defines the rotation as 90° clockwise.

$$\triangle ABC \rightarrow \triangle DEF$$

> → means *maps onto*.
> A rotation is a kind of mapping.

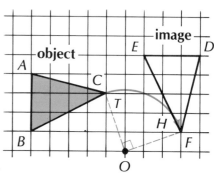

In the ¼ rotation, $\overline{OF} \perp \overline{OC}$ and $\overline{OF} \cong \overline{OC}$;
$\overline{OE} \perp \overline{OB}$ and $\overline{OE} \cong \overline{OB}$; $\overline{OD} \perp \overline{OA}$ and $\overline{OD} \cong \overline{OA}$.

EXERCISES

1. How many degrees are in each turn?

   a. a ¼ turn   b. a half turn   c. a ¾ turn   d. a full turn

2. Copy and complete. Refer to the diagram above.

   a. $A \rightarrow \blacksquare$ b. $\overline{AB} \rightarrow \blacksquare$ c. $\overline{BC} \rightarrow \blacksquare$ d. $\overline{AC} \rightarrow \blacksquare$
   e. $\blacksquare \rightarrow F$ f. $\angle B \rightarrow \blacksquare$ g. $\blacksquare \rightarrow \angle E$ h. $\triangle ABC \rightarrow \blacksquare$

3. What is the size of each angle?

   a. $\angle AOD$ b. $\angle BOE$ c. $\angle COF$

4. Compare the lengths of each segment.

   a. $\overline{OA}$ and $\overline{OD}$ b. $\overline{OB}$ and $\overline{OE}$ c. $\overline{OC}$ and $\overline{OF}$

5. Draw $\triangle EFG$, 120° arc TH, and centre O on
   plain paper.
   a. Trace $\triangle EFG$, arc TH, and centre O.
      Name the traced points T', H', E', F',
      and G'.
   b. Pin tracing paper at O. Turn tracing
      around O until T' meets H.
   c. Press E' F' G' onto the plain paper.
   d. Draw $\triangle E'F'G'$.

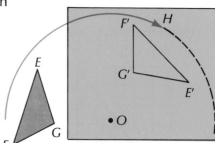

1. Make each diagram on grid paper. Draw an arc for each rotation. Use it to draw the rotation image for each clockwise rotation.

   a. 90°, centre A

   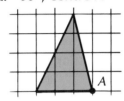

   b. 180°, centre O

   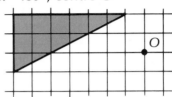

   c. 180°, centre M

   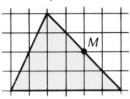

2. Describe the rotation by which 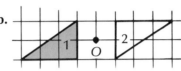 .

   a.

   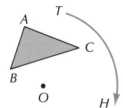

   b.

   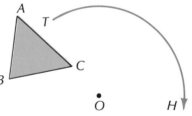

   c.

   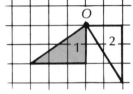

3. Make each diagram on plain paper.
   Use tracing paper to draw the image for the given rotation arc *TH* and centre O.

   a.

   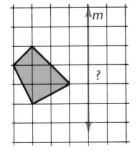

   b.

   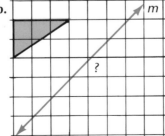

Flips and Reflections Revisited

Make each diagram on grid paper.
Then locate the *reflection image* of each object in line *m*.

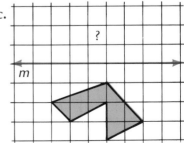

287

Transformations

A **transformation** maps each point in an object to its corresponding point in the image.

Translations, rotations, and reflections are transformations for which the image and object are congruent.

translation [L2, D3]	$\frac{1}{4}$ clockwise rotation about O	reflection in line *m*
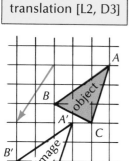	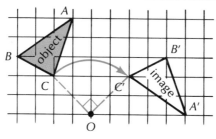	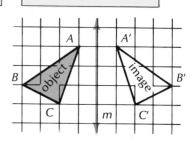

Sometimes two transformations are used to locate the image.

translation [R2, U1] and
$\frac{1}{4}$ clockwise rotation about O

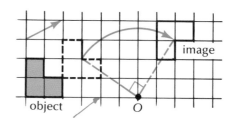

EXERCISES

Describe the transformation by which Figure 1 → Figure 2.

1.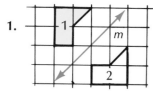

2.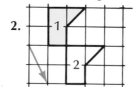

3.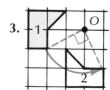

Describe the pair of transformations by which Figure 1 → Figure 2.

4.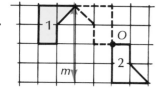

5.

6.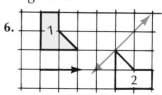

PRACTICE

Locate the image on grid paper.

1. 270° clockwise rotation, centre *A*

2. translation [L3, D4]

3. reflection in line *m*

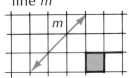

4. 180° clockwise rotation, centre *A*, and translation [L0, D2]

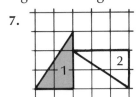

5. reflection in line *m* and translation [R1, U2]

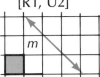

6. 90° clockwise rotation, centre *A*, and reflection in line *m*

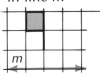

Describe a transformation or pair of transformations by which Figure 1 → Figure 2.

7.

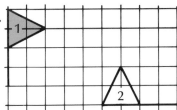

8.

9.

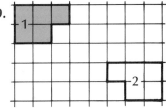

Transformation Patterns

Continue each pattern on grid paper to the end of the page.

a.

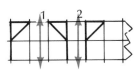

d.

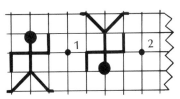

b.

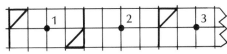

c.

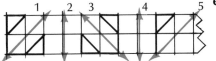

e.

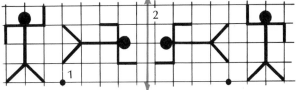

289

Rotational Symmetry

A figure has *rotational symmetry* if a tracing of the figure *fits onto* the original in less than one full turn.

You can use tracing paper to see that an equilateral triangle has rotational symmetry of *order 3*. This means that the tracing *fits onto* the triangle *three times* in one full turn.
The size of the angle for successive fits is 120° (360° ÷ 3).

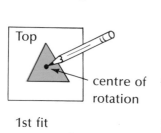

1st fit
(as traced)

centre of rotation

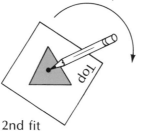

2nd fit

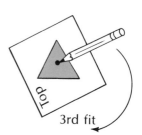

3rd fit

EXERCISES

These figures have rotational symmetry. Test them!

1.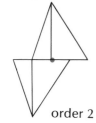
order 2

2.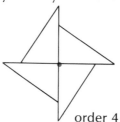
order 4

3.
order 6

4. Use tracing paper to find the order of rotational symmetry.

a.

b.

c.

d.

e.

f.

g.

h.

i.

5. Copy and complete the table.

Order of rotational symmetry	Size of angle for successive fits
1	360°
2	180°
3	
4	
5	
6	
7	
8	

290

1. Rotational symmetry of order 2 is called *half-turn symmetry*.
   Examine the digits at the right.
   a. Which digits have half-turn symmetry?
   b. Which pairs of digits are half-turn images of each other?

2. Which capital letters of the alphabet:
   a. have half-turn symmetry?
   b. are half-turn images of another letter?

   A, B, C, D, ...

3. Write two words that have half-turn symmetry.

4. Write a word that is a half-turn image of another word.
   (For example: WOW and MOM)

5. Playing cards use four suits:

   diamonds   hearts   spades   clubs

   Which suit symbols have rotational symmetry?

6. Does the playing card have rotational symmetry?

a.   b.   c.   d.   e.

7. *ABCD* is a parallelogram. Its diagonals intersect at *E*. Use tracing paper to show that *ABCD* has half-turn symmetry with centre *E*.

UNO

These are UNO cards:

Which is the six?

What number is this?

Quadrilaterals

Name / Classified by	Side-Angle Properties		Symmetry Properties
Quadrilateral	4 sides	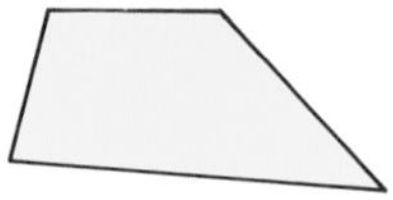	
Trapezoid	1 pair of parallel sides	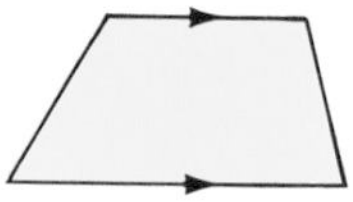	
Kite	2 pairs of congruent, adjacent sides	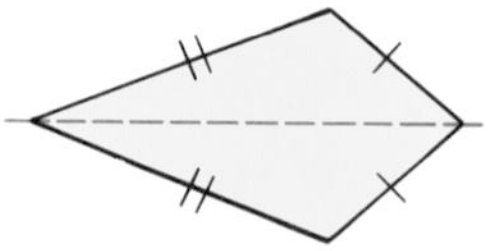	1 diagonal line of symmetry
Parallelogram	2 pairs of opposite, parallel sides	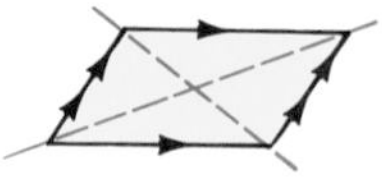	half-turn rotational symmetry
Rectangle	2 pairs of congruent opposite sides; 4 right angles	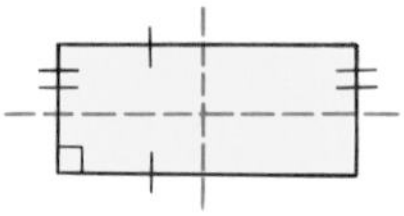	2 lines of symmetry through midpoints of sides; half-turn rotational symmetry
Rhombus	4 congruent sides	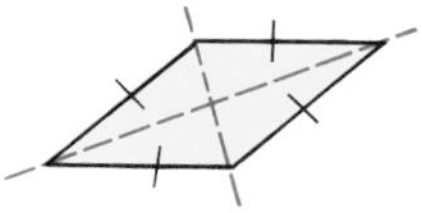	2 diagonal lines of symmetry; half-turn rotational symmetry
Square	4 congruent sides; 4 right angles	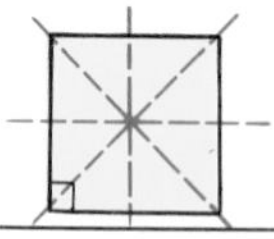	4 lines of symmetry; 4th order rotational symmetry

EXERCISES

Which quadrilaterals have the following properties?

1. 2 diagonal lines of symmetry

2. 4 congruent sides

3. 1 pair of parallel sides

4. 4th order rotational symmetry

5. 1 diagonal line of symmetry

6. half-turn rotational symmetry

7. 4 unequal sides

8. opposite congruent sides and 1 right angle

1. Name each quadrilateral. (Do not guess. Test each with a ruler and protractor.)

a.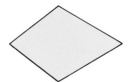

b.

c.

d.

e.

f.

2. Which of the seven types of quadrilateral are special parallelograms? What additional property does each have?

3. Is a square a rhombus? Explain.

4. Is a square a rectangle? Explain.

5. On grid paper, draw an example of each type of quadrilateral.

6. Copy the diagrams onto grid paper.
Complete each diagram into a quadrilateral that has the indicated lines of symmetry.

a.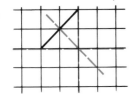

b.

c.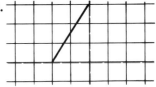

MIRA and Protractor Constructions

To construct a rectangle:

① Draw segment AB.

②, ③ Draw 2 segments perpendicular to $\overline{AB}$.

④ Draw a segment perpendicular to ② and ③.

Use a *MIRA* or a protractor to construct a square and a parallelogram.

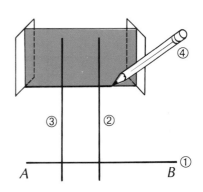

293

Regular Polygons

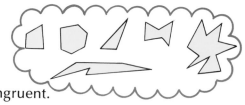

A closed figure consisting only of line segments is called a *polygon*.

A **regular polygon** has all sides and all angles congruent.

| equilateral triangle | square | regular pentagon | regular hexagon | regular heptagon | regular octagon |

EXERCISES

1. Is the polygon regular? Explain.

a.   b. 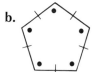 c. 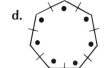 d.   e.

f. 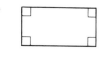 g.   h. i. j.

2. Copy and complete the table.

Regular Polygons

Name	Number of Sides	Number of Lines of Symmetry	Order of Rotational Symmetry	Number of Pairs of Parallel Sides
equilateral triangle	3			
	4			
	5			
	6			
	7			
	8			
regular dodecagon	12			

PRACTICE

1. a. Name some regular polygons that have an *odd* number of sides? Call them Set *A*.
   b. Name some regular polygons that have an *even* number of sides? Call them Set *B*.
   c. How do the lines of symmetry of the polygons in Set *A* differ from those in Set *B*?

2. Construct an *inscribed* equilateral triangle with a compass and a ruler.
   a. Draw a circle with any radius.
   b. Draw diameter *AD*.
   c. Using the circle's radius and centre *D*, draw arcs cutting the circle at *B* and *C*.
   d. Draw equilateral triangle *ABC*.

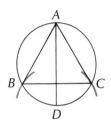

3. Construct an *inscribed* square.
   a. Draw a circle with any radius.
   b. Draw diameter *AC*.
   c. Draw diameter *BD* ⊥ diameter *AC*.
   d. Draw square *ABCD*.

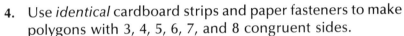

4. Use *identical* cardboard strips and paper fasteners to make polygons with 3, 4, 5, 6, 7, and 8 congruent sides.
   a. Which polygons are **rigid**?
   b. Use a protractor to adjust the angles of the non-rigid polygons to make regular polygons. Measure the size of each angle. Record the results in a table.

cardboard strip      punched hole   paper fastener

Logos

Regular polygons are often used in logos and signs.

Make a collage of signs and logos that use regular pentagons.

Describe the lines of symmetry and order of rotational symmetry for each.

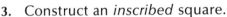

295

Floor Plans

The floor plan below shows four rooms in a motel.

a. Which rooms are reflection images of each other?

b. Which rooms are translation images of each other?

c. Why are the rooms planned this way?

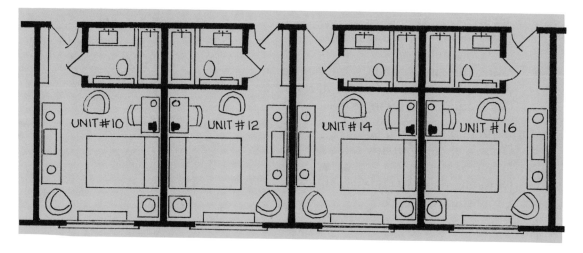

Dance Routines

Dance routines are often based on rotations, translations, and reflections.
Describe the transformation in each routine below.

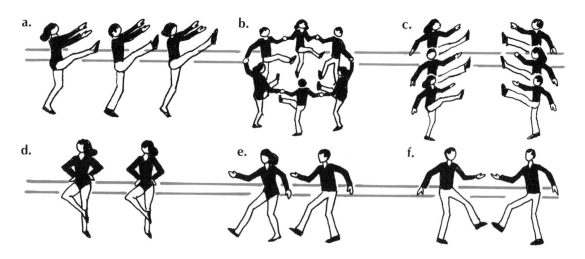

Identify the transformation that maps the object to its image. For example, write translation [R4, U7], or reflection in line *m*.

1.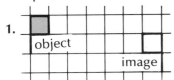

2.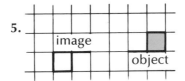

3.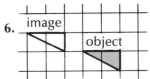

4.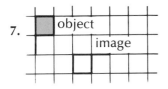

5.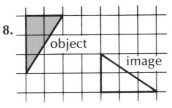

6.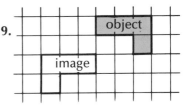

7.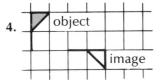

8.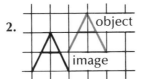

9.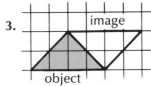

10. What is the order of rotational symmetry for each?

    a.
    b.
    c.
    d.
    e.

11. Identify each polygon. The dotted lines are lines of symmetry.

    a.
    b.
    c.
    d.
    e.

12. Define a regular pentagon.

13. What is the order of rotational symmetry for each?

    a.
    b.
    c.

14. How many pairs of parallel sides for each?
    a. regular octagon   b. square   c. regular pentagon

297

Tiles

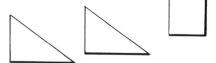

Geometric figures can be made by flipping
and turning *congruent tiles*.

The six polygons below were made from two congruent right triangle tiles.
Three polygons can be made by flipping across an edge. Another three
can be made by a half-turn about a midpoint of an edge.

Flip:

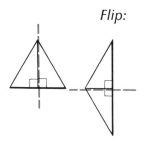

Half-Turn:

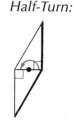

The quadrilaterals at the right
were made in the same way with
four congruent right triangle tiles.

Flips:

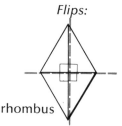

rhombus

Flips and turns:

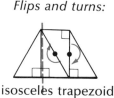

isosceles trapezoid

EXERCISES

Make two congruent right triangle tiles
out of cardboard.

1. Flip one tile across an edge to make and trace:
   a. a kite.   b. 2 different isosceles triangles.

2. Turn one tile about the midpoint of an edge to make and trace:
   a. a rectangle.   b. 2 different parallelograms.

3. Draw the lines of symmetry for each figure of problems 1 and 2.

4. Mark the corresponding congruent segments and angles for each figure.

Make two congruent isosceles triangle tiles
out of cardboard.

5. Draw and identify the figures made by a flip across an edge.

6. Draw and identify the figures made by a half-turn about the
   midpoint of an edge.

7. Repeat problems 3 and 4 for each figure from problems 5 and 6.

Make the following sets of congruent tiles out of cardboard.

Set *A*: (2 scalene triangles)

Set *B*: (2 obtuse triangles)

Set *C*: (2 equilateral triangles)

Set *E*: (3 equilateral triangles)

Set *F*: (4 equilateral triangles)

Do the following for each set of tiles.

1. Draw and identify the figures made by a flip across an edge.

2. Draw and identify the figures made by a half-turn about a midpoint of an edge.

3. Draw the lines of symmetry in each figure from problem 1 and 2.

4. Mark the corresponding congruent segments and angles in each figure from problem 1 and 2.

Polyominos

A **polyomino** is a figure formed by two or more squares placed edge to edge.

domino
2 squares

triomino
3 squares

tetromino
4 squares

pentomino
5 squares

hexomino
6 squares

1. Use square tiles to find and draw all the *different*:
   a. triominos. b. tetrominos. c. pentominos.

These triominos are the *same*.
They are related by a half-turn.

2. Some of the pentominos will fold to make an *open* cube. Identify them.

299

Tiling Patterns

Tiling patterns are constructed from congruent tiles which fit together to cover a surface without gaps or overlapping.

Such patterns have practical and artistic appeal.

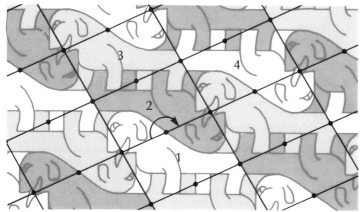

In the Escher tiling pattern at the left, each tile is a *transformation image* of every other tile.

Figure 1 is the *rotation image* of Figure 2 or the *translation image* of Figure 3.

Figure 4 is the *translation image* of Figure 2 or the *rotation image* of Figure 3.

EXERCISES

1. For parallelogram patterns *A* and *B* at the right, identify the transformation by which:
   a. tile 1 → tile 2.   b. tile 1 → tile 3.
   c. tile 1 → tile 4.   d. tile 2 → tile 5.
   e. How might tiles 6 and 7 have been positioned?

2. For the equilateral triangle pattern *C* at the right, identify the transformation by which:
   a. tile 1 → tile 2.   b. tile 1 → tile 4.
   c. In what ways might tiles 3, 5, 6, and 7 have been transformed?
   d. What figure is formed by tiles 1 and 2 together?

3. Repeat problem 2 for the scalene triangle tile pattern *D* at the right.

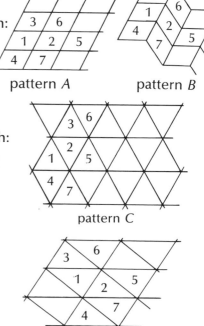

pattern *A*   pattern *B*

pattern *C*

pattern *D*

PRACTICE

1. Make four congruent quadrilaterals. Label the angles 1, 2, 3, and 4.
   a. Use rotation to continue the tiling pattern shown.
   b. What is the sum of angles 1, 2, 3, and 4?

2. Make congruent scalene triangles.
   a. Use different transformations to continue the tiling pattern shown.
   b. Trace three different parallelograms found in the tiling pattern.

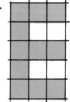

3. Make several regular polygons. Only 3 of the polygons shown will tile a surface. Experiment to find which ones they are.

4. Make each figure shown below. Which ones will tile a surface?

   a. 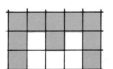   b.   c.   d.   e.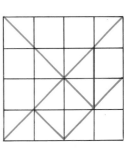

5. Make a set of tetrominos and a set of pentominos. (See page 299). Which tetrominos and pentominos will tile a surface?

Tangrams

Make the square design at the right on grid paper. Cut out the seven tangram pieces.

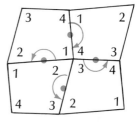

1. Fit the seven pieces edge to edge to make a:
   a. rectangle.
   b. parallelogram.
   c. right isosceles triangle.

2. Use the seven pieces to make these designs.

3. Then create your own!

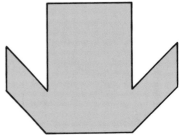

Enlar(ge)ments and Reductions

Enlargements and **reductions** are transformations. A given object
maps onto its enlargement image and reduction image.
The *size* of the image changes, but the *shape* stays the same.
The object and its image are **similar figures**.

Grids can be used to enlarge or reduce an object.

A. Given object:

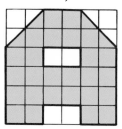

B. Enlargement image:

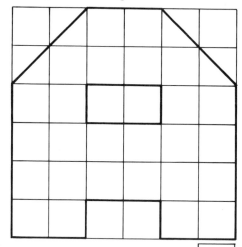

C. Reduction image:

The *scale ratio* is 1:2 (□:☐).
        image:object
The *scale factor* is 1 ÷ 2 or 0.5.

The *scale ratio* is 2:1 (☐ : ☐).
        image:object
The *scale factor* is 2 ÷ 1 or 2.

EXERCISES

1. How do the corresponding angles in the enlargement and the object compare in size?

2. How do the corresponding segments in the enlargement and the object compare in length?

3. How do the corresponding angles in the reduction and the object compare in size?

4. How do the corresponding segments in the reduction and the object compare in length?

5. Consider figure *C* above as the given object.
   a. What would be the *scale ratio* for its image *B*?
   b. What would be the *scale factor* for its image *B*?

302

PRACTICE

1. For each image of the object below, what is:
   a. the scale ratio? b. the scale factor?

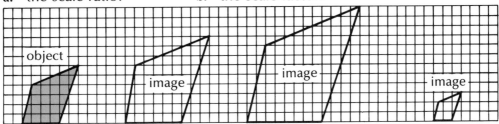

2. Use grid paper to enlarge and reduce the object below.
   a. Make an enlargement with a scale ratio 2:1.
   b. Make an enlargement with a scale factor 3.
   c. Make a reduction with a scale ratio 1:2.

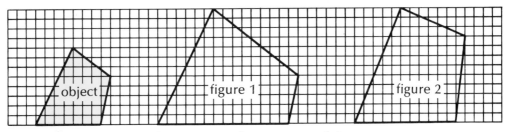

3. Show that figures 1 and 2 are not enlargements of the object above.

4. Construct each geometric figure and its image using a scale ratio 2:1.
   a. equilateral triangle   b. square
   c. regular hexagon   d. regular octagon
   e. right isosceles triangle

Distortions

In question 3 above, figures 1 and 2 are *distorted images* of the object.

Trace the figure at the right. Make images of it on distorted grids.

Distorted Grids

 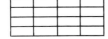

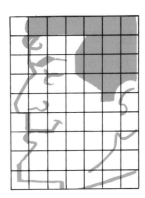

303

Three-Dimensional Figures

The objects of our world are *three-dimensional*.

They have *length, width,* and *height*.

They can be *solids, shells* or *skeletons*.

A brick is a **solid**.

A ping-pong ball is a **shell**.

Scaffolding is a **skeleton**.

A *polyhedron* is a 3-D figure whose faces are polygons.

Two kinds of polyhedrons are **prisms** and **pyramids**.

Prisms

Prisms have two congruent parallel bases. The lateral faces are congruent parallelograms or rectangles.

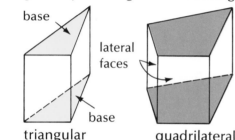

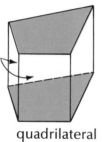

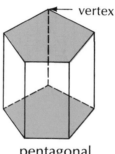

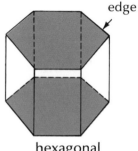

base

lateral faces

base

vertex

edge

triangular prism

quadrilateral prism

pentagonal prism

hexagonal prism

The *cube* and *cuboid* are **rectangular prisms**.

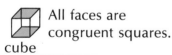

All faces are congruent squares.

All faces are rectangles. Opposite faces are congruent.

cube

cuboid

Pyramids

Pyramids have one base. All lateral faces in a pyramid are triangles.

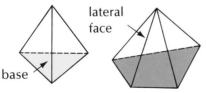

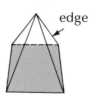

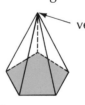

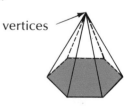

lateral face

edge

vertices

base

triangular pyramid

quadrilateral pyramid

square pyramid

pentagonal pyramid

hexagonal pyramid

EXERCISES

1. Classify each object as a solid, shell, or skeleton.
   - **a.** beach ball
   - **b.** wooden plank
   - **c.** pylon
   - **d.** a room
   - **e.** TV tower
   - **f.** cucumber

2. Which of the above objects is:
   - **a.** a prism?
   - **b.** a pyramid?
   - **c.** not a polyhedron?

3. The bases of the polyhedron below are shaded.
   Identify each as a kind of prism or pyramid.

   a.   **b.**   **c.**   **d.**

4. Copy and complete each table.

a.

Kinds of Pyramids	Number of		Total Faces
	Bases	Lateral Faces	
triangular			
quadrilateral			
pentagonal			
hexagonal			
octagonal			

b.

Kinds of Prisms	Number of		Total Faces
	Bases	Lateral Faces	
triangular			
quadrilateral			
pentagonal			
hexagonal			
octagonal			

PRACTICE

1. How many faces, vertices, and edges does a cuboid have?

2. *ABCD* is a triangular pyramid or a **tetrahedron**.
   Write the number of each for tetrahedron *ABCD*.
   - **a.** faces
   - **b.** lateral faces
   - **c.** vertices
   - **d.** edges
   - **e.** bases

3. Copy and complete the table. Include other prisms and pyramids.

Polyhedrons	Number of Faces (F)	Number of Vertices (V)	Number of Edges (E)	F + V − E
cube				
triangular prism				
tetrahedron				

Polyhedron Nets and Symmetry

The figure below is a **net** of a cuboid. It can be cut and folded to make the shell of a cuboid.

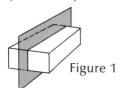   

A cuboid has three **planes of symmetry**.
Each plane of symmetry is shown below by a shaded cross-section.

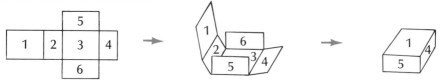

Figure 1   Figure 2   Figure 3

Each plane of symmetry divides the cuboid into two congruent halves.

Each half is a reflection image of the other half.

EXERCISES

Refer to the above drawings to answer each question.

1. How many rectangles are in the net of the cuboid?

2. How many faces are in a cuboid?

3. How many planes of symmetry does a cuboid have?

4. Name a cuboid face that is parallel and congruent to:
   a. face 1.   b. face 4.   c. face 5.

5. Which Figure above shows a plane of symmetry parallel and congruent to faces 5 and 6?

6. Make a cuboid using the net above.

7. Draw the lines of symmetry for each face of the cuboid. How do these relate to its planes of symmetry?

8. Place the cuboid against a mirror.
   a. Identify the figure made up of the cuboid and its image.
   b. What does the mirror represent?

1. a. Make nets for the following polyhedrons.
    b. Draw the lines of symmetry on each face.
    c. Cut and fold to make each polyhedron.

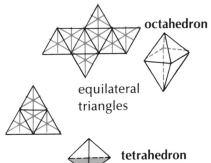

octahedron

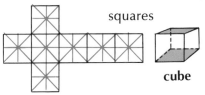

squares

equilateral
triangles

cube

tetrahedron

2. Copy and complete the table.

Regular Polyhedron	Number of Faces	Types of Faces	Number of Planes of Symmetry
regular tetrahedron			
cube			
regular octahedron			

3. The tetrahedron, cube, and octahedron (constructed above) are
    regular polyhedrons. All faces of each are congruent regular
    polygons. Is a cuboid a regular polyhedron? Why?

4. Which nets will fold to make a regular tetrahedron?

    a.   b.   c.   d.

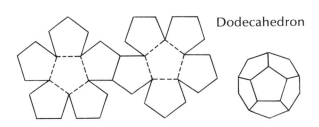

Big Nets

There are only five regular polyhedrons.
Three are shown above. The other two are shown below.
Construct these polyhedrons from their nets.

Dodecahedron

Icosahedron

Perspective Drawings

In *perspective drawings*, distant objects are smaller and appear to be farther away.

The drawing shown here is an overhead view to the right. The scene is put in perspective by the *vanishing point*.

The objects in the drawing are *distorted* but appear natural. The railroad tracks and telephone lines seem to converge (get close together). Yet these lines would be parallel in reality.

EXERCISES

Refer to the drawing at the top of the page.

1. Classify each segment as appearing parallel or converging in the drawing.
   a. sides of the road
   b. telephone poles
   c. railway tracks
   d. railroad ties
   e. telephone wires
   f. cross bars on telephone poles

2. The lines in which direction seem to converge?
   a. vertical
   b. left to right
   c. front to back

Answer the questions for both figures at the right. In reality, the length of $\overline{AE}$ is the same for both figures.

3. a. Is $\overline{AE}$ parallel to $\overline{DF}$?
   b. Is $\overline{AE}$ congruent to $\overline{AD}$?
   c. Is $\overline{AB}$ parallel to $\overline{DC}$?
   d. Is $\overline{AB}$ congruent to $\overline{DC}$?
   e. What three-dimensional figures do these represent?

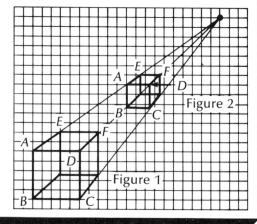

308

PRACTICE

The diagram shows the perspective drawing of a cube viewed from the front above eye level.

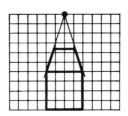

1. Make a perspective drawing of a cube viewed from:
   a. the left side above eye level.
   b. the right side above eye level.

2. Make a perspective drawing of a square pyramid viewed from:
   a. the front above eye level.
   b. the left side above eye level.

Below is the front, side, and top view of a cuboid when it is viewed at *eye level*.

  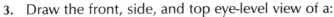

front   side   top

3. Draw the front, side, and top eye-level view of a:
   a. cube.   b. regular tetrahedron.   c. a TV set.

At the right is a front view of a billboard.

4. Make these two perspective drawings of the billboard.
   a. The viewer standing to the far right of the sign.
   b. The viewer standing to the far left of the sign.

Draw

Make a perspective drawing of a row of houses like the one at the right.
Label the lines which:
a. look parallel.
b. are parallel.
c. are converging.

Create your own perspective drawing.

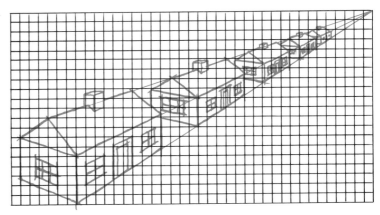

Making an Escher Drawing

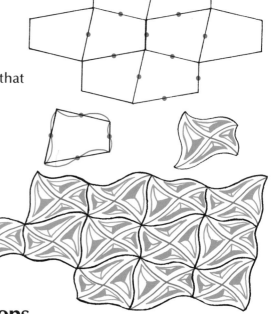

1. Tile a plane with quadrilaterals using half-turns about a midpoint.

2. Change each side of the quadrilateral so that the revised side has half-turn symmetry about its midpoint.

3. Decorate the revised figure.

4. Make a tile of the revised figure. Trace it repeatedly to make a tiling pattern.

Rigid and Non-rigid Polyhedrons

1. Make the polyhedron skeletons out of straws and pipe cleaners. Which are rigid? Explain.

   a.
   tetrahedron

   b.
   cube

   c.
   square pyramid

   d.
   triangular prism

   e.
   pentagonal pyramid

2. The geodesic dome is made of equilateral triangles on a pentagonal base. Is it rigid? Why?

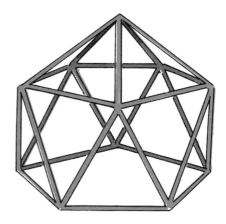

3. What can be done to this bookcase to make it rigid?

Soccer Ball Net

1. What are the basic figures on the surface of a soccer ball?

2. How many of these figures are there in all?

3. Construct a net for a soccer ball.

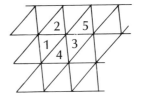REVIEW

1. Draw diagrams to illustrate how to place two congruent right triangle tiles so they form:
   a. an isosceles triangle
   b. a kite
   c. a rectangle

2. For the scalene triangle tiling pattern at the right, identify the translation by which:
   a. tile 1 → tile 2
   b. tile 1 → tile 3
   c. tile 1 → tile 4
   d. tile 1 → tile 5

3. Make an enlargement of the object at the right with a scale ratio of 3:1.

4. Identify each figure.
   a.
   b.
   c.
   d.

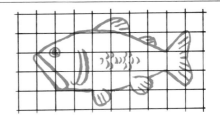

5. How many planes of symmetry are in each figure of question 4?

At the right is a perspective drawing of a cuboid, with vanishing point *P*.

6. Name 4 pairs of segments that are:
   a. drawn parallel.
   b. not drawn parallel.

7. Name a lateral face that is:
   a. a rectangle.
   b. a trapezoid.

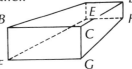

311

TEST   UNIT 12

1. Identify the transformation that maps the object onto its image. For example, write translation [L6, D2], or reflection in line *m*.

a.
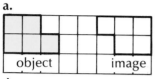

b.
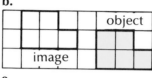

c. object   image
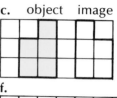

d.

e.

f.

2. What is the order of rotational symmetry?

a.   b.   c.   d.
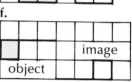

3. Make a drawing of each kind of polygon.
   a. scalene quadrilateral   b. trapezoid   c. kite
   d. parallelogram   e. rectangle   f. rhombus

4. Describe two regular polygons. Mention these features for each.
   a. sides   b. angles
   c. lines of symmetry   d. order of rotational symmetry

5. Draw two polygons which can be formed from two congruent isosceles triangle tiles.

6. Draw several block capital letters on a grid.
   Find two letters which will tile a surface.

7. Refer to the diagram at the right.
   a. Enlarge the object with a scale ratio of 4:1.
   b. Reduce the object with a scale ratio of 1:2.

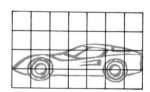

8. Identify each figure at the right.

   How many planes of symmetry are in each figure?

   a.   b.   c.

9. Make a perspective drawing showing the front eye-level view of a cuboid.

LOOKING BACK

Ratio, Proportion, and Percent

| R R R R W W W 2 2 2 2 2 2 2 2 S S 6 6 6 6 6 6 |

Write a ratio.

1. Rs to 6s   **2.** 2s to Ss   **3.** numbers to letters

Find the missing term.

4. $\dfrac{6}{9} = \dfrac{n}{27}$ **5.** $\dfrac{n}{16} = \dfrac{6}{24}$ **6.** $\dfrac{4}{12} = \dfrac{18}{n}$ **7.** $\dfrac{8}{n} = \dfrac{52}{26}$

Copy and complete.

8.

Kilograms of potatoes	0.5	1	1.5	2	2.5	3
Cost in dollars					$2.25	

Copy and complete.

9.

Time (h)	0.5	1	1.5	2	2.5	3
Distance (km)			937.5			

Find the actual distance.

10. Perry to Rand

11. Milton to Perry

Scale: 0.5 cm = 40 km

Perry • —————————— • Rand

Milton •

Write the equivalent decimal and percent.

12. $\dfrac{13}{20}$ **13.** $\dfrac{1}{4}$ **14.** 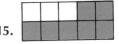   **15.**

Find the percent.	Find the part.	Find the whole.
16. 19 out of 25	**19.** 78% of 400	**22.** 45 is 20% of what?
17. 6 out of 40	**20.** 65% of 700	**23.** 120 is 75% of what?
18. 36 out of 50	**21.** 84% of 50	**24.** 350 is 40% of what?

Find the amounts of discount or sales tax.

25. regular price: $240
discount rate: 25%

26. selling price: $125
tax rate: 7%

Find the amount of interest earned.

27. principal: $2000
rate: 12%
time: 2 years

28. principal: $800
rate: 9½%
time: 6 months

Find the new height.

29. old height: 130 cm
increase: 25%

30. old height: 96 cm
decrease: 62%

UNIT 13
Statistics and Probability

Tally Charts and Frequency Tables

A survey was taken at a campground of the kinds of shelter.
A **tally chart** was used to keep a count of each kind of shelter.

Type of Shelter	Tally
Tent	卌 卌 卌 卌 卌 卌 卌 卌 ||||
Trailer Camper	卌 卌 卌 卌 ||
Camper Van	卌 卌 |||

Then the tallied *data* was transferred to a **frequency table**.

Type of Shelter	Frequency
Camper Van	13
Trailer Camper	22
Tent	44
Total Shelters	79

Sometimes the tally chart and frequency table are combined in one table.

1. Construct a frequency table from the tally chart.

Students' Pets	Tally
Dog	|||| |||| ||
Cat	|||| |||| ||||	
Bird	|||
Fish	|||| ||
Turtle	||
Hamster	|||| ||

2. Copy and complete the combined table for buttons.

Button Colour	Tally	Frequency
Green		
Blue		
Yellow		
Red		
Orange		

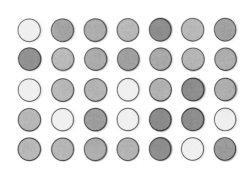

3. Construct a combined tally and frequency table for each set of data.

   a. Favourite digit: 0, 3, 2, 5, 5, 1, 3, 3, 2, 7, 7, 9, 9, 0, 2, 0, 3, 6, 4, 2, 8, 3, 3, 5, 6, 6, 9, 5, 0, 0, 1, 5, 5, 7, 9, 8, 5, 8, 4, 2, 1, 7, 7, 2

   b. Favourite letter: A, F, R, S, P, M, M, E, T, A, R, K, Z, S, A, I, B, T, R, P, N, M, Z, Y, D, H, H, K, S, K, Z, R, B, E, A, Z, M, S, S

   c. Favourite sports:
      11 Hiking
      18 Swimming
       9 Cycling
       7 Fishing
      12 Boating
      15 Skiing
       8 Tennis
      10 Soccer
       6 Bowling

1. Copy and complete the combined tally and frequency table for the kinds of licence plates found at a campground.

Licence Plate	Tally	Frequency
Alta.		
B.C.		
Man.		
N.B.		
Nfld.		
N.W.T.		
N.S.		
Ont.		
P.E.I.		
Que.		
Sask.		
Y.T.		

ALTA.	B.C.	MAN.	ALTA.
ONT.	SASK.	NFLD.	QUE.
ALTA.	MAN.	QUE.	ONT.
N.B.	SASK.	ONT.	NFLD.
SASK.	QUE.	Y.T.	QUE.
B.C.	N.S.	ALTA.	SASK.
ALTA.	P.E.I.	B.C.	QUE.
QUE.	B.C.	ONT.	MAN.
N.S.	ONT.	QUE.	ALTA.
N.S.	N.W.T.	B.C.	ONT.
MAN.	QUE.	NFLD.	P.E.I.

2. Construct a combined tally and frequency table for each.
   a. Test scores: 20, 18, 24, 22, 12, 13, 21, 25, 24, 19, 20, 12, 16, 22, 15, 25, 24, 10, 25, 21, 18, 24, 23, 20, 15, 19, 23.

   b. Arm spans: 160 cm, 154 cm, 171 cm, 162 cm, 175 cm, 152 cm, 154 cm, 162 cm, 164 cm, 160 cm, 158 cm, 154 cm, 150 cm, 152 cm, 160 cm, 165 cm, 164 cm, 160 cm, 162 cm, 156 cm, 162 cm, 154 cm, 166 cm, 152 cm.

   c. Daily high June temperatures for Sudbury, Ontario:
   29°C, 24°C, 21°C, 26°C, 24°C, 29°C, 21°C, 26°C, 26°C, 28°C, 22°C, 23°C, 24°C, 26°C, 25°C, 22°C, 28°C, 28°C, 26°C, 24°C, 28°C, 24°C, 29°C, 26°C, 25°C, 22°C, 25°C, 29°C, 26°C, 27°C.

   d. Travel times to get to school: 20 min, 15 min, half-hour, 5 min, 15 min, 10 min, 45 min, 30 min, 10 min, 60 min, 15 min, 20 min, 15 min, half-hour, 15 min, one hour, 20 min, 30 min, 10 min, 20 min, 30 min, 45 min, 60 min, 30 min.

3. Construct a combined tally and frequency table which summarizes the July precipitation in millimetres for these cities.

Calgary, 70   Charlottetown 70   Churchill 50
Edmonton 80   Fredericton 90   Frobisher Bay 50
Hamilton 70   Kitchener 90   London 80
Montreal 80   Ottawa 80   Quebec City 110
St. John 90   St. John's 80   Saskatoon 50
Toronto 80   Vancouver 30   Victoria 10
Windsor 80   Winnipeg 80   Sault Ste. Marie 70
Dawson 50   Moncton 80   Yellowknife 30
Halifax 80   Regina 60   Whitehorse 30

4. Survey the students in your class. Then construct a combined tally and frequency table to display your data.
   Choose one topic such as:
   a. How many students have blond, red, brown, and black hair?
   b. How many children are there in each family?
   c. In what month of the year does each student have a birthday?
   d. What is the favourite sport?

Licence Plate Math

Combine the digits from these licence plates with the computer symbols $+, -, *, /,$ and $\wedge$ to make the counting numbers: 1, 2, 3, and so on, to as high as possible. You do not have to use all the digits in the licence plate.

Beautiful
FAA 382
British Columbia

$1 = 3 - 1$
$2 = 2$ or $8 - 3 * 2$
$3 = 3$ or $8 - 3 - 2$
$4 = 8/2$

$5 = 8 - 3$
$6 = 2 * 3$

Saskatchewan
936 245

Friendly
143 847
Manitoba

Newfoundland
562 291
and Labrador

New Brunswick
37 396
Nouveau-Brunswick

Québec
884 962
Je me souviens

Prince Edward Island
861 124
Canada

Ontario
SEP 746
Yours To Discover

Nova Scotia
20 19 52
Canada's Ocean Playground

Wild Rose Country
278 356
Alberta

The Klondike
BA 63
Yukon

Northwest Territories
212

Range and Mean

Paul and Donna spent a week hiking in the Canadian Rockies. They recorded hiking data in a table.

Hiking Data

Day	Distance Hiked
Monday	14 km
Tuesday	15 km
Wednesday	14 km
Thursday	17 km
Friday	7 km
Saturday	11 km

The **range** and the **mean** are *statistics* that describe data.

The **range** describes how spread out data is. It is the difference between the smallest value and largest value.

Range = longest hike − shortest hike
$$= 17 - 7$$
$$= 10 \text{ km}$$

The **mean** is the sum of the numbers S divided by the number of items N. The mean tells the number of kilometres Paul and Donna *averaged* each day.

Mean $= \dfrac{S}{N}$ $\dfrac{14 + 15 + 14 + 17 + 7 + 11}{6} = 13 \text{ km}$

EXERCISES

Find the *range*.

1. 6, 5, 4, 3 $6 - 3 = \blacksquare$

2. 57, 21, 34, 48, 25

3. 8, 10, 9, 5, 9, 13

4. 4, 7, 3, 6, 7, 5, 5, 7

5. 6, 8, 11, 3, 2, 7, 5, 1, 2

6. 10, 15, 14, 12, 11, 15, 8

Find the *mean*.
Round to the nearest tenth.

7. 3, 6, 5, 2 $\dfrac{3 + 6 + 5 + 2}{4} = \blacksquare$

8. 8, 5, 13, 6, 12, 2

9. 5, 1, 5, 9, 4, 6

10. 4, 8, 3, 4, 6, 6, 3, 6

11. 8, 13, 4, 1, 7, 2, 3, 7, 5, 10, 5, 9, 6, 8, 4, 3, 9, 5, 2, 7, 1, 12, 8, 6

Find the *range* and the *mean*.
Round to the nearest tenth.

12. 5, 7, 3, 8, 6

13. 4, 2, 3, 5, 9, 6, 4

14. 36, 47, 29, 35, 38, 36

15. 95, 80, 100, 78, 62, 88, 75

Find the range and the mean. Round to the nearest tenth.

1. 7, 8, 3, 1, 1

2. 3, 7, 9, 4, 2

3. 7, 4, 9, 2, 8, 3, 7, 2, 8

4. 4, 3, 9, 6, 4, 1, 2, 7, 6, 4

5. 12, 16, 11, 29, 13, 19

6. 16, 17, 27, 16, 35, 18

7. 3, 11, 4, 16, 9, 10, 14, 15

8. 29, 20, 21, 14, 26, 38, 35, 30

9. test scores: 39%, 81%, 74%, 90%, 40%

10. test scores: 82%, 53%, 86%, 93%, 52%, 47%, 76%, 61%, 78%

11. Tom's 50 m Sprints

Race 1	8.4 s
Race 2	8.9 s
Race 3	8.5 s
Race 4	7.9 s
Race 5	8.6 s

12. People Hiking

Group 1	12
Group 2	10
Group 3	14
Group 4	9
Group 5	8

Find the value of x in each set.

13. {4, 8, 4, 5, 6, 7, 2, x}
    Mean = 5

14. {9, 8, 9, 7, 5, 7, 8, 4, 5, x}
    Mean = 7

Computer Means

Use the computer program to find the means of several sets of numbers.

a. Explain the purpose of the instructions in lines 40 and 50.

b. In which line of the program does the computer print the method for finding the mean?

The variable N, as used in line 110, is called a counter.

```
10 PRINT "TO FIND THE MEAN,"
20 PRINT "INPUT THE NUMBERS ";
30 PRINT "ONE AT A TIME."
40 PRINT "TYPE -1 AT END ";
50 PRINT "OF THE LIST."
60 PRINT
70 LET N = 0
80 LET S = 0
90 INPUT A
100 IF A = - 1 THEN 140
110 LET N = N + 1
120 LET S = S + A
130 GOTO 90
140 PRINT
150 PRINT "N = ";N,
160 PRINT "SUM = ";S
170 PRINT "MEAN = ";
180 PRINT S / N
190 PRINT
200 GOTO 10
210 END
```

Median and Mode

Mount Logan	6060 m
Mt. St. Elias	5490 m
Mt. Lucania	5230 m
King Peak	5170 m
Mt. Steele	5070 m
Mt. Wood	4840 m

The *median* and the *mode* are statistics. They can be used to describe the data on the highest mountains of Canada.

The **median** is the middle number when the data are arranged in order from largest to smallest.

6060   5490   5230   5170   5070   4840

$$\text{Median} = \frac{5230 + 5170}{2} = 5200 \text{ m}$$

The **mode** is the number that occurs most often.
The data above have *no mode.*

If the heights were rounded to the nearest hundred, the mode would be 5200 m.

6000   5500   5200   5200   5000   4800

Mode = 5200 m

EXERCISES

Find the median for each.

1. 3, 4, 7, 9, 10

2. 76, 79, 80, 80, 81, 83, 85

3. 6, 7, 8, 9, 10, 11

4. 25, 27, 28, 30, 31, 34

5. 9, 11, 2, 5, 6, 10, 4, 8, 3

6. 17, 14, 20, 19, 15, 18

7. 210, 250, 230, 300, 270, 220, 180, 250, 260, 310, 290, 320

Find the mode for each.

8. 6, 9, 10, 11, 11

9. 2, 9, 13, 15, 15, 16, 20, 25

10. 8, 8, 4, 4, 4, 3, 4, 8

11. 16, 25, 14, 16, 25, 25, 30

12. 18, 14, 10, 11, 12, 15

13. 42, 48, 35, 41, 46

Data may have several modes.
Find all the modes.

14. 7, 7, 8, 9, 9, 10, 11, 12

15. 26, 27, 27, 27, 28, 28, 28, 29

16. 2, 1, 2, 4, 1, 5, 2, 1, 6, 7, 2, 1

17. 3, 9, 6, 2, 9, 5, 3, 2, 8, 7

Find the median and the mode for each.

1. 1, 4, 8, 4, 5, 4, 6, 6, 7, 2, 4

2. 24, 26, 27, 26, 23, 26, 22, 24, 21

3. 2, 7, 6, 6, 4, 4, 6, 8, 2, 4

4. 6, 4, 9, 5, 8, 7, 7, 9, 8, 9, 7, 5, 7

5. 92, 98, 97, 95, 89, 99, 96, 94

6. 19, 25, 14, 22, 13, 19, 20, 21

7. Daily telephone calls: 6, 12, 2, 0, 5, 18, 5, 4, 3, 4, 2, 0, 10, 2

8. Misspelled words: 3, 2, 5, 8, 2, 6, 1, 0, 1, 0, 0, 2, 0, 1, 4

9. Test scores: 75%, 79%, 100%, 100%, 92%, 95%, 60%

10. Kilometres hiked: 9 km, 6 km, 8 km, 5 km, 8 km, 7 km

11. Times for a 3 km Jog

Day 1	18 min
Day 2	16 min
Day 3	17 min
Day 4	20 min
Day 5	16 min

12. Money Earned

May	$35
June	$50
July	$65
August	$58
September	$42

Find the mean, median, and mode for each.

13. 3, 4, 3, 6, 6, 5, 5, 6, 4

15. 6, 5, 3, 8, 4, 9, 7, 10, 2, 12

16. 7, 9, 10, 9, 10, 11, 9, 10

17. 1, 4, 3, 4, 1, 0, 4, 3, 4, 0

14.

Heights	Tally	Frequency
175 cm	||	2
170 cm	|||| ||	7
165 cm	|||	3
160 cm	ⅢⅠ ||||	9

1. Construct a combined tally and frequency table for the colours of these squares.

Find the range and the mean to the nearest tenth.

2. 76, 92, 85, 88, 80, 90, 86

3. 650, 720, 700, 615, 725, 695

Find the median and the mode.

4. 4, 6, 7, 2, 3, 6, 8, 7, 9, 6, 1

5. 12, 19, 11, 16, 12, 17, 17, 14

Bar and Line Graphs

The table at the right lists the normal monthly precipitation in Regina. Can you quickly find in which months there are the greatest amounts of precipitation?

Regina's Rainfall in Millimetres					
Jan.	18	May	41	Sept.	36
Feb.	17	June	83	Oct.	19
Mar.	18	July	58	Nov.	18
Apr.	23	Aug.	50	Dec.	16

The answer is easy to see on a vertical **bar graph** or a **line graph**.
The greatest amounts of precipitation normally fall in June, July, and August.

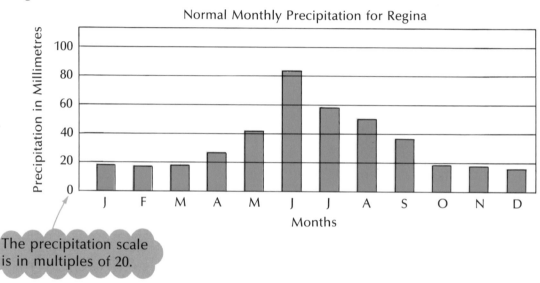

Normal Monthly Precipitation for Regina

The precipitation scale is in multiples of 20.

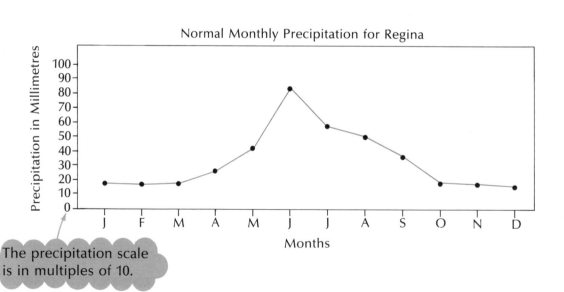

Normal Monthly Precipitation for Regina

The precipitation scale is in multiples of 10.

EXERCISES

Use the graphs on the previous page to answer the question.

1. Which month has the most precipitation?

2. Which month has the least?

3. What is the precipitation in August?

4. Approximately what is the difference in precipitation between January and June?

5. Make a vertical bar graph to display the data below.

Normal Monthly Precipitation for Winnipeg in Millimetres					
January	24	May	57	September	53
February	19	June	80	October	35
March	26	July	80	November	27
April	37	August	74	December	23

6. Make a *line graph* displaying the precipitation data for Winnipeg.

7. Complete a *bar graph* displaying the data on the average wind speeds in eight Canadian cities.

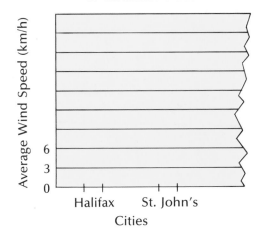

Average Wind Speeds in Canadian Cities

City	Average Wind Speed
Halifax	18 km/h
St. John's	24 km/h
Edmonton	15 km/h
Toronto	17 km/h
Fredericton	14 km/h
Quebec City	17 km/h
Victoria	18 km/h
Regina	22 km/h

8. Construct a *line graph* to show the progress of John's flu.
Sun. 38°C, Mon. 38.8°C, Tues. 37.7°C, Wed. 37.5°C,
Thurs. 37.5°C, Fri. 37°C.

PRACTICE

Use the horizontal *bar graph* to answer the questions.

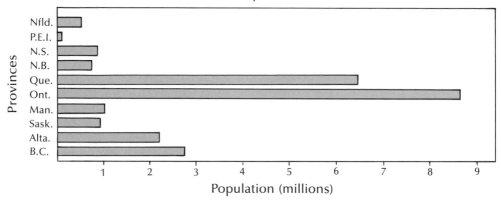

Canadian Population 1981

1. Which province has the greatest population?

2. Which province has the least population?

3. What is the approximate population of Manitoba?

4. What is the approximate difference in population between Quebec and Ontario?

Copy and complete the horizontal *bar graph* with data from the table.

5.

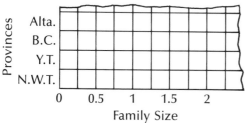

Average Number of Persons Per Family			
Nfld.	3.8	Ont.	3.2
P.E.I.	3.5	Man.	3.2
N.S.	3.3	Sask.	3.3
Que.	3.3	Alta.	3.3
N.B.	3.4	Y.T.	3.3
B.C.	3.1	N.W.T.	4.0

Copy and complete the *line graph* with data from the table.

6.

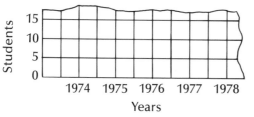

Grade 7 Students at Middle School			
1974	26	1979	44
1975	28	1980	50
1976	34	1981	48
1977	42	1982	43
1978	46	1983	44

Copy and complete the *double vertical bar graph*. Use the data given in the table.

7.

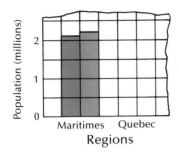

Canadian Population by Region		
Region	1976	1981
Maritime Prov.	2 181 775	2 234 032
Quebec	6 234 445	6 438 403
Ontario	8 264 465	8 625 107
Prairie Prov.	3 780 866	4 232 278
B.C. and Terr.	2 531 053	2 813 361

Use the table below to make a *line graph*.

8.

Normal Monthly Precipitation and Temperature in Vancouver					
Month	Precipitation	Temperature	Month	Precipitation	Temperature
Jan.	147 mm	2°C	July	30 mm	17°C
Feb.	117 mm	4°C	Aug.	37 mm	17°C
Mar.	94 mm	6°C	Sept.	61 mm	14°C
April	61 mm	9°C	Oct.	122 mm	10°C
May	48 mm	12°C	Nov.	141 mm	6°C
June	45 mm	15°C	Dec.	165 mm	4°C

Alphabet Tally

List the letters from A to Z. Tally the number of times each letter is used in the paragraph below.

Canada is the world's second largest country in land size. It stretches from the North Pole to the United States border and from the Atlantic Ocean to the Pacific. The climate of Canada is generally temperate, but varies from freezing winter cold to blistering summer heat. The range is more than fifty degrees Celsius.

The frequencies of some letters are given below. Replace these with the appropriate letters to decode a message.

8	20	16	8		17	36	21		30	16		17	36	21

Histograms and Frequency Polygons

The frequency of each running time from the table can be displayed on either a *histogram* or a *frequency polygon*.

Grade 7 Students' 4 km Run Times		
Time	Tally	Frequency
12 min	⫶⫶⫶ ⫶⫶⫶	10
14 min	⫶⫶⫶ ⫶⫶⫶ |||	13
16 min	⫶⫶⫶ ⫶⫶⫶ ⫶⫶⫶	15
18 min	⫶⫶⫶ ⫶⫶⫶ ⫶⫶⫶ ⫶⫶⫶ ⫶⫶⫶ ⫶⫶⫶	30
20 min	⫶⫶⫶ ⫶⫶⫶ ||||	14

A **histogram** is a bar graph of frequencies with no spaces between the bars.

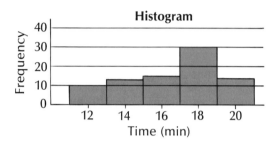

A **frequency polygon** is a line graph of the frequencies. It is made into a polygon by bringing the line down to zero before the first number and after the last.

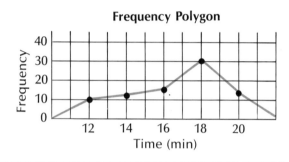

EXERCISES

Copy and complete the histogram and frequency polygon.

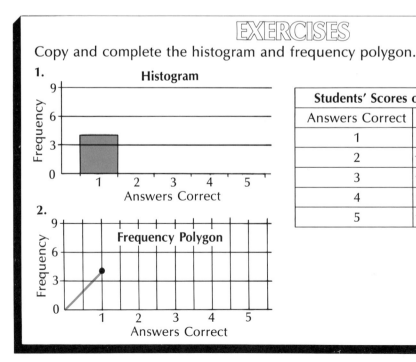

1.

Students' Scores on a 5-Question Test		
Answers Correct	Tally	Frequency
1						4
2	⫶⫶⫶ |||	8
3	⫶⫶⫶ ⫶⫶⫶ ||	12
4	⫶⫶⫶ ⫶⫶⫶ ⫶⫶⫶|	16
5	⫶⫶⫶ ⫶⫶⫶	10

2.

PRACTICE

Copy and complete the frequency table, histogram, and frequency polygon.

1.

Number of Children in Students' Families		
Children in Family	Tally	Frequency
1	⦀⦀ ⦀⦀⦀	
2	⦀⦀⦀⦀ ⦀⦀⦀⦀ ⦀⦀⦀⦀ ⦀	
3	⦀⦀⦀⦀ ⦀⦀⦀⦀ ⦀⦀⦀⦀ ⦀⦀⦀	
4	⦀⦀⦀⦀ ⦀⦀⦀⦀ ⦀	
5	⦀⦀⦀⦀	

2. Histogram

Children In Family

3. Frequency Polygon

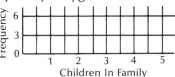

Children In Family

Make a histogram and frequency polygon from the data in the table.

4.

Weekly Earnings of Students		
Earnings	Tally	Frequency
$ 1 to $3	⦀⦀⦀⦀ ⦀	
$ 4 to $6	⦀⦀⦀⦀ ⦀⦀⦀	
$ 7 to $9	⦀⦀⦀⦀ ⦀⦀⦀⦀ ⦀⦀	
$10 to $12	⦀⦀⦀⦀ ⦀⦀⦀	

Make a histogram and frequency polygon for the following data:

5. Test scores: 24, 19, 26, 31, 28, 32, 25, 27, 30, 32, 31

6. Daily high temperatures: 19°C, 21°C, 18°C, 19°C, 25°C, 28°C, 27°C, 28°C

Average Earnings

The fifteen students who deliver newspapers earn an average of $20 per week. Ten students who baby-sit earn an average of $16 per week.

The average of 16 and 20 is 18. But $18 is *not* the average earnings of the 25 students described above.

a. What is the average earnings of the 25 students?

b. Why isn't $18 the average? Under what conditions would it be?

Stem-and-Leaf Graphs

Another way to display data is by making a **stem-and-leaf graph**.

160, 185, 188, 174, 187, 190, 191, 186, 176, 158, 178, 168, 179, 188, 195, 194, 188, 185, 150, 201, 186, 175, 166, 159, 161, 168, 178, 193, 188, 172, 182.

To construct a stem-and-leaf graph, split each number in the set of data into a *stem* and a *leaf*. For the data above, the stems could be the first two digits of the height and the leaf could be the last digit.

For example:

stem	leaf
1 8	5

The possible stems for this data are 15, 16, 17, 18, 19, and 20. To complete the graph, arrange the stems in a column.

A finished graph would look like this:

```
15 : 8 0 9
16 : 0 8 6 1 8
17 : 4 6 8 9 5 8 2
18 : 5 8 7 6 8 8 5 6 8
19 : 0 1 5 4 3
20 : 1
```

A graph can also be ordered:

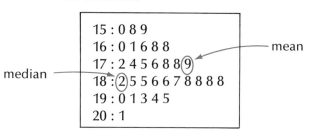

```
15 : 0 8 9
16 : 0 1 6 8 8
17 : 2 4 5 6 8 8 9        ← mean
18 : 2 5 5 6 6 7 8 8 8 8
19 : 0 1 3 4 5
20 : 1
```
median   18 : 2 ...

Using the ordered stem-and-leaf graph, it is easy to find the *median*, by counting halfway. There are 31 heights, so the 16th height will be the median: 182.

Because no numbers are "lost" in the stem-and-leaf graph, the *mean* is possible to compute: 179.

The stem-and-leaf graph is like a *histogram* of the data.

Make ordered stem-and-leaf graphs for the following sets of data.

Find the median and mean for each set of data.

1. 23, 25, 13, 19, 34, 40, 28, 20, 18, 19, 31.

2. 54, 67, 57, 46, 58, 45, 62, 55, 41, 57, 50, 56, 52, 71, 39.

3. 55, 77, 51, 119, 117, 96, 90, 105, 101, 51, 73, 51, 95, 101, 49, 44, 63, 75, 88, 92, 67.

Box-and-Whisker Graphs

A **box-and-whisker graph** provides a quick but complete summary of data. It shows the extremes as *whiskers* and the median and middle half of the data as *boxes*.

To construct a box-and-whisker graph, it is best to work from a stem-and-leaf graph.

At the right is a stem-and-leaf graph for 19 masses (kg).

```
4 : 8
5 : 1 3 3 7
6 : 0 1 3 4 ④ 5 5 8          ──median
7 : 1 2 2 5 6
8 : 0
```

Step 1: Draw a horizontal scale at least as long as the range between the extremes, 48 and 80. Plot the box and whisker beneath the scale.

Step 2: Draw a box around the median and the two hinges as shown below. Draw a line from each hinge to an extreme.

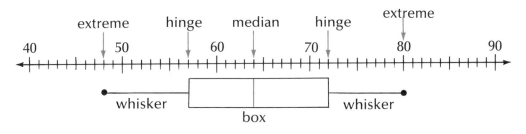

Since there are 19 masses, the **median**, is the 10th mass: 64.

The **hinges** are the middle numbers between the median and the extremes of the data. Since there are 9 numbers between the median and each extreme, the hinges are the fifth numbers from each end: 72 and 57.

1. Construct three box-and-whisker graphs beneath the same scale using the information below. All three sets of data have different medians and extremes, but one set of data is very much different than the other two. Explain why.

   a. median 78; hinge points: 75 and 82; extremes: 55 and 91
   b. median 68; hinge points: 74 and 58; extremes: 48 and 95
   c. median 70; hinge points: 73 and 61; extremes: 52 and 93

2. Construct a box-and-whisker graph of the following data.
   59, 74, 77, 63, 76, 89, 90, 75, 65, 67, 67, 57, 68, 77, 84, 83, 77, 74, 46, 90, 64, 55, 48, 50, 57, 67, 82, 77, 61, 71, 59

Probability

When a die is tossed, what is the probability of rolling a 2?

The probability of rolling a 2 is *1 chance in 6.*

This is written: $P(2) = \frac{1}{6} = 0.1\overline{6}$.

$\frac{1}{6}$ ← There is *one* favourable event.
  ← There are *six events (faces)* in total.

The probability of rolling a die and having a 1, 3, 4, 5, or 6 show up is *5 chances in 6,* or $P(1, 3, 4, 5, 6) = \frac{5}{6} = 0.8\overline{3}$.

$\frac{5}{6}$ ← There are *five* favourable events.
  ← There are *six* events in total.

The probability of rolling a die and having a 7 show up is *0 chances in 6,* or $P(7) = \frac{0}{6} = 0$.

The probability of rolling a die and having a 1, 2, 3, 4, 5, or 6 show up is *6 chances in 6,* or $P(1, 2, 3, 4, 5, 6) = \frac{6}{6} = 1$.

Remember:
The probability of an *impossible* event is 0.
The probability of a *certain* event is 1.
The probability of any other event is between 0 and 1.

$$\text{Probability of an event} = \frac{\text{number of favourable events}}{\text{total number of possible events}}$$

EXERCISES

1. How many events are there in all for one die?

2. Copy and complete the probabilities for one die as a fraction and as a decimal.

   a. $P(3)$ = ■   b. $P(8)$ = ■

   c. $P(1, 2, 3, 4, 5,$ or $6)$ = ■   d. $P($even number$)$ = ■

   e. $P(4$ or $5)$ = ■   f. $P($not $6)$ = ■

3. A bag contains 6 blue and 9 green marbles. If you reach into the bag and draw one marble:

   a. How many marbles are there in all?

   b. How many outcomes are there in all?

4. For the bag in question 3, copy and complete the probabilities as a fraction and as a decimal.

   a. $P($blue$)$ = ■   b. $P($green$)$ = ■

   c. $P($not blue$)$ = ■   d. $P($not green$)$ = ■

   e. $P($blue or green$)$ = ■   f. $P($not blue and not green$)$ = ■

5. Toss two coins.

   a. Copy and complete the table that lists all possible outcomes.

   b. $P($two tails$)$ = ■

   c. $P($head and tail$)$ = ■

   d. $P($two heads$)$ = ■

Coin 1	Coin 2
Head	Head
■	■
■	■
■	■

6. Toss two coins 40 times and keep a tally of the possible outcomes.

   a. How many times out of the 40 tosses would you expect 2 tails?

   b. How many times did you get 2 tails?

Coin Tosses	Tally
2 heads	
2 tails	
head and tail	

7. For each event, is the probability 0, 1, or between 0 and 1?

   a. The sun will shine on the weekend.

   b. New Year's Eve will fall on January 31st.

   c. You will have one birthday each year.

   d. It will rain in April.

   e. February will have 28 days in a Leap Year.

1. How many outcomes in all are there for each spinner?
   Find *P*(red) for each as a fraction and as a decimal.

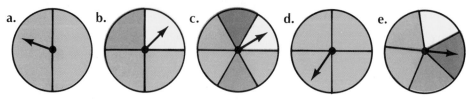

   a.   b.   c.   d.   e.

2. For each event, is the probability 0, 1, or between 0 and 1?

   a. Snow will melt at −10°C.
   b. The temperature will be warmer in Winnipeg than in St. John's.
   c. Water will boil at 100°C.
   d. Icicles will form at 10°C.

3. Spread a deck of cards face down on a table
   and draw one card. Find each probability as
   a fraction and as a decimal.

   a. *P*(Queen of Hearts)
   b. *P*(Ace)
   c. *P*(Jack, Queen, or King)
   d. *P*(2, 3, 4, 5, 6, 7, 8, or 9)
   e. *P*(Ace of Spades)

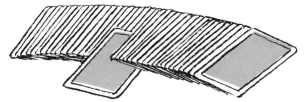

4. Draw one card from a deck of 52 cards 50 times.
   Shuffle the cards between each draw. Keep a tally of the results.

   a. How many times out of the 50 draws would you expect to
      draw a Queen?
   b. How many times did you draw a Queen?

5. Do you have a better chance of winning if you buy 3 tickets for a
   raffle that has 350 tickets or 5 tickets for a raffle that has 600
   tickets?

6. If you flip 2 coins together 100 times in a row, about how many
   times would you expect both to land tails?

7. Lottery tickets are numbered 000 to 999. You win the grand
   prize if the number drawn is the number of the ticket you have.
   What is the probability that you will win the grand prize?
   (Remember that all 3 digits must match to win the grand prize.)

8. Frank spins the spinner twice and adds the numbers.
Find each probability as a fraction and as a decimal.

a. *P*(sum of 2) **f.** *P*(sum of 1)
b. *P*(sum of 6) **g.** *P*(sum of 3 or 4)
c. *P*(sum of 7) **h.** *P*(even-numbered sum)
d. *P*(sum of 8) **i.** *P*(sum of 2 or 5)
e. *P*(sum of 5) **j.** *P*(sum of 10)

Hint:
List all the
outcomes first.

First Spin	Second Spin	Sum
1	1	2
1	2	■
■	■	■
■	■	■

Computer Probability

This computer program simulates the tossing of 2 dice 200 times.

Find the probability of tossing each sum. Then run the program on your own and see if the sums tossed were what you expected.

P(sum of 3)   *P*(sum of 10)
P(sum of 6)   *P*(sum of 2)
P(sum of 9)   *P*(sum of 5)
P(sum of 12) *P*(sum of 8)
P(sum of 4)   *P*(sum of 11)
P(sum of 7)

> The REM statement remarks about what is happening in the program. REMarks are not printed during a RUN.

> The DIMension statement sets aside memory space for 12 possible sums.

```
100 REM PROGRAM THAT SIMULATES
    THE THROW OF TWO DICE
    200 TIMES
110 DIM M(12)
120 FOR I = 1 TO 200
130 REM THROW ONE DIE
140 LET A=INT(RND(1)*6+1)
150 REM THROW THE OTHER DIE
160 LET B=INT(RND(1)*6+1)
170 REM ADD THE DICE TOGETHER
180 LET C=A+B
190 REM KEEP TRACK OF THE NUMBER
    OF TIMES EACH SUM OCCURS
200 M(C)=M(C)+1
210 NEXT I
220 PRINT"SUM OF 2 DICE",
230 PRINT"NUMBER OF TIMES"
235 PRINT
240 FOR I = 2 TO 12
250 PRINT "A ";I;"WAS ROLLED";
255 PRINT M(I);" TIMES."
260 NEXT I
270 END
```

Problem Solving

Jody wears blue socks to school half the time. Brad wears his red sweater to school half the time. What is the probability that Jody will be wearing blue socks and Brad will be wearing his red sweater on the same day?

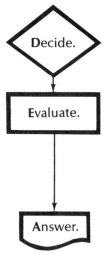

A *diagram* can help you solve the problem. It shows all four possible outcomes.

Brad   *Jody*
red sweater —1—blue socks

               2

               3

other sweater —4—other socks

The probability that Jody will be wearing blue socks and Brad will be wearing his red sweater on the same day is *1 chance in 4.*

P(red sweater, blue socks) $= \frac{1}{4} = 0.25$

EXERCISES

Solve by making a table or diagram of possible outcomes.

1. What is the probability that Jody will not be wearing blue socks and Brad will not be wearing his red sweater on the same day? (Refer to the diagram above.)

2. Angie has a tan jacket and a navy blue jacket which she randomly alternates wearing with her brown, her plaid, and her red skirt. What is the probability that Angie will be wearing her tan jacket with her plaid skirt?

3. To make a sundae, a snack shop uses vanilla, chocolate, or mint ice cream along with caramel, strawberry, or chocolate sauce.

   If a friend orders a surprise sundae for you, what is the probability that it will be made with mint ice cream and chocolate sauce?

PRACTICE

Solve by making a table or diagram of possible outcomes.

1. Jack and George each hold one hand behind their backs. At the signal, they each bring that hand to the front showing either 1, 2, 3, 4, or 5 fingers. What is the probability that both boys show 5 fingers at the same time?

2. What is the probability of getting a sum of 5 by adding the results of the spinners?

3. A new limited-edition sports car comes with these choices:
   a. diesel or gas engine.
   b. red, blue, or black exterior.
   c. sunroof or vinyl roof.

   How many different combinations of engine, paint, and roof options are there?

REVIEW

1. Construct a vertical bar graph which displays the altitude data.

Altitudes of Capital Cities			
St. John's	140 m	Toronto	111 m
Charlottetown	55 m	Winnipeg	239 m
Halifax	145 m	Regina	577 m
Fredericton	20 m	Calgary	1084 m
Québec City	73 m	Victoria	69 m

2. Construct a tally chart and a histogram to show the amounts of each coloured square.

3. There are 100 marbles in a jar. Thirty are white, 10 are blue, and 60 are yellow. Draw one marble from the jar. Find the probability.

   a. *P*(blue)   b. *P*(white)   c. *P*(yellow)   d. *P*(not white)

335

Estimating the Number of Fish in a Lake

To estimate the number of fish in a lake, a
scientist might do the following.

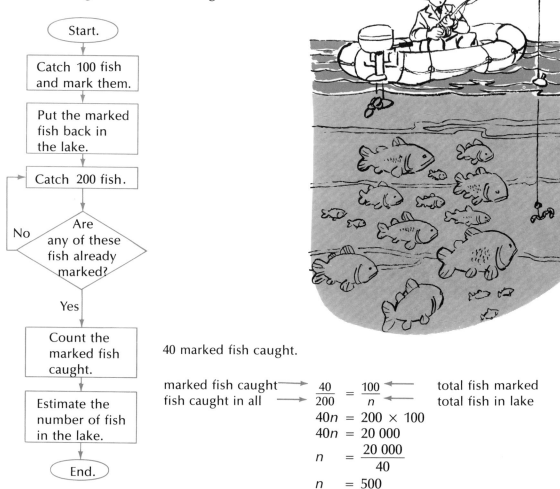

```
      Start.

Catch 100 fish
and mark them.

Put the marked
fish back in
the lake.

Catch 200 fish.

        Are
No   any of these
     fish already
       marked?

       Yes

Count the
marked fish
caught.

Estimate the
number of fish
in the lake.

      End.
```

40 marked fish caught.

marked fish caught ⟶ $\dfrac{40}{200} = \dfrac{100}{n}$ ⟵ total fish marked
fish caught in all ⟶   ⟵ total fish in lake

$$40n = 200 \times 100$$
$$40n = 20\,000$$
$$n = \frac{20\,000}{40}$$
$$n = 500$$

There are probably 500 fish in the lake.

1. What would the total number of fish be if 150 were marked and
   the scientist then caught 100 fish, of which 10 were marked?

2. What would be the total number of fish if 100 were marked and
   the scientist then caught 250 fish, of which 32 were marked?

3. **a.** Do you think that this method will always give us the exact
   number of fish in the lake? Explain your answer.
   b. What other problems would the scientist have using this
   technique?

Choosing Cards With and Without Replacing Them

Choose a card from
a box containing:

Choose a card from
a box containing:

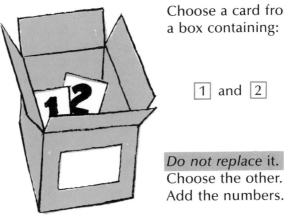

1 and 2

1 and 2

Replace it.
Choose another.
Add the numbers.

Do not replace it.
Choose the other.
Add the numbers.

Three Possible Outcomes:

One Possible Outcome:

$1 + 1 = 2$
$1 + 2 = 3$
$2 + 2 = 4$

$1 + 2 = 3$

For each problem, two cards are chosen, one at a time from a box.

1. The box contains 1, 2, and 3.
   What are the possible outcomes:
   a. with replacement?   b. without replacement?

2. The box contains 1, 2, and 3, and 4.
   What are the possible outcomes:
   a. with replacement?   b. without replacement?

3. The box contains 1, 2, 3, 4, and 5.
   What are the possible outcomes:
   a. with replacement?   b. without replacement?

4. For the box in question 3, find the probability of choosing each
   sum, with and without replacement.

   a. *P*(sum 3)   b. *P*(sum 5)   c. *P*(sum 7)   d. *P*(sum 9)   e. *P*(sum 2)

   f. *P*(sum 4)   g. *P*(sum 6)   h. *P*(sum 8)   i. *P*(sum 10)   j. *P*(sum 1)

5. How many possible outcomes would there be if six cards were
   in the box and the first card chosen was replaced? was not
   replaced?

337

1. Construct a tally chart and a frequency table to show the numbers of each polygon.

2. Find the range and mean of these sets of numbers. Round to the nearest hundredth.

   a. 5, 4, 10, 7, 5, 2, 3

   b. 39, 30, 31, 24, 36, 48, 45, 40

3. Find the median and mode of these sets of numbers. Round to the nearest tenth.

   a. 10, 6, 10, 4, 12, 8, 10

   b. 3, 6, 10, 6, 7, 6, 8, 9, 4, 6

4. Construct a bar graph displaying the amounts of snow that fell one week.

   Monday 20 mm, Tuesday 45 mm, Wednesday 70 mm, Thursday 60 mm, Friday 0 mm, Saturday 150 mm, Sunday 80 mm.

5. Construct a line graph for this data.

Population of Canada		1871-1981	
Year	Population	Year	Population
1871	3 700 000	1931	10 400 000
1881	4 300 000	1941	11 500 000
1891	4 800 000	1951	14 000 000
1901	5 400 000	1961	18 200 000
1911	7 200 000	1971	21 600 000
1921	8 800 000	1981	24 300 000

6. Construct a frequency polygon for this set of students' weekly earnings.
   $15, $11, $10, $7, $13, $7, $14, $12, $16, $14, $5, $10, $11, $12, $13, $5, $10, $13, $14, $12, $11, $8, $6, $9, $15, $9, $10, $23

7. Find the probabilities.
   a. $P(3)$

   b. P(an even number)

   c. $P(0)$

   d. P(a number less than 9)

1. Identify the transformation (or combination of transformations) that maps the object to its image. For example, translation [L2, D4].

a.
object
image

b.
object
image

c.
object
image

2. What is the order of rotational symmetry?

a.

b.

c.

3. Draw an example of each polygon.
   a. parallelogram   b. trapezoid   c. kite
   d. regular octagon   e. square   f. regular pentagon

4. Draw a figure with more than four sides that will tile a surface.

British Columbia
Vancouver

5. a. Enlarge the map with a scale ratio of 3:1.
   b. Reduce the map with a scale ratio of 1:2.

6. Identify each figure below.
   How many planes of symmetry does each figure have?
   a.   b.   c.

7. Make a perspective drawing of your teacher's desk as viewed from your seat.

UNIT 14

Integers

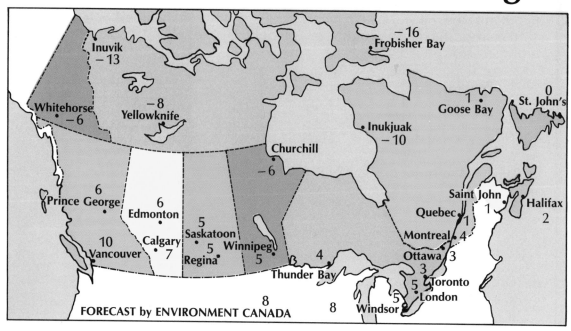

FORECAST by ENVIRONMENT CANADA

Temperature

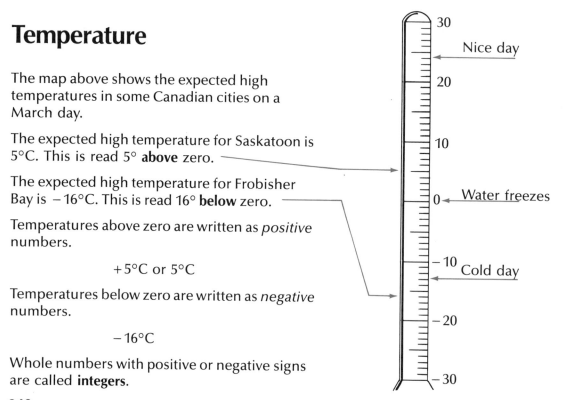

The map above shows the expected high temperatures in some Canadian cities on a March day.

The expected high temperature for Saskatoon is 5°C. This is read 5° **above** zero.

The expected high temperature for Frobisher Bay is −16°C. This is read 16° **below** zero.

Temperatures above zero are written as *positive* numbers.

$$+5°C \text{ or } 5°C$$

Temperatures below zero are written as *negative* numbers.

$$-16°C$$

Whole numbers with positive or negative signs are called **integers**.

30 — Nice day

20

10

0 — Water freezes

−10 Cold day

−20

−30

340

EXERCISES

Write the temperature shown in degrees Celsius.

1.   2. 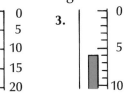   3.   4.   5.

Use *integers* to write the temperature.

6. four below zero   7. one above zero   8. minus ten degrees

9. minus five   10. twelve above   11. nine degrees below zero

12. minus forty   13. fifteen below   14. twenty

Copy and complete using "is warmer than" or "is colder than".

15. 4°C ● 10°C   16. −8°C ● −15°C   17. −3°C ● 3°C

18. 21°C ● 0°C   19. −2°C ● 0°C   20. 1°C ● −5°C

PRACTICE

Write a temperature that would be reasonable for each.

1. a classroom   2. a cold winter day   3. a hot oven

4. boiling water   5. a hot summer day   6. ice

Use the weather map on the previous page to answer each question.

7. What is the highest expected temperature found on the map? How many degrees above zero is this?

8. What is the lowest expected temperature found on the map? How many degrees below zero is this?

9. Which city's expected high temperature is the same as the freezing point of water?

10. How many degrees difference is there between the expected high temperature for these cities?
    a. Montreal and Saint John   b. Prince George and Whitehorse
    c. Goose Bay and Halifax   d. Yellowknife and Inuvik
    e. Vancouver and Frobisher Bay   f. Edmonton and Yellowknife

11. What is the mean expected temperature for all cities on the map in Alberta and British Columbia?

Integers

The number line shows the set of integers is *infinite* in both positive and negative directions.

Set of integers = {. . ., −2, −1, 0, 1, 2, . . .}

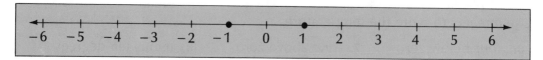

Two numbers are called **opposites** if they are the same distance from zero but on opposite sides of zero.

−1 and 1 are opposites. They are *graphed* on the number line above.

A number line can be used to compare two integers.
The integer to the left on the number line is the lesser integer.

−5 is to the left of −4 so   −5 < −4   or   −4 > −5

EXERCISES

Is the number an integer?

1. 12   **2.** −6   **3.** 0.2   **4.** 0   **5.** $\frac{1}{4}$

Is the integer *positive* or *negative*?

6. 8   **7.** −3   **8.** −10   **9.** 75   **10.** −92

Write the opposite of each integer.

11. −2   **12.** 4   **13.** 11   **14.** −5   **15.** 20

Copy and complete using < or >.

16. 3 ● −5   **17.** 6 ● −8   **18.** −2 ● 0

19. −11 ● −15   **20.** 0 ● −4   **21.** −6 ● −12

22. −5 ● −3   **23.** −2 ● −3   **24.** 3 ● −2

Copy the number lines. *Graph* the sets of integers.

25. {−2, 2}   **26.** {−4, −1, 2}

342

Write the *opposite* of the integer.

1. -2 2. 4   3. -7 4. -8 5. 1

6. 10   7. -12 8. 0   9. 48   10. -73

Compare each pair of numbers using the $>$ sign.

11. $-6, 3$ 12. $-10, 4$ 13. $2, -3$ 14. $-1, 0$ 15. $-4, -1$

16. $1, 4$ 17. $-6, -8$ 18. $3, -7$ 19. $-2, -5$ 20. $0, 7$

Compare each pair of numbers using the $<$ sign.

21. $-1, -5$ 22. $7, 5$ 23. $0, -8$ 24. $-4, 2$ 25. $-2, -15$

26. $9, 8$ 27. $-3, -2$ 28. $6, -1$ 29. $0, 4$ 30. $-1, -2$

Write in order from smallest to largest.

31. $-11, 25, 6, 0, -10, 4, -17$ 32. $6, -5, -8, 0, 3, -2, 4$

Graph the sets of integers on separate number lines.

33. $\{-6, -4, -2\}$ 34. $\{-2, 1, 3\}$ 35. $\{-3, -1, 1, 3\}$

36. {the integers that are both <2 and >-5}

37. {the integers that are both >-1 and <4}

Computer Relations

Computers can identify true number statements and false number statements with PRINT.

For true statements, some computers reply with 1. For false statements some computers reply with 0.

Computer Relations Symbols	
$>$	greater than
$<$	less than
$=$	equal to
$>=$	greater than or equal to
$<=$	less than or equal to
$<>$	not equal to

You type:	Computer replies:
PRINT 5>3	1
PRINT -2>1	0

Will 0 or 1 be printed?

a. PRINT -7>4

b. PRINT (6+2)<9

c. PRINT -2<>2

d. PRINT -2>-4

e. PRINT 7<>(10-3)

f. PRINT -9<=-8

g. PRINT -4<2

h. PRINT 1>=-1

i. PRINT 0<>(5-5)

343

Adding Integers

A number line can be used to show how integers are added.
Arrows pointing *right* are for *positive* integers.
Arrows pointing *left* are for *negative* integers.

Win $4. Then win $6 more.
How much *profit* or *loss*?

$10 profit.

$4 + 6 = 10$

Lose $5. The lose $3 more.
How much *profit* or *loss*?

$8 loss.

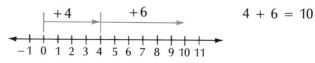

$(-5) + (-3) = -8$

The sum of two positive integers is a positive integer.
The sum of two negative integers is a negative integer.

EXERCISES

Write an integer addition equation for each.

1.

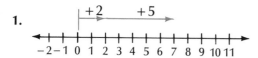

2.

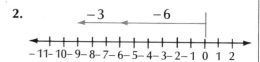

3.

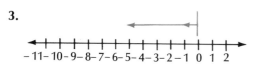

4.

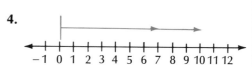

5.

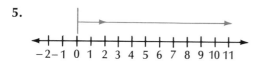

6.

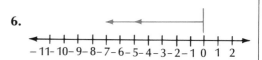

7. Win $7.
   Then win $6 more.
   How much profit or loss?

8. Lose $8.
   Then lose $6 more.
   How much profit or loss?

Add.

9. $(-5) + (-2)$

10. $6 + 9$

11. $(-9) + (-4)$

12. $(-3) + (-8)$

13. $(-2) + (-2)$

14. $8 + 9$

15. $0 + (-1)$

16. $5 + 8$

17. $0 + 6$

Add.

1. $4 + 5$ 　　　2. $(-3) + (-2)$ 　　3. $1 + 7$ 　　　4. $(-8) + (-3)$

5. $0 + (-6)$ 　　6. $9 + 8$ 　　　7. $(-2) + (-1)$ 　　8. $5 + 0$

9. $7 + 8$ 　　　10. $0 + (-2)$ 　　11. $(-4) + (-3)$ 　　12. $(-6) + (-2)$

What is the missing addend?

13. $5 + \blacksquare = 7$ 　　14. $(-5) + \blacksquare = 9$ 　　15. $0 + \blacksquare = -9$

16. $(-4) + \blacksquare = -8$ 　　17. $3 + \blacksquare = 10$ 　　18. $(-1) + \blacksquare = -6$

Write an integer addition equation for each.

19. What is the gain or loss if a football player:
    a. gains six and then gains three?
    b. loses nine and then loses three?
    c. gains nothing and then loses four?

20. What is the gain or loss if a worker:
    a. cashes a cheque for $5 and then cashes another cheque for $8?
    b. pays two bills, one for $7 and then one for $4?
    c. cashes two cheques, one for $8 and then one for $9?

21. What is the gain or loss if a card player:
    a. wins 6 points and then wins 9 points?
    b. wins 0 points and then wins 2 points?
    c. loses 5 points and then loses 1 point?

Magic Integer Square

Copy and complete the square so that each row, column, and diagonal has a sum of -15.

-8	-1	
	-5	

Adding Positive and Negative Integers

A number line can be used to show how a positive integer and a negative integer are added.

Win $4. Then lose $5.
How much profit or loss?

$1 loss.

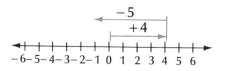

$$4 + (-5) = -1$$

Lose $1. Then win $4.
How much profit or loss?

$3 profit.

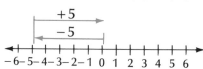

$$(-1) + 4 = 3$$

Lose $5. Then win $5.
How much profit or loss?

No profit. No loss.

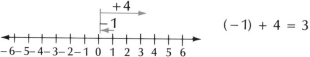

$$(-5) + 5 = 0$$

> The sum of an integer and its opposite is always zero.

EXERCISES

Copy and complete each pattern.

1.

$$2 + \quad 1 = \blacksquare$$
$$2 + \quad 0 = \blacksquare$$
$$2 + (-1) = \blacksquare$$
$$2 + (-2) = \blacksquare$$
$$2 + (-3) = \blacksquare$$

2.

$$0 + \quad 2 = \blacksquare$$
$$0 + \quad 1 = \blacksquare$$
$$0 + \quad 0 = \blacksquare$$
$$0 + (-1) = \blacksquare$$
$$0 + (-2) = \blacksquare$$

3.

$$4 + \quad 1 = \blacksquare$$
$$4 + \quad 0 = \blacksquare$$
$$4 + (-1) = \blacksquare$$
$$4 + (-2) = \blacksquare$$
$$4 + (-3) = \blacksquare$$

Write an integer addition equation for each.

4.

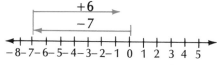

5.

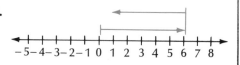

6.

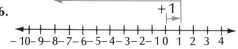

7.

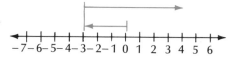

Add.

8. $6 + (-4)$

9. $(-3) + 9$

10. $(-2) + 2$

11. $(-5) + 3$

12. $8 + (-8)$

13. $7 + (-1)$

Add.

1. $(-2) + 9$
2. $1 + (-7)$
3. $(-6) + 0$
4. $0 + (-4)$
5. $(-8) + 8$
6. $4 + (-7)$
7. $(-1) + (-9)$
8. $(-2) + 3$
9. $(-6) + (-5)$
10. $(-2) + 7 + (-5)$
11. $8 + (-9) + 1$
12. $(-4) + (-3) + (-2)$

Write an integer addition equation for each.

13. a loss of 5 points and then a win of 9 points.
14. a rise of 9°C and then a fall of 6°C.
15. a loss of 6 kg and then a gain of 3 kg.

16. Jack is experimenting with a way for scoring golf. Par is 0, one over par is $+1$, one below par is -1, and so on.
    a. Which golfer had the best eighth hole?
    b. Which golfer had the best fourth hole?
    c. What is each golfer's total score?
    d. Who won the match?

    Remember in golf the person with the *lowest* score wins.

Hole	Jack	Helen	Tom	Sue
1	-1	$+1$	0	$+2$
2	-2	-1	$+3$	-1
3	$+1$	0	$+1$	$+2$
4	0	$+3$	$+2$	$+1$
5	$+2$	-1	-1	-1
6	-1	0	-1	$+1$
7	$+3$	$+2$	$+4$	$+2$
8	0	0	$+1$	-1
9	$+3$	$+2$	$+1$	$+2$

Copy and complete using "is warmer than" or "is colder than".

1. 6°C ● 12°C
2. -7°C ● -8°C
3. 2°C ● -1°C

Write the opposite of each integer.

4. -1
5. 7
6. 24
7. 0
8. -42

Add.

9. $(-7) + (-1)$
10. $0 + (-2)$
11. $8 + 4$
12. $(-6) + (-8)$
13. $(-4) + 5$
14. $2 + (-3)$
15. $1 + (-8)$
16. $(-6) + 9$

Subtracting Integers

To subtract an integer, add its opposite.

The temperature was 5°C and dropped by 7°C. What is the new temperature?

The temperature was 5°C and fell to −2°C. What is the change in temperature?

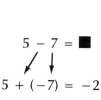

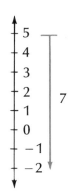

5 − 7 = ■

5 + (−7) = −2

The temperature is −2°C.

5 − (−2) = ■

5 + (2) = 7

The temperature change is 7°C.

EXERCISES

Subtract.

1.
8 − 6
8 − 7
8 − 8
8 − 9
8 − 10
8 − 11

2.
4 − 2
4 − 1
4 − 0
4 − (−1)
4 − (−2)
4 − (−3)

3.
3 − 1
2 − 1
1 − 1
0 − 1
(−1) − 1
(−2) − 1

4.
(−2) − 1
(−2) − 0
(−2) − (−1)
(−2) − (−2)
(−2) − (−3)

Copy and complete.

5. 4 − 9 = ■
4 + (−9) = ■

6. 4 − (−6) = ■
4 + 6 = ■

7. (−5) − 6 = ■
(−5) + (−6) = ■

8. 2 − 8 = ■
2 + (−8) = ■

9. 7 − (−3) = ■
7 + 3 = ■

10. (−3) − (−3) = ■
(−3) + 3 = ■

Subtract.

11. 8 − 9

12. (−5) − 3

13. 4 − (−6)

14. 2 − 11

15. 4 − (−2)

16. 3 − 10

17. (−6) − 6

18. 3 − (−9)

19. 3 − 7

20. (−4) − 6

21. (−7) − (−2)

22. (−6) − (−7)

PRACTICE

Subtract.

1. $1 - (-4)$ **2.** $(-6) - 10$ **3.** $4 - (-8)$ **4.** $(-10) - 10$

5. $9 - 9$ **6.** $(-2) - 7$ **7.** $(-3) - 3$ **8.** $2 - (-3)$

9. $(-5) - (-2)$ **10.** $(-8) - (-8)$ **11.** $(-15) - 4$ **12.** $1 - 1$

Simplify.

13. $(-2) + (5 - 7)$ **14.** $(4 + 6) - (3 - 4)$ **15.** $(-8) - (2 - 9)$

16. $(2 - 4) + (6 - 7)$ **17.** $(-1) + (6 - 6)$ **18.** $(9 + 5) - (5 - 9)$

Copy and complete.

19. $3 - 4 = 3 + \blacksquare$ **20.** $m - 7 = m + \blacksquare$ **21.** $m - n = m + \blacksquare$

22. $3 - (-4) = 3 + \blacksquare$ **23.** $m - (-7) = m + \blacksquare$ **24.** $m - (-n) = m + \blacksquare$

Each thermometer shows how the temperature changed.
Match each equation to a thermometer that shows the difference.

25. $1 - 2 = (-1)$ **a.**

26. $2 - (-1) = 3$ **b.**

27. $1 - (-2) = 1$ **c.**

Copy and complete.

28. 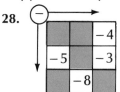   **29.** 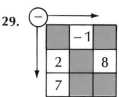   **30.**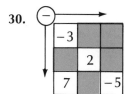

Calculate Integers

Some calculators have a **change-sign key** to allow you to enter integers on a calculator. The key is labelled ⌷CS⌷ or ⌷+/−⌷.

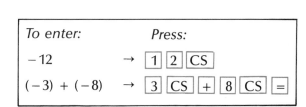

To enter:	Press:
-12	→ ⌷1⌷⌷2⌷⌷CS⌷
$(-3) + (-8)$	→ ⌷3⌷⌷CS⌷⌷+⌷⌷8⌷⌷CS⌷⌷=⌷

Use a calculator to find the sum.

1. $69 + (-48)$ **2.** $(-95) + (-38)$ **3.** $245 + (-186)$

4. $(-24) + 113$ **5.** $127 + (-215)$ **6.** $(-77) + (-99)$

Graphing Ordered Pairs

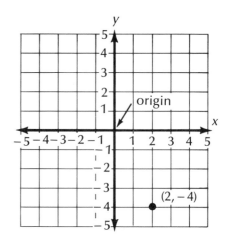

origin

(2, −4)

The grid at the right shows the **coordinate plane.**

The *horizontal* number line is called the **x-axis.**

The *vertical* number line is called the **y-axis.**

The x- and y-axes intersect at the **origin.** The axes divide the coordinate plane into four sections.

An ordered pair locates prints on a grid.

| The **x-coordinate** describes the *horizontal* distance, right or left, from the origin. | The **y-coordinate** describes the *vertical* distance, up or down, from the origin. |

(2, − 4)

right 2 units   down 4 units

EXERCISES

Write the coordinates for these directions from the origin.

1. 5 units right, 3 units up

2. 2 units left, 5 units up

3. 0 units right, 2 units down

4. 4 units left, 4 units down

Write the letter at each ordered pair.

5. (1, 1)   **6.** (−3, −4)   **7.** (−2, 2)

8. (0, 0)   **9.** (−5, 5)   **10.** (−2, −3)

11. (−4, 1)   **12.** (3, 5)   **13.** (5, 3)

14. (0, −3)   **15.** (−5, −3)   **16.** (2.5, 2.5)

Write the ordered pair for each point.

17. B   **18.** J   **19.** S

20. K   **21.** R   **22.** E

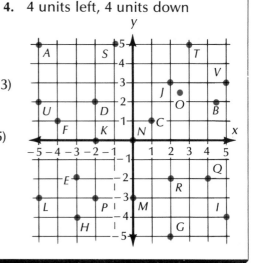

PRACTICE

Write the ordered pair describing the halfway point between:

1. (4, −2) and (4, 2)　　**2.** (−5, 6) and (−5, 0)　　**3.** (−1, −1) and (5, −5)

For each figure, write the ordered pairs which were joined in the order shown by the arrow.

4. 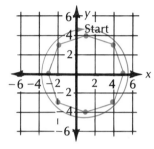　　　　**5.**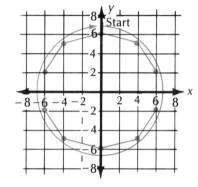

Graph and connect the ordered pairs on a grid in the order given.

6. (−1, 0) (2, 0) (2, 1) (−1, 1) (−1, 0)

7. (2, −1) (3, 1) (−3, 1) (−2, −1) (2, −1)

8. (−1, 4) (−6, −2) (−6, −3) (−1, 0) (−1, −5) (−3, −7) (−3, −8) (−1, −7)
(3, −8) (3, 7) (1, −5) (1, 0) (6, −3) (6, −2) (1, 4) (1, 8) (0, 10) (−1, 8) (−1, 4)

Computer Screen

A 40-column computer display is usually a 40 × 24 grid.

Commonly, the columns are numbered from left to right, 0 to 39.
The rows are numbered from top to bottom, 0 to 23.

1. List the coordinates of the letters.

2. What is the ordered pair of the centre of the display?

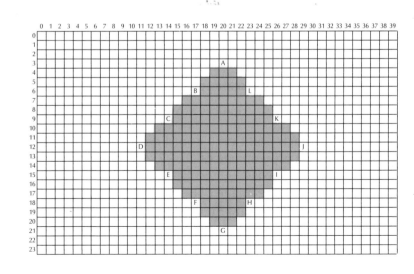

Transformations

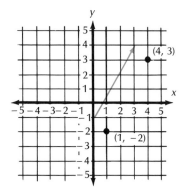

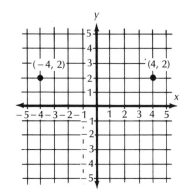

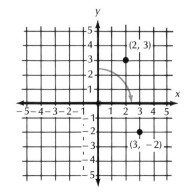

(4, 3) is the *image* of (1, −2) resulting from the *translation* [R3, U5].

(4, 2) is the *image* of (−4, 2) resulting from a *reflection* in the y-axis.

(3, −2) is the *image* of (2, 3) resulting from a $\frac{1}{4}$ clockwise *rotation* around (0, 0).

EXERCISES

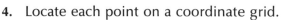

1. Draw and label each translation image of (−3, 1).
   a. [L1, D4]   b. [R7, U3]

2. On a second grid, draw each reflection image of (−3, 1).
   a. in the x-axis   b. in the y-axis

3. On a third grid, draw each rotation image of (−3, 1).
   a. $\frac{1}{4}$ clockwise rotation around (0, 0)
   b. $\frac{1}{2}$ clockwise rotation around (0, 0)

4. Locate each point on a coordinate grid.
   a. What is the image of (2, −2) resulting from a reflection in the y-axis?
   b. What is the image of (−3, −4) resulting from a $\frac{1}{4}$ clockwise rotation around (0, 0)?
   c. What is the image of (−3, 5) resulting from the translation [R5, D7]?

PRACTICE

1. Describe the transformation of (−5, 3) on each grid.
   For example: translation, [L2, D8].

   a.

   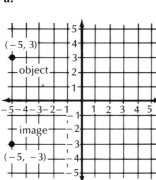

   b.

   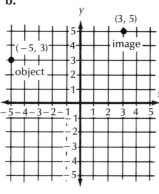

   c.

   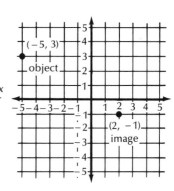

2. Locate the image point on a coordinate grid.
   a. What is the image of (1, 2) resulting from a $\frac{1}{2}$ clockwise rotation around (0, 0)?
   b. What is the reflection image of (−2, 3) in the x-axis?
   c. What is the image of (−5, −2) resulting from the translation [R7, U6]?
   d. What is the image of (1, −3) resulting from a $\frac{3}{4}$ clockwise rotation around (0, 0)?
   e. What is the reflection image of (−2, −4) in the y-axis?

Triangle Transformations

Triangle (−2, 2) (−4, 0) (−2, −3) can be transformed in many ways on a coordinate grid. Its reflection image in the y-axis is shown at the right.

Write the triangle's image for each transformation.

a. $\frac{1}{4}$ clockwise rotation around (0, 0)
b. reflection in the x-axis
c. translation [R7, U2]
d. $\frac{3}{4}$ clockwise rotation around (0, 0)
e. translation [L1, D2]

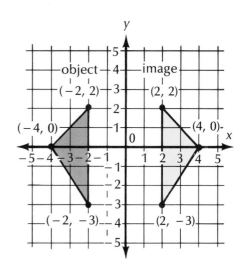

353

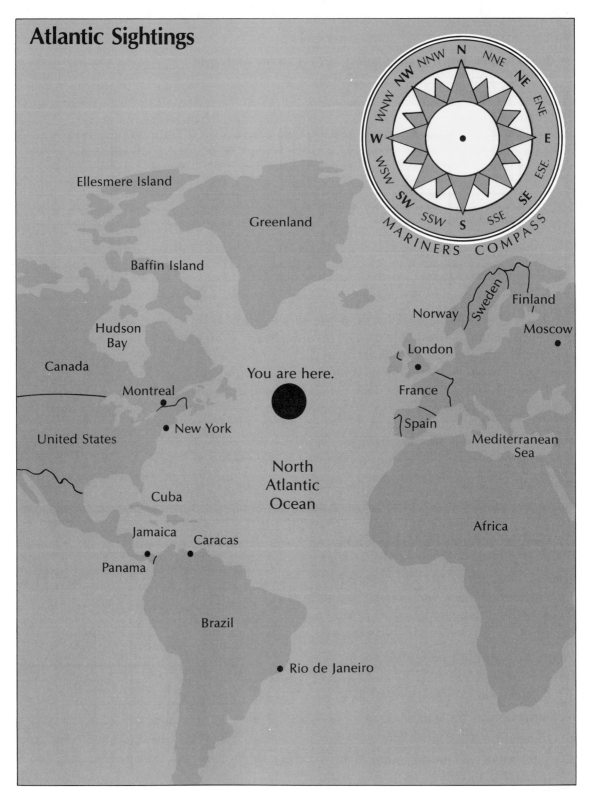

Atlantic Sightings

Ellesmere Island

Greenland

Baffin Island

Hudson Bay

Canada

Montreal

United States

New York

Cuba

Jamaica

Panama

Caracas

Brazil

Rio de Janeiro

You are here.

North Atlantic Ocean

Norway

Sweden

Finland

Moscow

London

France

Spain

Mediterranean Sea

Africa

MARINERS COMPASS

N
NNE
NE
ENE
E
ESE
SE
SSE
S
SSW
SW
WSW
W
WNW
NW
NNW

What city appears in the following direction?

1. East Northeast
2. West
3. West Southwest
4. South
5. Southwest
6. West Northwest

What island is located in the following direction?

7. SW   8. N   9. NNW   10. ENE   11. W   12. NW

Give the approximate location for each.

13. Mediterranean Sea
14. Lake Ontario
15. Hudson Bay
16. North Sea
17. Gulf of St. Lawrence
18. Gulf of Mexico
19. South America
20. Canada
21. Africa
22. Norway
23. Spain
24. France

REVIEW

Subtract.

1. $(-3) - (-3)$ 2. $0 - (-7)$ 3. $8 - (-2)$ 4. $4 - 6$

Write an ordered pair describing the halfway point between:

5. $(1, 4)$ and $(-3, 4)$ 6. $(-3, 2)$ and $(-1, 0)$ 7. $(-2, -2)$ and $(0, 2)$

8. What is the image of $(-4, 2)$ resulting from a reflection in the y-axis?

9. What is the image of $(-4, 2)$ resulting from a $\frac{1}{4}$ clockwise rotation around $(0, 0)$?

10. What is the image of $(-4, 2)$ after the translation [R8, U6]?

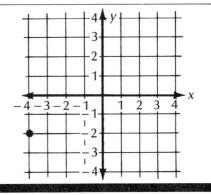

Which is the warmer temperature?

1. −8°C, −10°C   **2.** 0°C, −1°C   **3.** 3°C, 7°C   **4.** −6°C, 0°C

Write the opposite of each integer.

5. −4   **6.** 1   **7.** 15   **8.** −10   **9.** 0

Compare the two integers using the < sign.

10. 7, 5   **11.** −2, 4   **12.** −9, −7   **13.** 0, −2

Add.

14. (−5) + (−7)   **15.** (−9) + (−9)   **16.** 5 + 8   **17.** 0 + 4

18. (−10) + 4   **19.** 9 + (−2)   **20.** 6 + (−6)   **21.** (−1) + 7

Subtract.

22. 18 − (−9)   **23.** 10 − 5   **24.** 4 − (−7)   **25.** (−3) − 4

Write the point located by each ordered pair.

26. (5, −1)   **27.** (0, −5)   **28.** (4, 4)

Write the coordinates for each point.

29. H   **30.** B   **31.** F

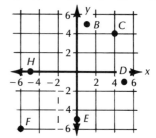

32. a. Graph the ordered pairs on a grid. Join the points in order.
(−4, 0) (−5, −2) (−3, −4) (−1, −2) (−2, 0) (−4, 0)
b. Describe the figure formed.
c. Add 8 to the first coordinate and 6 to the second coordinate for each pair. Join the points in order. Describe the new figure.

33. What is the image of (−2, 3) resulting from a reflection in the x-axis?

34. What is the image of (−2, 3) resulting from the translation [L3, D6]?

35. What is the image of (−2, 3) resulting from a $\frac{3}{4}$ clockwise rotation around (0, 0)?

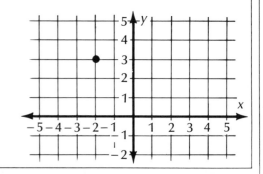

Statistics and Probability

Doug took a survey of the heights of the girls in his Grade 7 class.
The tallest girl was 170 cm tall and the range of heights was 30 cm.

1. How tall was the shortest girl?

2. The mean height of boys 13 years old is 155 cm. Does this mean that most boys 13 years old are 155 cm tall? Explain.

Doug also took a survey of the masses of the boys and girls in Grade 7. He got the results shown below.

3. What are the range and the mean of the boys' masses?

4. What are the range and the mean of the girls' masses?

5. What is the difference between the average girl's and the average boy's mass?

6. What are the range and mean for the masses of the boys and girls combined?

7. What are the median and mode for the masses of the boys and girls combined?

8. Does the mean, median, or mode most clearly describe the *average* mass?

9. Construct a frequency polygon for the masses of the boys and girls combined.

Mass (kg)	Boys	Girls
32	|	
34		||
36		
38	||	
40	|	|||
42	‖‖‖‖‖	||
44	‖‖‖‖‖ ||||	‖‖‖‖‖ |
46	‖‖‖‖‖ |	‖‖‖‖‖ ||
48	|||	‖‖‖‖‖
50	||	|
52		
54	||	
56	||	|
58	||	
60		

10. One student in the Grade 7 class will be randomly selected to win a prize. What is the probability that the winner will be a girl?

UNIT 15   Sets and Relations

Sets

A set is a well-defined collection of objects.
Capital letters can be used to name sets.
Braces { } enclose the objects belonging to a set.

The set of commonly used Canadian coins:

$A = \{$ ... $\}$

The set of counting numbers <5:

$B = \{1, 2, 3, 4\}$

The symbols $\in$ and $\notin$ are used to show the relationship of an object and a set.

$3 \in B$ means *3 is a member of set B.*
$7 \notin A$ means *7 is not a member of set A.*

A set containing no members is called the *empty set* or *null set.*
The symbols for empty set are { } or $\emptyset$.

The set of pink elephants is set C, where $C = \{\ \}$ or $C = \emptyset$.

Write each as a set using { }.

1. Set B = the even numbers between 1 and 9, B = {■, ■, ■, ■}

2. Set D = the days of the week. D = {■, ■, ■, ■, ■, ■, ■}

3. Set P = the letters in the word computer.

4. Set O = the odd, one-digit prime numbers.

5. Set W = the whole numbers >3 and <7.

6. Set Z = the months of the year having 32 days.

7. Set J = the prime numbers >13 and <17.

8. Set M = the odd numbers divisible by 2.

Describe each set.

9. F = {1, 2, 3}   10. S = {spring, summer, fall, winter}   11. B = {b, o, a, t}

Rewrite using ∈ or ∉.

12. 6 is a member of set G.

13. △ is not a member of set F.

14. 17 is not a member of set K.

15. John is a member of set X.

Write each as a set.

1. Set P = the prairie provinces.

2. Set N = the provinces east of Newfoundland.

3. Set F = the factors of 12.

4. Set R = the whole numbers <30 that are divisible by 4.

5. Set O = the three oceans bordering Canada.

6. If S = {the factors of 60}, which are true?
   a. $12 \in S$ b. $18 \in S$ c. $24 \in S$
   d. $14 \notin S$ e. $36 \notin S$ f. $16 \in S$

7. If C = {the provincial capitals}, which are false?
   a. Windsor $\in C$ b. Regina $\in C$ c. Kamloops $\notin C$
   d. Charlottetown $\notin C$ e. Victoria $\in C$ f. Red Deer $\notin C$

8. If B = {all two-digit prime numbers}, which are false?
   a. $93 \in B$ b. $7 \notin B$ c. $81 \in B$
   d. $47 \in B$ e. $29 \in B$ f. $57 \notin B$

Union and Intersection of Sets

Set Union:

Two or more sets can be *united* to make a new set called the **union** of the sets.

The symbol for union is U.
The union of sets can be pictured on a *Venn Diagram*.

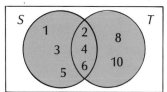

$S = \{1, 2, 3, 4, 5, 6\}$

$T = \{2, 4, 6, 8, 10\}$

$S \cup T = \{1, 2, 3, 4, 5, 6, 8, 10\}$ ←No members are written twice.

Set Intersection:

The making of a new set from the *common* members of two or more sets is called the **intersection** of the sets.

The symbol for intersection is ∩.

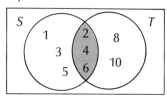

$S \cap T = \{2, 4, 6\}$

EXERCISES

List the members of each set.

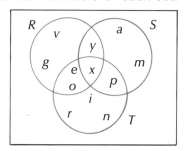

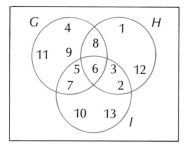

1. $R = \{\blacksquare, \blacksquare, \blacksquare, \blacksquare, \blacksquare, \blacksquare\}$

2. $R \cup S = \{\blacksquare, \blacksquare, \blacksquare, \blacksquare, \blacksquare, \blacksquare, \blacksquare, \blacksquare, \blacksquare\}$

3. $S \cup T$

4. $R \cup S \cup T$

5. $H = \{\blacksquare, \blacksquare, \blacksquare, \blacksquare, \blacksquare, \blacksquare\}$

6. $G \cap H = \{\blacksquare, \blacksquare\}$

7. $H \cap I$

8. $G \cap H \cap I$

PRACTICE

List the numbers of each set.

1.

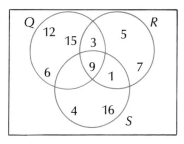

a. $R \cap Q$ **b.** $Q \cup R$

c. $R \cup S$ **d.** $Q \cap S$

e. $Q \cap R \cap S$ **f.** $S \cup (Q \cap R)$

2.

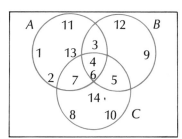

a. $A \cup B$ **b.** $A \cap C$

c. $B \cap C$ **d.** $A \cup C$

e. $B \cap A \cap C$ **f.** $(B \cap C) \cup A$

Describe each set.

T = {all triangles}	R = {all rectangles}	B = {all big things}
G = {all green things}	Y = {all yellow things}	

3. $T \cup R$ **4.** $T \cap Y$ **5.** $T \cap R$

6. $Y \cup G$ **7.** $Y \cap B \cap R$ **8.** $Y \cap B \cap D$

Draw a Venn Diagram. Then list the set members.

A = {the factors of 32}	B = {the factors of 30}	C = {the factors of 20}

9. $A \cap C$ **10.** $B \cap C$ **11.** $B \cap A$

12. $A \cup C$ **13.** $A \cap B \cap C$ **14.** $C \cap (A \cup B)$

Get Ready, Get Set

Call me X. I'm a number between 30 and 90.

Use these set clues to figure out my name.

$X \in P$, $X \in Q \cup R$, and $X \in S$

P = {numbers that leave a remainder of 2 when divided by 8}

Q = {numbers whose digits add to 6}

R = {numbers whose digits add to 12}

S = {numbers divisible by 10 or 11}

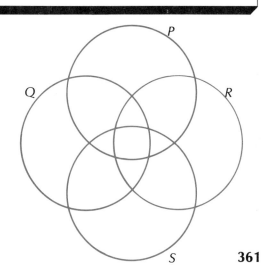

361

Using Diagrams to Solve Problems

Mrs. Thomson's class has 28 students. Twelve students own dogs and 15 students own cats. Five of those students own both dogs and cats. How many of Mrs. Thomson's students own neither a dog or cat?

Step 1: Describe the sets.
    D = {students owning a dog}
    C = {students owning a cat}

Step 2: Make a Venn Diagram.
    12 dog owners (7 + 5).
    15 cat owners (10 + 5).
    5 dog and cat owners.

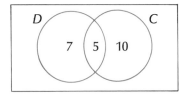

Step 3: Calculate the solution.
    28 students in all.
    22 students, 7 + 5 + 10, own a dog or a cat.

    6 students, 28 − (7 + 5 + 10), own neither a dog nor a cat.

EXERCISES

Use a Venn Diagram to solve these problems.

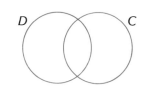

1. Twelve Grade 7 students have dogs or cats. Seven own dogs and 8 own cats. How many students own both dogs and cats?

2. There are 12 people in the Willowbrook 4-H Club. Six people own cows, five people own pigs, and eight people own horses. One person owns all three animals, two people own just horses and pigs, two people own just cows and pigs, and one person owns just cows and horses. How many people own just cows? just pigs? just horses?

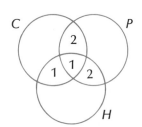

Use a Venn Diagram to solve these problems.

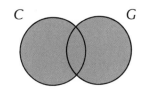

1. At Highline school, there are 28 students in the chess club and 18 students in the gymnastics club. Seven of the chess players are also gymnasts. How many students belong to only one club?

2. Bob, Jack, Paul, Sarah, Holly, and Kim are singing or dancing in the school musical. Bob, Sarah, Jack, and Kim are dancing. Only Bob and Kim are singing and dancing. Who are singing?

3. At a school party, 77 people ate a hamburger, 106 ate a plate of fries, and 66 ate the ice cream dessert. Fifty-six people ate a hamburger and fries, 43 ate fries and ice cream, and 26 ate a hamburger and ice cream. Eleven people ate a hamburger, a plate of fries, and the ice cream dessert. How many people attended the school party?

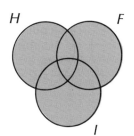

4. Twenty of the 35 football team members play offence. Six of those players play defence as well.
    a. How many players play just defence?
    b. How many players play just offence?

Finite and Infinite

A set having a limited number of members is a *finite set*.

The set of letters in the word Canada = {c, a, n, d}

A set having an unlimited number of members is an *infinite set*.

The set of multiples of 5 = {0, 5, 10, ...}

Is the set finite or infinite?

a. {all even numbers}
b. {h, o, u, s, e}
c. {stars in the sky}
d. {books in a library}
e. {multiples of 8}
f. {atoms in the Earth}
g. {whole numbers $>1\,000\,000$}
h. {whole numbers >3 and <10}
i. {grains of sand on a beach}
j. {factors of 1000}
k. {all people who have ever lived}
l. {multiples of 6}

Relations

A **relation** or **mapping** pairs the members of two sets.

A relation between two sets can be described by a **rule**.
It can be described by an arrow diagram, a table, or a set of
ordered pairs.

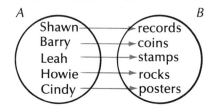

A	B
Shawn	records
Barry	coins
Leah	stamps
Howie	rocks
Cindy	posters

(Shawn, records)
(Barry, coins)
(Leah, stamps)
(Howie, rocks)
(Cindy, posters)

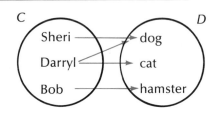

C	D
Sheri	dog
Darryl	dog
Darryl	cat
Bob	hamster

(Sheri, dog)
(Darryl, dog)
(Darryl, cat)
(Bob, hamster)

In the above example, Darryl has two pets.
So Darryl (in set C) is "mapped" onto two pets (in set D).

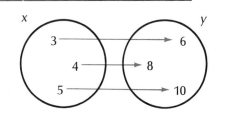

x	y
3	6
4	8
5	10

(3, 6)
(4, 8)
(5, 10)

364

EXERCISES

1. List the set of ordered pairs for the relation.

a. | **Rule:** favourite colour |

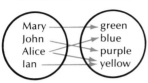

b. **Rule:** capital city

Province	Capital
Alta.	Calgary
N.S.	Halifax
Ont.	Toronto
B.C.	Victoria

c. **Rule:** $y = x \div 3$

x	y
27	9
24	8
21	7
18	6

2. Draw an arrow diagram.

a. **Rule:** subject taught

Teacher	Subject
Foster	Science
Foster	Math
Taylor	English
Akune	P.E.
Orser	French

b. **Rule:** instrument played

(Jody, piano)
(Harry, trumpet)
(Celia, flute)
(Norman, drums)
(Kathi, clarinet)

c. **Rule:** round to ones

x	y
1.2	1
1.5	2
2.4	2
2.5	3
3.8	4

3. Complete the table according to the rule.

a. **Rule:** number of days in a month

Month	Days
Jan.	?
Mar.	?
June	?
Aug.	?
Oct.	?
Nov.	?

b. **Rule:** $y = x + 7$

x	y
9	?
4	?
3	?
7	?
5	?
8	?

c. **Rule:** $y = 3x - 1$

x	y
2	?
4	?
6	?
8	?
10	?
12	?

4. Show the relation as a table. Include a rule.

a.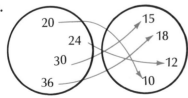

b.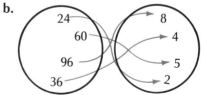

c. (2, 6) (7, 21) (0, 0) (11, 33) (4, 12) (20, 60) (5, 15)

d. (4, 11) (2, 7) (0, 3) (3, 9) (6, 15) (1, 5) (5, 13)

PRACTICE

Show the relation as an arrow diagram. Include a rule.

1.

Sport	Trophy
Hockey	Stanley Cup
Football	Grey Cup
Tennis	Davis Cup
Sailing	America's Cup
Sailing	Admiral's Cup

2.

x	y
3	6
5	8
10	13
7	10
9	12

3.

(Canada, Ottawa)
(England, London)
(France, Paris)
(Italy, Rome)
(Spain, Madrid)

List a set of ordered pairs for the relation. Include a rule.

4.

Fir — tree
rose — flower
mushroom — fungus
carrot — vegetable
apple — fruit

5.

x	y
2	5
4	11
6	17
8	23
10	29

6.

x	y
4	24
2	30
5	18
3	12
9	54

Complete the table according to the rule.

7.

Rule: $y = 2x$

x	y
3	?
7	?
1	?
4	?
5	?

8.

Rule: $y = 3x - 2$

x	y
4	?
2	?
1	?
5	?
7	?

9.

Rule: $y = 5x + 3$

x	y
8	?
6	?
3	?
?	23
?	48

Show the relation as a table. Include a rule.

10. (1, 2) (2, 3) (3, 4) (4, 5) (5, 6) (6, 7) (8, 9)

11. (0, 0) (1, 5) (2, 10) (3, 15) (4, 20) (5, 25) (6, 30)

12. (8, 2) (12, 3) (4, 1) (6, 1.5) (16, 4) (26, 6.5)

13. (10, 41) (7, 29) (5, 21) (9, 37) (12, 49) (3, 13)

14.

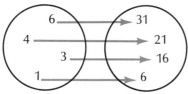

15.

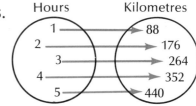

Make a table to answer each question. Include a rule.

16. Movie tickets cost $5.50 each. What is the cost of 2 tickets? 3 tickets? 4 tickets? 5 tickets?

17. Tim and Tina want to sell their used books and games and then split the profit. How much money would each make if there were $22 profit? $54 profit? $38 profit? $110 profit?

18. Mrs. Bixby is 35 years older than her daughter. How old is Mrs. Bixby if her daughter is 12 years old? 25 years old? 32 years old? 49 years old?

19. George types at a rate of 45 words/min. How many words would he type after 5 min? 10 min? 15 min? 20 min?

20. One fourth of the ingredients of a punch recipe is ginger ale. How much ginger ale is used if 3 L of punch is made? 4 L? 5 L? 6 L?

21. How many equal parts are formed when a piece of paper is folded in half once? twice? three times? four times?

REVIEW

If R = {the factors of 72}, which are true?

1. $18 \notin R$ 2. $24 \in R$ 3. $15 \notin R$

4. $6 \in R$ 5. $R = \{ \}$ 6. $R = \emptyset$

Draw a Venn Diagram. Then list the members of each set.

$A = \{5, 10, 15, 20\}$ $B = \{3, 6, 9, 12, 15\}$ $C = \{2, 4, 6, 8, 10\}$

7. $B \cup C$ 8. $A \cap C$ 9. $(A \cap B) \cup C$

Use a diagram to solve the problem.

10. There are 40 students who play rugby, tennis, or soccer. Fifteen students play rugby and 18 students play soccer. Four of those students play rugby and soccer. How many students play only tennis?

Show each relation in a table. Include a rule.

11. (3, 11) (5, 13) (7, 15) (9, 17) (11, 19) (13, 21) (15, 23)

12. (1, 5) (4, 14) (8, 26) (10, 32) (12, 38) (15, 47) (20, 62)

Linear Relations

A relation is *linear* if its
graph is a set of points
which lie on a *straight line*.

Rule: $y = 2x + 1$	
x	y
7	15
6	13
5	11
4	9
3	7
2	5
1	3
0	1

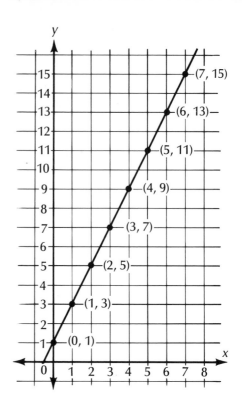

EXERCISES

Copy and complete the table. Then draw the graph.

1.

Rule: $y = x + 1$	
x	y
1	?
2	?
3	?
4	?
5	?

2.

Rule: $y = 3x$	
x	y
12	?
11	?
10	?
9	?
8	?

3.

Rule: $2x - 1$	
x	y
10	?
9	?
8	?
7	?
6	?

List the ordered pairs from each graph.

4.

5.

6.

7. For problems 4 to 6, which relation is not linear?

Copy and complete each table. Then draw the graph.

1.

Rule: $y = x - 5$	
x	y
12	
11	
10	
9	
8	
7	

2.

Rule: $y = 4x + 2$	
x	y
0	
1	
2	
3	
4	
5	

3.

Rule: $y = x$	
x	y
2	
4	
6	
8	
10	
12	

List the ordered pairs for each graph.

4.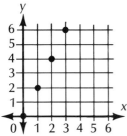

5.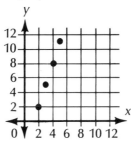

6.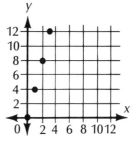

7. For problems 4 to 6, write the rule.

8. Graph the relations.
   Which relations are not linear?
   a. (3, 4) (2, 2) (−1, −4) (0, −2)
   b. (−2, 3) (4, 2) (2, 0) (1, −2)
   c. (4, −4) (0, 0) (−3, 3) (2, −2)

Mass Mystery

Sarah was trying to find the mass of a chicken, a rabbit, and a duck by using a balance scale and two 1 kg masses.

She found that the rabbit's mass was 2 kg more than the duck's, and that the duck's mass was 2 kg more than the chicken's.

The combined mass of the duck and the chicken was 1 kg less than the rabbit's mass.

What was the mass of each animal?

Solving Equations

Equations can be solved by using **opposite operations**.

Example:

$$\boxed{x + 6 = 20}$$

$x + 6 - 6 = 20 - 6$ $\begin{cases}\text{Do the opposite.}\\ \text{Subtract 6 from}\\ \text{both sides.}\end{cases}$

$x + 0 = 14$

$x = 14$

Check: $14 + 6 = 20$

$$\boxed{3x = 45}$$

$\dfrac{3x}{3} = \dfrac{45}{3}$ $\begin{cases}\text{Do the opposite.}\\ \text{Divide both}\\ \text{sides by 3.}\end{cases}$

$x = 15$

Check: $3 \times 15 = 45$

$$\boxed{5x + 4 = 19}$$

$5x + 4 - 4 = 19 - 4$ $\begin{cases}\text{Do the opposite.}\\ \text{Subtract 4.}\end{cases}$

$5x + 0 = 15$

$5x = 15$

$\dfrac{5x}{5} = \dfrac{15}{3}$

$x = 3$

Check: $5 \times 3 + 4 = 19$

$$\boxed{2x + 3x = 10}$$

$2x + 3x = 5x$ $\begin{cases}\text{Combine}\\ \textbf{like terms.}\end{cases}$

$5x = 10$

$\dfrac{5x}{5} = \dfrac{10}{5}$

$x = 2$

Check: $2 \times 2 + 3 \times 2 = 10$

EXERCISES

Solve the equation by doing the opposite operation.
Then check the solution.

1. $x + 13 = 52$

$x = 52 - \blacksquare$

$x = \blacksquare$

2. $x - 16 = 41$

3. $2x = 78$

$x = \dfrac{78}{\blacksquare}$

$x = \blacksquare$

4. $5x = 115$

5. $2x - 11 = 31$

$2x = 31 + \blacksquare$

$2x = \blacksquare$

$x = \dfrac{\blacksquare}{\blacksquare}$

$x = \blacksquare$

6. $3x + 5 = 61$

7. $6x - 4x = 6$

$\blacksquare x = 6$

$x = \dfrac{6}{\blacksquare}$

$x = \blacksquare$

8. $4x + 5x = 108$

9. $x - 14 = 69$

10. $9x = 117$

11. $8x - 9 = 87$

12. $5x + 9x = 98$

370

PRACTICE

Is the given value of x a solution to the equation?
Answer *yes* or *no*.

1. $x + 14 = 25$
for $x = 9$

2. $x - 45 = 32$
for $x = 77$

3. $x + 18 = 105$
for $x = 97$

4. $6x = 252$
for $x = 42$

5. $18x = 54$
for $x = 3$

6. $45x = 270$
for $x = 5$

7. $12x + 3 = 87$
for $x = 7$

8. $32x - 5 = 635$
for $x = 20$

9. $9x + 18 = 126$
for $x = 12$

10. $3x + 5x = 32$
for $x = 4$

11. $7x - 2x = 15$
for $x = 3$

12. $8x + 2x = 70$
for $x = 6$

Solve the equation. Then check the solution.

13. $x - 24 = 17$

14. $x + 114 = 209$

15. $x - 95 = 132$

16. $9x = 342$

17. $12x = 168$

18. $15x = 375$

19. $5x - 2 = 18$

20. $3x - 10 = 215$

21. $4x + 78 = 182$

22. $6x + 3x = 63$

23. $3x + 10x = 208$

24. $5x + 9x = 350$

Solve.

25. The product of a certain number and 7 less 24 is 200.
What is the number?

26. Nineteen more than the product of a number and 15 is 364.
What is the number?

Calculator Solutions

You can use a calculator to do the *opposite operation* needed to solve an equation.

$15.9x + 226.85 = 236.39$

  9.54

  0.6

Solution: $x = 0.6$

Check: $15.9(0.6) + 226.85 = 236.39$

Solve these equations
with a calculator.
a. $438.72x = 403.6224$
b. $b + 26.9 = 35.4 + 43.1$
c. $6.19a - 45.5 = 301.14$
d. $22.44s + 10.24 = 100$
e. $3.5n + 0.2n = 0.925$

Using Equations to Solve Problems

Lucy can fill a 20 L container with three full pails
of water plus 2 L.
What is the capacity of each pail?

Step 1: Let x represent the unknown amount of water a pail holds.

Step 2: Write an equation. $3x + 2 = 20$

Step 3: Solve the equation. $3x + 2 = 20$

$$3x = 20 - 2$$ — Do the opposite. Subtract 2.
$$3x = 18$$
$$x = \frac{18}{3}$$ — Do the opposite. Divide by 3.
$$x = 6$$
Check: $3 \times 6 + 2 = 20$

Each pail holds 6 L of water.

EXERCISES

Complete the equation for the problem.
Then solve the equation to solve the problem.

1. Three kilograms more than Bob's mass is
   52 kg. What is *Bob's mass*?

   $m + \blacksquare = \blacksquare$

2. Two times the number of centimetres in the
   length of a pen is 28. What is the *length*
   of the pen?

   $\blacksquare \times L = \blacksquare$

3. Marie has $79 in the bank at the end of the
   year. This amount is five dollars more than
   double the money she had at the start of the
   year. How much money did Marie have at
   the *start* of the year?

   $\blacksquare \times s + \blacksquare = \blacksquare$

4. Nine less than half the total number of
   deliveries on Bob's paper route lie on Elm
   Street. If Bob delivers 27 papers on Elm
   Street, how many deliveries must he make
   in *total*?

   $\blacksquare \times t - \blacksquare = \blacksquare$

Set up an equation for the problem.
Then solve the equation to solve the problem.

1. After a day of buying and trading at the stamp fair, Joan found that she has three less than double the number of stamps in her original collection. If she now has 75 stamps, how many stamps were in her *original* collection?

2. Tom delivered fliers one weekend. He delivered half of the fliers on Saturday morning and 35 more after lunch. Altogether he delivered 115 fliers on Saturday. How many fliers did Tom deliver altogether that *weekend*?

3. Sally needs to work 12 h to earn enough money to add to the $141 already in her savings account to buy a new violin. New violins cost $237. What is Sally's *hourly* wage?

4. Bill now has 41 guppies. This is seven less than four times the number of guppies he had at first. How many guppies did Bill have at the *start*?

5. The cost of renting a video recorder is $12.95 plus $2.99 for each movie rented. If Mr. Baker paid $30.89 for the rental, how many *movies* did he get with the recorder?

Draw the graph for each.

1. (1, 8) (2, 16) (3, 24) (4, 32)   2. (1, 2) (2, 5) (3, 8) (4, 11)

Solve the equation. Then check the solution.

3. $x + 23 = 111$ 4. $3x + 12 = 57$ 5. $7x + 5x = 84$

Set up an equation for the problem.
Then solve the equation to solve the problem.

6. To buy a new 10-speed bike for $220, Jason needs $50 less than triple his present amount of money. How much *money* does he have now?

A Linear Relations Computer Program

The BASIC computer program below computes the value of y in the rule $y = 3x + 1$.

Rule: $y = 3x + 1$	
x	y
5	
100	
6	
8	
13	

```
100 REM
110 REM THIS PROGRAM COMPUTES LINEAR RELATIONS.
120 REM PUT FIVE NUMBERS IN THE DATA STATEMENT 300.
130 REM THE PROGRAM WILL USE THE FIVE NUMBERS
140 REM TO CALCULATE THE Y VALUE.
150 REM THE LINEAR RELATION IS DEFINED IN STATEMENT 220.
160 REM
200 FOR I = 1 TO 5
210 READ X
220 LET Y = 3*X+1
230 PRINT TAB(12);X;TAB(18);"--->";TAB (23);Y
240 NEXT I
300 DATA 5,100,6,8,13
310 END
```

```
]RUN
          5      ---)  16
          100    ---)  301
          6      ---)  19
          8      ---)  25
          13     ---)  40
```

The READ and DATA statements are used together in a program. The DATA statement includes a list of values for the computer to READ. With an INPUT statement, one value at a time can be entered from the keyboard. But if you have a lot of data which doesn't change, it is faster to use the READ and DATA statements for inserting values into a program.

The TAB ( ) function moves the cursor to a specified printing position, counting from the left edge of the current cursor line. TAB (12) moves the cursor right 12. This function is always used within a PRINT statement.

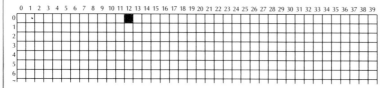

Refer to the computer program on the previous page to answer each question.

1. In which line of the program is the linear relation defined?

2. Write each rule in BASIC.

   a. $y = x + 3$
   b. $y = x - 2$
   c. $y = 3x$

   d. $y = 5x$
   e. $y = 3.4x$
   f. $y = 2.5x$

   g. $y = \frac{x}{7}$
   h. $y = \frac{x}{2}$
   i. $y = 5x - 2$

   j. $y = 3x + 3$
   k. $y = 2x - 8$
   l. $y = 4x + 7$

   m. $y = \frac{x}{2} - 3$
   n. $y = \frac{x}{5} + 4$
   o. $y = \frac{3}{x}$

   p. $y = \frac{10}{x}$
   q. $y = 3.5x - 2.8$
   r. $y = 4.2x + 0.8$

   s. $y = 5(x + 3)$
   t. $y = 2(x + 4)$
   u. $y = 7(x - 1)$

3. Change line 220 to each of the following. What is the output if the program were RUN?

   a. `LET Y = 5*X-2`
   b. `LET Y = 2.5*X`
   c. `LET Y = 5*(X + 3)`

4. Change lines 200 and 300 to each of the following. What is the output if the program were RUN?

   a. `200 FOR I = 1 TO 4`
      `300 DATA 3,9,10,12`

   b. `200 FOR I = 1 TO 3`
      `300 DATA 3.7,4.2,1.5`

   c. `200 FOR I = 1 TO 6`
      `300 DATA 2,7,10,15,18,24`

5. How could some program lines be changed in order to compute the y values for each rule?

   a. **Rule:** $y = 5x - 7$

x	y
8	
3	
7	
4	

   b. **Rule:** $y = 2x + 8$

x	y
34	
18	
6.5	
0	
1	

   c. **Rule:** $y = 4.2x + 0.8$

x	y
7	
9	
3.2	

6. Experiment with changing the TAB positions in the program. Describe what happens for TAB (20), TAB (30), TAB (40), TAB (80), TAB (200), TAB (255), TAB (256).

$A = \{a, b, c, d, e, f, g\}$ $B = \{a, c, e, f, h, j\}$ $C = \{b, c, d, k, l, m\}$

True or false?

1. $g \in B$ **2.** $a \in A$ **3.** $C = \{\}$ **4.** $m \notin A$

Draw a Venn Diagram for sets A, B, and C.
Then list the members in each set.

5. $A \cup B$ **6.** $B \cap C$ **7.** $A \cap B \cap C$ **8.** $A \cup (C \cap B)$

Find the rule for each.

9.

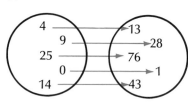

10.

x	y
2	9
0	5
5	15
3	11
6	17
1	7

11.

(0, 3)
(1, 5)
(2, 7)
(3, 9)
(4, 11)
(5, 13)

Copy and complete the table. Then draw the graph.

12.

Rule: $y = 4x$	
x	y
0	?
1	?
2	?
3	?
4	?
5	?

13.

Rule: $y = 2x - 2$	
x	y
5	?
4	?
3	?
2	?
1	?
0	?

14.

Rule: $y = 3x + 1$	
x	y
5	?
4	?
3	?
2	?
1	?
0	?

Solve for x.

15. $3x = 57$ **16.** $5x + 6 = 71$ **17.** $7x - 3x = 72$

Write an equation to help you solve the problem.

18. The Hillcrest pizza parlor served 197 pizzas on Friday night. This is eight more than triple the number of pizzas sold on Thursday night. How many pizzas were sold on Thursday night.

1. Write the temperatures in order from coldest to warmest.
   −8°C   0°C   −12°C   1°C   5°C   −3°C   −9°C

Write the opposite of each integer.

2. 4   **3.** −25   **4.** −81   **5.** 0   **6.** 295

Compare the two integers using the > sign.

7. −4, 9   **8.** 0, 3   **9.** −6, −7   **10.** −2, 2

Add.

11. (−5) + (−9)   **12.** 0 + (−4)   **13.** 4 + 8   **14.** (−1) + (−10)

15. 3 + (−3)   **16.** (−16) + 17   **17.** (−6) + (−9)   **18.** (−10) + 10

Subtract.

19. 2 − 3   **20.** (−2) − (−8)   **21.** 0 − (−5)   **22.** (−4) − 7

23. (−4) − 4   **24.** 0 − 5   **25.** (−3) − (−1)   **26.** 12 − (−9)

Write the ordered pair describing the halfway point between.

27. (−2, 2) and (2, 2)   **28.** (3, 2) and (3, −5)   **29.** (−1, −1) and (3, 3)

30. (4, −3) and (4, −1)   **31.** (−5, 1) and (−3, −1)   **32.** (−6, 0) and (−2, 4)

33. Graph the ordered pairs on a grid. Join the points in the order given.
(0, −2) (0, −7) (1, −7) (0, −2) (2, −4) (2, −3) (5, −3) (4, −1)
(6, 1) (5, 1) (6, 3) (5, 3) (5, 4) (3, 3) (3, 5) (2, 5) (2, 6) (1, 5) (0, 7)
(−1, 5) (−2, 6) (−2, 3) (−4, 4) (−4, 3) (−6, 3) (−5, 1) (−6, 0)
(−5, −1) (−6, 0) (−5, −1) (−5, −2) (−3, −2) (−4, −3)
(−1, −3) (0, −2)

34. What is the reflection image of (4, 2) in the y-axis?

35. What is the image of (4, 2) resulting from the translation [L7, D4]?

36. What is the image of (4, 2) resulting from a $\frac{1}{2}$ clockwise rotation around (0, 0)?

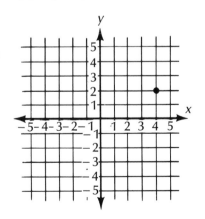

Cumulative Test:

Units 1–3

Use the driving distance table to answer questions 1–3.

Kilometre Guide	Banff	Flin-Flon	Gaspé	Moncton	Windsor
Banff		1362	4823	4904	3370
Flin-Flon	1362		4252	4324	2799
Gaspé	4823	4252		669	1856
Moncton	4904	4324	669		1936
Windsor	3370	2799	1856	1936	

1. Between which two cities is the driving distance
   a. the shortest?
   b. the longest?

2. What is the total driving distance for each trip?
   a. Flin-Flon to Banff and back.
   b. Moncton to Gaspé and back.

3. If you average about 600 km/d when driving, between which two cities could you drive in three days?

4. The Mackenzie River is about 4240 km long. The driving distance between which two cities is about the same length.

Add or subtract.

5.
$$500 - 79$$

6.
$$7\,426 + 35\,299$$

7.
$$29\,600\,000 - 856\,713$$

8.
$$87\,145 + 996\,255$$

9.
$$226\,174\,825 - 28\,079\,374$$

10.
$$\$492\,364 + 79\,985$$

11.
$$\$75\,000 - 2\,965$$

12.
$$\$12.88 + 6.27$$

13. $2000 - 456$

14. $38\,109 + 9758$

15. $349 + 74\,757$

16. $\$3.70 + \$19.56$

17. $\$25 - \$6.79$

18. $4.08 + 29.674$

Evaluate each expression. Suppose $x = 1.2$, $y = 8.4$, and $z = 3.5$.

19. $y + z$

20. $27 - x$

21. $y - z$

22. $95 + y$

Guess and test the solution for each equation.

23. $a + 75 = 117$

24. $68 - x = 49$

25. $354 + b = 402$

26. $18 - m = 5.7$

27. $1.5 + y = 7.2$

28. $40.2 - c = 25.5$

Write an equation. Then guess and test the solution.

29. The sum of 19.6 and a number is 32.4. What is the number?

Find the product.

30. $10\,000 \times 14$ **31.** 2.65×100 **32.** 0.08×1000 **33.** 12.7×10

Find the quotient.

34. $27 \div 10$ **35.** $38 \div 1000$ **36.** $27\,184 \div 1000$ **37.** $0.4 \div 100$

Estimate the product or quotient.

38. 689×52 **39.** $38\overline{)4172}$ **40.** $\$1.99 \times 18$ **41.** $9\overline{)\$32.95}$

Multiply.

42. $\begin{array}{r} 28 \\ \times 75 \\ \hline \end{array}$ **43.** $\begin{array}{r} 7624 \\ \times\ 397 \\ \hline \end{array}$ **44.** $\begin{array}{r} 2.78 \\ \times 0.03 \\ \hline \end{array}$ **45.** $\begin{array}{r} 724.5 \\ \times 0.005 \\ \hline \end{array}$

Divide.

46. $72\overline{)864}$ **47.** $4.6\overline{)174.8}$ **48.** $0.25\overline{)1361}$ **49.** $0.6\overline{)518.7}$

Evaluate each expression. Suppose $a = 24$, $b = 0.8$, and $c = 168$.

50. $2c$ **51.** $\dfrac{a}{b}$ **52.** $5ab$ **53.** $\dfrac{c}{b}$

Write in expanded form using powers of 10.

54. $29\,300$ **55.** $7\,500\,000$ **56.** 1872 **57.** $264\,850\,000$

Find the value of n.

58. $237 + 9641 = n + 237$ **59.** $(24 \times 500) \times 64 = 24 \times (500 \times n)$

60. $(60 + 7) \times 9 = 60n + 7n$ **61.** $(100 - 4) \times n = (100 \times 8) - (4 \times 8)$

Simplify.

62. $2^1 + 3^0$ **63.** $9^0 \times 1$ **64.** $(112 - 38) \times 10^2 - 250$

65. $18 \div 1 \times 5^1$ **66.** $49 + (35 \div 35)$ **67.** $(18 - 18) \times 6^3 + 9^2$

68. $2^6 \times 3^1 \div 7^0$ **69.** $3^3 - (4 + 2^0) \div 5$ **70.** $25 + 26 - (6^2 + 14) \div 10$

Solve.

71. Allan rented three movies on the weekend. Two of the movies had 122 min playing times. It took 359 min to view all three movies. What was the playing time of the third movie?

72. The product of three different whole numbers is 60. What are the three numbers?

73. When you subtract 28.5 from a number, the result is 35.8. What is the number?

Cumulative Test:

Choose the operation which would solve the problem.

1. On the average, Janet spells 0.9 of the words correctly on her weekly tests. How many words would she be expected to spell correctly on a 50-word test?
   - a. divide
   - b. multiply
   - c. multiply and divide

Estimate the area of each lake on the Canadian side of the boundary. Then use a calculator to find the *exact* area.

Lake	Total Area (km²)	Area on American Side of Boundary (km²)
Superior	2. 82 103	4. 53 354
Erie	3. 25 667	5. 12 898

Copy and complete.

6. 29.5 m = ■ cm
7. 38 m = ■ km
8. 1256 mm = ■ m
9. 45 L = ■ mL
10. 0.5 kL = ■ L
11. 1875 L = ■ kL
12. 2.8 t = ■ kg
13. 655 g = ■ kg
14. 12 kg = ■ g

15. Find the perimeter of a hexagon whose sides are 4.5 cm each.

16. Find the circumference of a circle whose diameter is 16 cm.

Find the area.

17. triangle: base = 6 cm, height = 9 cm

18. square: side = 14 m

19. rectangle: length = 12 km, width = 24 km

20. parallelogram: base = 17 cm, height = 11 cm

21. circle: radius = 48 cm

Find the volume.

22. *rectangular prism*
    length: 15 cm
    width: 28 cm
    height: 9 cm

23. *triangular prism*
    triangular base: 15 cm
    triangular height: 12 cm
    prism height: 5 cm

24. *cylinder*
    radius of base: 6 cm
    height: 18 cm

Match each question with one of the letters below.

25. *AD*

26. Point *F*

27. Point *J*

28. ∠*BAE*

29. ∠*ABD*

30. Figure *BCD*

31. Figure *ABDE*

32. ∠*FHI*

33. ∠*ACB*

34. *BC*

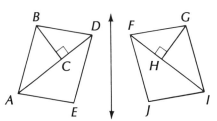

A. ≅ ∠*FJI*	**B.** = 180°	**C.** is a scalene triangle
D. ≅ *FI*	**E.** = 90°	**F.** is the image of point *E*
G. is a right triangle	**H.** ≅ ∠*FGI*	**I.** is a parallelogram
J. is the image of point *D*	**K.** ⊥ *AD*	**L.** ≅ ∠*GIJ*

Make the construction described.

35. a. Construct ∠*ABC* = 80° with a protractor.
   b. Construct *BX* to bisect ∠*ABC* with a compass.
   c. Construct ∠*DEF* ≅ ∠*ABC* with a protractor or tracing paper.

36. Construct an equilateral triangle *QRS* with your own choice of equipment.

Is 731 412 divisible by the number?

37. 2   38. 3   39. 4   40. 6   41. 9

Write the set of factors for each number.

42. 57   43. 72   44. 86   45. 200   46. 120

Identify the number as prime or composite.

47. 9   48. 37   49. 2   50. 61   51. 87

Write each as a product of prime factors.

52. 36   53. 124   54. 500   55. 128   56. 144

Write the set of the first six multiples for each.

57. 6   58. 11   59. 15   60. 400   61. 150

Find:

62. GCF (8, 20); LCM (8, 20).   63. GCF (12, 18); LCM (12, 18).

64. GCF (9, 15); LCM (9, 15).   65. GCF (42, 56); LCM (42, 56).

Cumulative Test:

Units 8–11

Copy and complete.

1. $\frac{4}{5} = \frac{\blacksquare}{25}$
2. $\frac{7}{12} = \frac{35}{\blacksquare}$
3. $\frac{3}{8} = \frac{\blacksquare}{40}$
4. $\frac{9}{16} = \frac{27}{\blacksquare}$

Write the fractions in simplest terms.

5. $\frac{15}{24}$
6. $\frac{28}{42}$
7. $\frac{36}{48}$
8. $\frac{21}{35}$
9. $\frac{60}{144}$

Copy and compare. Use < or >.

10. $\frac{3}{8} \bullet \frac{4}{5}$
11. $\frac{7}{9} \bullet \frac{7}{10}$
12. $1\frac{2}{3} \bullet 1\frac{3}{4}$
13. $1\frac{5}{6} \bullet 1\frac{4}{5}$

Write the fraction as a decimal.

14. $\frac{3}{4}$
15. $\frac{5}{8}$
16. $\frac{1}{2}$
17. $\frac{1}{3}$
18. $\frac{13}{20}$

Write the decimal as a fraction in simplest terms.

19. 0.2
20. 0.75
21. 0.96
22. 0.08
23. 0.85

Add or subtract.

24. $\frac{2}{8} + \frac{3}{4}$
25. $\frac{5}{6} - \frac{5}{8}$
26. $\frac{3}{7} + \frac{1}{9}$
27. $\frac{4}{5} - \frac{1}{2}$

28. $\frac{3}{4} + \frac{9}{10}$
29. $\frac{7}{12} - \frac{3}{8}$
30. $1\frac{1}{2} - \frac{3}{4}$
31. $2\frac{1}{2} + 3\frac{2}{3}$

32. $2\frac{7}{8} - 1\frac{1}{6}$
33. $3\frac{7}{9} + 1\frac{7}{8}$
34. $5\frac{1}{6} - 3\frac{4}{5}$
35. $1\frac{9}{10} + 2\frac{11}{12}$

For each diagram, write a multiplication equation involving fractions.

36.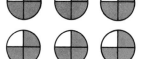
37.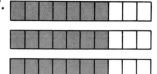
38.

Write the reciprocal for each.

39. 25
40. $\frac{9}{11}$
41. $\frac{1}{5}$
42. $1\frac{3}{4}$
43. $3\frac{7}{12}$

Multiply or divide.

44. $12 \times \frac{5}{6}$
45. $\frac{3}{4}$ of 128
46. $18 \times \frac{2}{3}$
47. $\frac{7}{9}$ of 72

48. $28 \div \frac{4}{7}$
49. $\frac{3}{5} \times 150$
50. $\frac{5}{6} \div \frac{1}{3}$
51. $\frac{3}{8} \times \frac{1}{12}$

52. $4\frac{4}{5} \times 5$
53. $10 \div 6\frac{4}{5}$
54. $1\frac{1}{2} \times 2\frac{2}{3}$
55. $7\frac{3}{8} \div 1\frac{1}{2}$

56. How many rectangles in all?

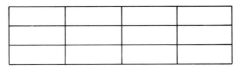

57. The design at the right has 4 small triangles and uses 9 toothpicks. How many toothpicks would be needed to extend the design to make 18 small triangles?

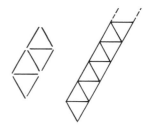

58. Work backwards to find the input number if the output number is 15.

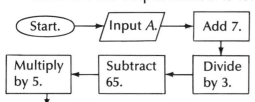

59. Calculate the results.

a. $\boxed{3}\boxed{2}\boxed{\times}\boxed{3}\boxed{4}\boxed{=}$

b. $\boxed{3}\boxed{3}\boxed{2}\boxed{\times}\boxed{3}\boxed{3}\boxed{4}\boxed{=}$

c. $\boxed{3}\boxed{3}\boxed{3}\boxed{2}\boxed{\times}\boxed{3}\boxed{3}\boxed{3}\boxed{4}\boxed{=}$

Predict the results.

d. $33\ 332 \times 33\ 334 = \blacksquare$

e. $\blacksquare \times \blacksquare = 111\ 110\ 888\ 888$

Write the ratio for each.

```
ABCABCABC
ABCABCABC
ABCABCABC
```

60. As to Bs.

61. Cs to letters.

Write an equivalent fraction, decimal, and percent.

62. 38 out of 100   **63.** 6 out of 8   **64.** 18 out of 25

Find the percent, the part, or the whole.

65. What percent is 42 out of 50?   **66.** What percent is 75 out of 200?

67. What part of 150 is 30%?   **68.** What part of 24 is 75%?

69. 18 is 40% of what?   **70.** 45 is 15% of what?

Find the amount of discount and of sales tax.

71. regular price: $299
discount rate: 30%

72. selling price: $129.95
tax rate: 7%

Cumulative Test:

Units 12–15

On grid paper, draw each transformation of the figure at the right.

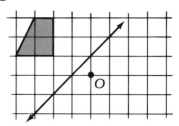

1. translation, [R7, U3]

2. $\frac{3}{4}$ clockwise rotation about print O.

3. reflection in line m.

Make a drawing of an isosceles triangle, a trapezoid, and a kite on grid paper.

4. What is the order of rotational symmetry for each?

5. Which of these polygons will tile a surface?

6. Enlarge the kite with a scale ratio of 3:1.

Identify these figures.

7.

8.

9.

10. How many planes of symmetry are in each figure?

11. Make a drawing of each figure showing the view from directly overhead.

At the right are Betty's scores on her weekly 25-word vocabulary tests.

18	25	25	24
25	23	19	19
24	22	25	23
23	23	17	21
19	23	23	25
22	19	18	23

12. Find the mean, median, and mode for Betty's scores.

13. Construct a combined tally and frequency table for the scores.

14. Construct a histogram for the scores.

Find the probabilities.

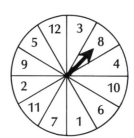

15. $P(4)$

16. P(prime number)

17. $P(15)$

18. P(odd number)

Add or subtract.

19. $(-2) + (-3)$ **20.** $9 + 2$ **21.** $(-7) + 8$ **22.** $(-9) + (-1)$

23. $(-5) + 2$ **24.** $16 - 20$ **25.** $3 - (-4)$ **26.** $(-12) - (-15)$

27. $(-8) - (-9)$ **28.** $(-2) + 5$ **29.** $(-8) + 0$ **30.** $0 - (-6)$

Graph the ordered pairs on a grid. Join the points in order.

31. (0, 3) (2, 0) (0, −3) (−2, 0) (0, 3)

32. (1, 4) (3, 3) (4, 1) (4, −1) (3, −3) (1, −4) (−1, −4) (−3, −3)
(−4, −4) (−4, 1) (−3, 3) (−1, 4) (1, 4)

Write the ordered pair.

33. What is the image of (−4, −2) resulting from a reflection in the *y*-axis?

34. What is the image of (2, −1) resulting from a $\frac{1}{4}$ clockwise rotation around (0, 0)?

35. What is the image of (0, 3) resulting from the translation [L5, D4]?

$Q = \{3, 5, 7, 8, 9, 2\}$ $R = \{1, 2, 4, 8, 9\}$ $S = \{2, 4, 6, 8, 10\}$

True or false?

36. $3 \in Q$ **37.** $9 \notin S$ **38.** $R = \emptyset$

39. $6 \in Q \cup R$ **40.** $4 \in R \cap S$ **41.** $2 \notin Q \cap R \cap S$

Copy and complete the table. Then draw the graph.

42.

Rule: 1.5*x*	
x	*y*
0	?
1	?
2	?
3	?

43.

Rule: 3*x* − 6	
x	*y*
0	?
1	?
2	?
3	?

44.

Rule: 2*x* + 2	
x	*y*
0	?
1	?
2	?
3	?

Solve for *x*.

45. $9x = 198$ **46.** $3x + 45 = 249$ **47.** $4x + 3x = 168$

Write an equation to help you solve the problem.

48. The sum of 8 times a mystery number and 148 is 428. What is the mystery number?

Extra Practice: Units 1–3

Add.

1. $43.75
    + 5.99

2. $265.70
    + 82.35

3. $269.38
    + 98.64

4. 0.3 + 64.2

5. 2.7 + 0.863

6. 9.78 + 49.149

Subtract.

7. $419.50
    − 69.59

8. $374.10
    − 28.95

9. $7150.00
    − 1925.79

10. 12 − 6.7

11. 31.2 − 8.67

12. 9 − 0.34

Multiply.

13. 2.65
    × 0.3

14. 752
    × 0.86

15. 8.64
    × 73.5

16. 73 × 0.1

17. 0.01 × 35

18. 2743 × 0.001

Divide.

19. 65)$83.85

20. 48)$112.80

21. 23)$104.88

22. 76 ÷ 0.001

23. 0.9 ÷ 0.01

24. 16.3 ÷ 0.001

Evaluate each expression. Suppose $c = 3$, $d = 7.8$, and $e = 4.5$.

25. cde

26. $\dfrac{18}{e}$

27. $36 - de$

28. $c + de$

29. $c \times (d + e)$

30. $cd - ce$

Simplify.

31. $7^0 + 17 \times 2^1$

32. $18 - 4^3 \div 2^2$

33. $16 \times (4^0 - 1^4)$

34. $5 \times (9^2 + 10^0) - 410$

35. $(63 - 63) \times 5^3 + 2^8$

36. $(4^2 - 2^4) \times (2^5 + 3^4)$

Solve.

37. The sum of 463 and a mystery number is 904. What is the number?

Extra Practice: Units 4–7

Find the perimeter or circumference.

1.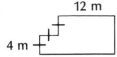

2.

3.

Find the area.

4. rectangle
length: 12.5 m
width: 6.25 m

5. circle
radius: 7 cm

6. parallelogram
base: 9.8 cm
height: 5.5 cm

Find the volume.

7. rectangular prism
base length: 4.6 cm
base width: 6.2 cm
prism height: 9 cm

8. triangular prism
triangle base: 18 cm
triangle height: 9.5 cm
prism height: 0.8 cm

9. cylinder
circle radius: 19.2 m
cylinder height: 25 m

Make the construction described.

10. Draw line segment *FG*.
Use a protractor to construct right angles at *F* and *G*.

11. Construct triangle *MNO* with sides 4 cm, 5 cm, and 6 cm.
Construct the perpendicular bisectors of each side of the
triangle.

Find the GCF.

12. 15, 17

13. 27, 33

14. 16, 24

15. 12, 18

16. 30, 45

17. 26, 39

18. 20, 35, 60

19. 28, 56, 42

20. 72, 54, 36

Find the LCM.

21. 4, 6

22. 8, 9

23. 10, 12

24. 10, 25

25. 12, 14

26. 72, 144

27. 24, 32

28. 18, 15

29. 36, 42

Estimate. Then use a calculator to find the exact answer.

30. If light travels at the rate of 299 792.5 km/s, how far
will it travel in one minute?

Extra Practice: Units 8–11

Add. Write the sum in simplest terms.

1. $\frac{7}{10} + \frac{19}{25}$

2. $\frac{7}{12} + \frac{5}{12}$

3. $\frac{3}{18} + \frac{7}{12}$

4. $\frac{5}{6} + \frac{3}{16}$

5. $2\frac{3}{4} + 7\frac{7}{8}$

6. $9\frac{6}{7} + 4\frac{3}{5}$

7. $12\frac{2}{5} + 6\frac{1}{4}$

8. $9\frac{3}{8} + 4\frac{7}{12}$

Subtract. Write the difference in simplest terms.

9. $3\frac{1}{3} - \frac{5}{6}$

10. $18 - 2\frac{3}{5}$

11. $23 - \frac{11}{12}$

12. $15\frac{3}{5} - 9$

13. $7\frac{4}{5} - 2\frac{1}{9}$

14. $6\frac{3}{4} - 3\frac{7}{10}$

15. $3 - 2\frac{3}{5}$

16. $8\frac{8}{9} - 4\frac{3}{4}$

Multiply. Write the product in simplest terms.

17. $\frac{2}{3}$ of $\frac{3}{4}$

18. $\frac{5}{8} \times \frac{16}{25}$

19. $\frac{1}{4}$ of $\frac{8}{9}$

20. $\frac{7}{8} \times \frac{32}{35}$

21. $1\frac{3}{5} \times 5\frac{1}{2}$

22. $3\frac{1}{5} \times 2\frac{1}{2}$

23. $8\frac{1}{9} \times 1\frac{1}{2}$

24. $1\frac{1}{4} \times 2\frac{7}{10}$

Divide. Write the quotient in simplest terms.

25. $\frac{1}{2} \div \frac{3}{4}$

26. $\frac{2}{3} \div \frac{5}{6}$

27. $\frac{1}{4} \div \frac{1}{2}$

28. $\frac{5}{8} \div \frac{7}{10}$

29. $15 \div 1\frac{1}{2}$

30. $3\frac{1}{8} \div 1\frac{1}{4}$

31. $35 \div 2\frac{1}{3}$

32. $2\frac{2}{3} \div 1\frac{3}{4}$

33. Use a calculator to find the value of n.

   a. $n^7 = 823\ 543$ b. $n^3 = 15\ 625$ c. $n^4 = 160\ 000$

34. Find the percent.

   a. 125 marching band members.
      45 are male.
      What percent are male?

   b. $380 deposited in the bank.
      $34.20 interest earned.
      What is the interest rate?

35. Find the part.

   a. $22.45 dinner bill.
      15% tip.
      What is the tip?

   b. $2550 selling price.
      7% sales tax.
      What is the sales tax?

36. Find the whole.

   a. 12% interest rate.
      $168 interest earned.
      How much money was deposited?

   b. $18 sale price.
      25% discount rate.
      What was the original price?

Extra Practice: Units 12–15

1. Draw the object and its transformation image on grid paper.

   a. [R3, D6]

   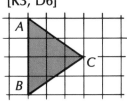

   b. $\frac{3}{4}$ clockwise rotation around P

   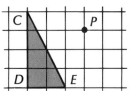

   c. reflection in line *m*

   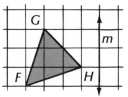

2. For the set of test scores, find the
   a. mean.
   b. median.
   c. mode.

3. Make a tally and frequency table of the scores.

4. Make a frequency polygon of the scores.

5. Make a stem-and-leaf graph of the scores.

Geography Test Scores
76, 87, 89, 86, 90, 88, 77,
85, 90, 86, 75, 76, 97, 74,
93, 72, 93, 92, 99, 84, 73,
95, 94, 88, 84, 91, 74, 77,
88, 91, 87, 96, 83, 94, 81,
77, 71, 71, 74, 73, 88, 80,
76, 72, 71, 77, 88, 83, 85,
94, 80, 97, 88, 76, 71, 83.

6. Copy and complete the tables.

   a.

+	2	−1	−8	0	−3
7					
−2					
3					

   b.

−	−3	4	0	−1	5
2					
0					
−4					

7. Copy and complete the table. Then draw the graph.

   a.

Rule: $y = 2x$	
x	*y*
0	
1	
2	
3	
4	

   b.

Rule: $y = 3x - 4$	
x	*y*
0	
1	
2	
3	
4	

   c.

Rule: $y = 4x + 2$	
x	*y*
0	
1	
2	
3	
4	

Glossary

Acute angle An angle measuring less than 90°.

Acute triangle A triangle with three acute angles.

Adjacent sides Two sides of a polygon with a common vertex.

Altitude (of a triangle) The perpendicular distance from the base of a triangle to the opposite vertex.

Angle Two line segments having a common endpoint.

Arc A part of a circle.

Area The measure of a plane region, usually in square units.

Array An arrangement of objects in rows and columns.

Associative property The property stating that when three or more numbers are added or multiplied, the operations can be performed in any order.

$$(46 + 57) + 23 = 46 + (57 + 23)$$
$$(3 \times 25) \times 8 = 3 \times (25 \times 8)$$

Base (in a power) The factor repeated in a power.

$6^2 \leftarrow$ base

Base (of a polygon) Any side can be called the base.

Bisect To divide into two congruent parts.

Box-and-whisker graph An arrangement of data which facilitates a quick summary. It highlights the median, the extremes, and the hinge points.

Capacity The amount a container can hold.

Centi- A prefix meaning a hundredth.

Chord (of a circle) A segment from a point on a circle to any other point on the circle.

Circle A closed curve whose points are all the same distance from one point (the centre).

Circumference The rim of a circle.

Common denominator Any common multiple of two or more denominators.

Commutative property The property stating that two numbers can be added or multiplied in any order.

$$36 + 45 = 45 + 36$$
$$8 \times 12 = 12 \times 8$$

Compass An instrument for drawing arcs.

Composite number Any whole number having 3 or more factors.

Congruent angles Angles having the same size.

Congruent figures Figures having the same size and shape.

Consecutive numbers Numbers obtained by counting by ones from any given integer.

$$57, 58, 59, 60, \ldots$$

Coordinate plane A number grid on a plane with an x-axis and a y-axis.

Coordinates The two numbers in an ordered pair that locate a point on a grid.

Corresponding angles In two congruent figures, two angles that match and are congruent to each other.

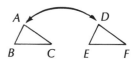

Corresponding segments In two congruent figures, two segments that match and are congruent to each other.

Cylinder A three-dimensional figure having two parallel, congruent, circular bases.

Data Facts.

Deca- A prefix meaning ten.

Deci- A prefix meaning a tenth.

Degree Celsius A unit for measuring temperature.

Degree (of an angle) A unit for measuring angles.

Degree (of longitude and latitude) A unit for measuring the earth's surface.

Denominator The bottom number of a fraction.

Diagonal A segment connecting two vertices of a polygon that is not a side of the polygon.

Diameter A chord of a circle passing through its centre.

Difference The result of a subtraction.

Digit Any one of the ten Arabic number symbols, 0 through 9.

Discount The amount of decrease in the price of an item.

Discount rate A percent of the original price.

Distortion A change in the shape of a figure.

Distributive property The property stating that a product can be written as a sum of or the difference between two products.

$$5 \times (40 + 8) = (5 \times 40) + (5 \times 8)$$
$$6 \times (100 - 2) = (6 \times 100) - (6 \times 2)$$

Dividend The number you divide.

$$\overset{15}{6)\overline{90}} \leftarrow \text{dividend}$$

Divisible A number is divisible by a second number if the quotient has a remainder of zero.

Divisor The number by which you divide.

$$\text{divisor} \rightarrow \overset{16}{3)\overline{48}}$$

Edge The intersection of two faces of a solid.

Equation A number sentence showing two numbers or quantities are equal.

Equilateral triangle A triangle with three congruent sides and three congruent angles.

Equivalent fractions Fractions that represent the same number.

Equivalent ratios Ratios that name the equivalent fractions.

Evaluate an expression Replace each variable in an expression by a given value of the variable and then simplify the result.

Expanded form The writing of a numeral as a sum of the products of each digit in the numeral and its place value.

Exponent (in a power) The number of times the base occurs as a factor.

$$3^4 \leftarrow \text{exponent}$$

Expression A combination of mathematical symbols, variables, and numerals.

Faces The flat surfaces that form a three-dimensional figure.

Factor Any one of the numbers used in multiplication to form a product.

Factor tree A tree-like diagram showing a number as a product of prime factors.

Finite set A set having a limited number of members.

Flow chart A drawing of a sequence of events or instructions.

Frequency The number of times an event occurs.

Frequency polygon A line graph that shows the frequencies of data.

Graph A pictorial device that displays a numerical relationship.

Greatest common factor (GCF) The largest number that is a factor of each of a set of numbers.

Half-turn symmetry A figure has half-turn symmetry if it has rotational symmetry of order 2 (if a tracing of the figure fits onto the figure twice in one full turn).

Hecto- A prefix meaning one hundred.

Height (of a polygon) A line segment from any vertex perpendicular to the opposite side (or an extension of the opposite side).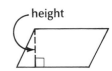

Heptagon A polygon having seven sides.

Hexagon A polygon having six sides.

Histogram A bar graph showing the frequencies of data.

Identity element The number 0 is the identity element for addition. The number 1 is the identity element for multiplication. For any number a:

$$a + 0 = a \quad \text{and} \quad a \times 1 = a.$$

Image The figure resulting from a transformation.

Infinite set A set having an endless number of members.

Integers The set of numbers consisting of . . ., $-2, -1, 0, 1, 2, \ldots$

Interest Money paid for use of money.

Interest rate A percent of the original amount of money deposited in the bank.

Intersecting lines Two lines that meet and share a point.

Intersection (set) The making of a new set from the common members of two or more sets.

Intersection point The one common point to intersecting lines.

Inverse operation One operation that "undoes" the other.

Isosceles triangle A triangle with two congruent sides and two congruent angles.

Kilo- A prefix meaning one thousand.

Kilogram The basic unit of mass in the metric system.

Kite A quadrilateral with two pairs of congruent, adjacent sides.

Latitude The angular distance north or south of the equator, measured in degrees along a meridian, as on a map or globe.

Least common denominator (LCD) The least common multiple of the denominators.

Least common multiple (LCM) The smallest non-zero number that is a multiple of each of two or more given numbers.

Line A set of points in a straight path extending infinitely in both directions.

Line graph A graph made up of line segments used to show data representing changes over a period of time.

Line of symmetry A line that divides a figure into two congruent parts that are reflection images of each other.

Line segment A part of a line with two endpoints.

Linear relation A relation whose graph is a set of points which lie on a straight line.

Line symmetry A figure has line symmetry if it can be divided into two congruent parts that are reflection images of each other.

Litre A metric unit of capacity.

Longitude The angular distance on the earth or on a globe or map, east or west of the prime meridian at Greenwich, England, to the point on the earth's surface for which the longitude is being determined; expressed in degrees, hours, minutes, or seconds.

Magic square An array of numbers in which the sum of each column, row, and diagonal is the same.

Mapping A correspondence of points. For example, $\triangle QRS$ maps onto $\triangle Q'R'S'$, with Q corresponding to Q', R corresponding to R', and S corresponding to S'.

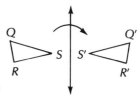

Mass The amount of matter in a body.

Mean The sum of the values divided by the number of values.

Median The middle value when data are arranged in order from largest to smallest.

Metre The basic unit of length in the metric system.

Midpoint The point which bisects a line segment.

Milli- A prefix meaning a thousandth.

MIRA A transparent plastic mirror used for geometric construction.

Mixed numeral A numeral consisting of a whole number and a fraction.

Mode The value that occurs most often in a set of data.

Multiple The product of a number and an integer.

Nautical mile A unit of length used in sea and air navigation, based on the length of one minute of arc of a great circle (1852 m).

Negative integers The number in the set $\{-1, -2, -3, \ldots\}$.

Net A pattern which can be folded into a 3-dimensional shell.

Nonagon A polygon having nine sides.

Number expression A sum, difference, product, or quotient of numerical values.

Numerals The symbols we write to represent numbers: 1, 2, 3, and so on.

Numerator The top number in a fraction.

Obtuse angle An angle measuring between 90° and 180°.

Obtuse triangle A triangle with an obtuse angle.

Octagon A polygon having eight sides.

Opposite angles Angles formed by intersecting lines which have a common vertex, are opposite each other, and are congruent.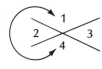

Order of rotational symmetry The number of times the tracing of a figure fits onto the figure in one full turn.

Ordered pair A pair of numbers in which order is important. (3, − 2) and (− 2, 3) are different ordered pairs.

Origin The point where the x-axis and the y-axis intersect.

Palindrome A number of two or more digits that reads the same forwards or backwards. 747 and 36 463 are palindromes.

Parallel lines Two lines in a plane that do not intersect.

Parallelogram A quadrilateral having opposite sides parallel.

Pentagon A polygon having five sides.

Pentomino A polyomino made up of 5 squares touching edge-to-edge.

Percent The ratio of a number to 100.

Perimeter The distance around a closed figure.

Perpendicular bisector A line which bisects a segment as well as being perpendicular to it.

Perpendicular line(s) Lines that form 90° angles when they intersect.

Perspective drawing A sketch of three-dimensional objects and depth relationships on a two-dimensional surface.

Pi (π) The ratio of the circumference of a circle to its diameter. π ≈ 3.1416.

Plane figure A set of points in one flat surface.

Plane of symmetry The plane which divides a three-dimensional figure into two congruent parts that are reflection images of each other.

Point A point has an exact position. It is shown by a dot.

Polygon A closed figure whose sides are three or more line segments.

Polyhedron A three-dimensional figure whose faces are polygons.

Polyomino A polygon made up of equal size squares touching edge-to-edge. (See pentomino.)

Positive integers The numbers in the set {1, 2, 3, . . .}.

Power A product of equal factors; for $216 = 6^3$, 216 is the *third power* of 6.

Power of 10 A product in which all factors are ten: 10^1, 10^2, 10^3, and so on.

Prime factor A factor that is a prime number.

Prime number Any whole number greater than 1 whose only factors are itself and one.

Principal Money on which interest is paid.

Prism A three-dimensional figure whose bases are congruent polygons in parallel planes and whose faces are parallelograms.

hexagonal prism

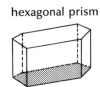

Probability The ratio of the number of times a certain outcome can occur to the total possible outcomes.

Product The result of a multiplication.

Protractor An instrument for measuring the size of angles.

Pyramid A three-dimensional figure whose base is a polygon and whose lateral faces are triangles.

rectangular pyramid

Quadrilateral A polygon having four sides.

Quotient The result of a division.

13 ← quotient
7)91

Radius A line segment that joins the centre of a circle with any point on its circumference.

Range The difference between the smallest and largest values of a set of data.

Ratio A comparison of numbers. The ratio of two numbers is their quotient.

Reciprocal Either of a pair of numbers, such as 7 and $\frac{1}{7}$, whose product is 1.

Rectangle A parallelogram having four right angles.

Rectangular prism
A three-dimensional figure having two parallel congruent rectangular bases.

Reflection A rigid motion that flips the points of a plane over a line.

Reflection image The image of an object resulting from its reflection in a line.

Reflection line A line in which an object is reflected (or mapped) onto its image.

Regular polygon A polygon that is equilateral and equiangular.

Regular polyhedron A polyhedron whose faces are regular congruent polygons.

Relation A pairing or mapping of each element in a first set with an element of a second set.

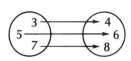

Remainder The number left when division is not exact.

Repeating decimal A decimal of infinite length in which one or more of the digits repeat.

Rhombus A parallelogram with four congruent sides.

Right angle An angle measuring 90°.

Right triangle A triangle with a 90° angle.

Rotation A rigid motion in which the points of the plane are turned about a fixed point.

Rotation image The image of an object resulting from a rotation.

Rotational symmetry A figure has rotational symmetry if a tracing of the figure fits onto itself in less than one full turn.

Rounding An approximation of a quantity by dropping digits after a given place.

Sale price The original price of an item minus the discount.

Sales tax rate A percent of the original price which is paid to the provincial government for items purchased.

Scale drawing A sketch of an object with all distances in proportion to corresponding actual distances.

Scale factor A number representing the amount the distances on an object are multiplied by to get the distances on its image.

Scale ratio The ratio of the size of the enlarged or reduced image to the object in a scale drawing.

Scalene triangle A triangle with no congruent sides or angles.

Set A group or collection of objects.

Shell A model of a solid whose interior is completely empty.

Similar figures Figures having the same shape but not always the same size.

Simplest terms fraction A fraction made up of whole numbers that have no common factor greater than 1.

Skeleton A model of a solid having only edges and vertices.

Solid A three-dimensional figure whose inside is completely filled.

Square A rectangle with four congruent sides.

Statistics The science of analysing numerical information.

Stem-and-leaf graph An arrangement of data that facilitates the finding of the mean, median, mode. It is also a graph or histogram of data.

Straight edge An angle measuring 180°.

Sum The result of an addition.

Surface area The total of the surface of a solid.

Tally chart A chart used to record stroke marks for each occurrence of an event.

Tangram A Chinese puzzle consisting of a square cut into five triangles, a square, and a parallelogram to be reassembled into different figures.

Tetrahedron A poly-
hedron with four
faces.

Tetromino A polyomino made up of four
squares touching edge-to-edge.

Tiling pattern A repeated pattern of
geometric figures which will completely
cover a plane without gaps or overlapping;
a tessellation.

Transformation A mapping of an object
onto its image: a translation, rotation or
reflection.

Translation A rigid motion in which each
point of the plane is moved the same
distance and in the same direction.

Translation image The image of an object
resulting from a translation.

Triangle A polygon having three sides.

Triangular prism A three-dimensional figure
having two parallel, congruent, triangular
bases.

Union (set) The making of a new set from
the uniting of two or more sets.

Vanishing point A point in a perspective
drawing at which parallel lines appear to
converge.

Variable An unknown value that is
represented by a letter.

Variable expression An expression
containing a variable.

Venn Diagram A
diagram used to show
the relationship
between two or more
sets.

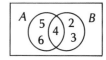

Vertex The common point of any two sides
of an angle or polygon.

Volume The measure of space of a figure in
terms of cubic units.

Whole numbers The numbers in the set {0,
1, 2, 3, . . .}.

x-**axis** The horizontal number line on a
coordinate plane.

y-**axis** The vertical number line on a
coordinate plane.

Computer BASIC Glossary

Commands:

LIST   —prints the program currently in memory.

NEW   —erases the program currently in the computer's memory.

RUN   —causes the computer to execute the program in memory.

Statements:

DIM A (N)   —declares maximum sizes for the array named. (p. 333)

`50 DIM A(4)`

A(1)	A(2)	A(3)	A(4)

END   —ends the execution of a program. (p. 30)

FOR . . . NEXT   —sets up and runs a loop a stated number of times. (p. 66)

`50 FOR C=1 TO 10`

GOTO   —during execution, sends the program control to another line. (p. 113)

`50 GOTO 10`

IF . . . THEN   —provides a decision-making capability within a program. If a stated condition is *true*, the instructions following the THEN statement are executed. If the stated condition is *false*, the program's execution continues as though the entire statement were not there. (p. 133)

`50 IF A = 2 THEN GOTO 40`

`50 IF A = 2 THEN PRINT "YES"`

396

INPUT	—allows a value to be assigned to a variable name by the user from the keyboard during the execution of a program. (p. 113)	`50 INPUT A`
LET	—allows a value to be assigned to a variable name. (p. 30)	`50 LET A = 5`
PRINT	—types out values of numerical expressions. (p. 30)	`50 PRINT A * 6`
PRINT " "	—prints everything inside the quotation marks. (p. 30)	`50 PRINT "AGE"`
PRINT " ";	—causes the next item to be printed *immediately after* the message inside the quotation marks. (p. 66)	`50 PRINT "THE ANSWER IS ";`
PRINT " ",	—causes the next item to be printed *ten spaces after* the message inside the quotation marks. (p. 333)	`50 PRINT "NAME", "DATE"`
PRINT TAB ( )	—formats a program's output by setting the number of spaces in from the left margin at which the output will begin. (p. 333)	`50 PRINT TAB(20); "*****"`

READ . . . DATA	—READ assigns values from DATA statements. DATA holds the data values for READ statements. (p. 374)	`10 READ P,Q,R,S`
		
		 `50 DATA 3,4,5,10`

REM	—remarks or comments about the program (ignored by the computer when the program is RUN). (p. 333)	`50 REM THIS PROGRAM FINDS THE VOLUME OF CYLINDERS`

Functions:

INT	—converts a number to a whole number or INTeger. (p. 235)	`50 LET A = INT(C/X)`
RND	—generates random numbers within a given range. (p. 333)	`50 LET A = INT (RND(1)*6+1)`

397

Metric Equivalents

Length
1 cm (centimetre) = 10 mm (millimetres)
1 m (Metre)   = 100 cm
1 km (kilometre) = 1000 m

Mass
1 g (gram)   = 1000 mg (milligrams)
1 kg (kilogram)   = 1000 g
1 t (metric tonne) = 1000 kg

Capacity
1 L (litre)   = 100 mL (millilitres)
1 kL (kilolitre) = 1000 L

Area
$1 cm^2$ (square centimetre) = $100 mm^2$
$1 m^3$ (square metre)   = $10\ 000\ cm^2$
1 ha (hectare)   = $10\ 000\ m^2$

Symbols

$=$ is equal to
$\neq$ is not equal to
$>$ is greater than
$<$ is less than
$\approx$ is approximately equal to
$:$ the ratio of
π pi, ($\approx$ 3.1416)
$\cong$ is congruent to
$\perp$ is perpendicular to
  congruent sides
$\angle$ $\angle$-   congruent angles
  parallel sides
$\emptyset$ empty set
$\cup$ union
$\cap$ intersection
$\in$ is a member of
$\notin$ is not a member of

Formulas

Perimeter of a polygon	P = sum of sides
Perimeter of a rectangle	$P = 2l + 2w$
Circumference of a circle	$C = \pi d$
Area of a rectangle	$A = lw$
Area of a square	$A = s^2$
Area of a parallelogram	$A = bh$
Area of a triangle	$A = \dfrac{bh}{2}$
Area of a circle	$A = \pi r^2$
Volume of prisms and cylinders	V = (area of base) $\times$ height

Index